Born in the East End of London in the early 1950s, the retired draughtman has witnessed and lived through many life-changing social and economic developments.

The sports loving man with an enjoyment of life grew up and attended schools in Dagenham. Here, living within a working-class community, the novelist learned friendship, respect and trust were just as equal if not more important than money.

Notorious for animatedly narrating 'exaggerated' tales from his youth, with a cockney wit inherited from his father, he always looks for a reason to laugh.

STEWART PERKINS

Dead Serious

*Life is just a series
of short stories*

AUSTIN MACAULEY PUBLISHERS™
LONDON • CAMBRIDGE • NEW YORK • SHARJAH

A CIP catalogue record for this title is available from the British
Library.

ISBN 9781398488229 (Paperback)
ISBN 9781398488236 (ePub e-book)

www.austinmacauley.com

First Published 2023
Austin Macauley Publishers Ltd
1 Canada Square
Canary Wharf
London E14 5AA

To my wife and daughter for their love and support.

Acknowledgements

I would like to thank everyone at the publishing team, with a special thank you to Walter Stephenson and Victoria White.

01

JOURNEY

Chapter Marker

THOMAS

"Yeah, do you remember playing at that school in Barham?" asked Stan.

"Er, what one?" Mike queried.

"The one where we had to get changed in the school, then walk twenty minutes to the pitch in our kit," continued Stan.

Mike replied, "Oh yeah, where they played in the big park with a boating lake."

Stan confirmed, "That's it. If the ball went in, the other school sent a kid with a net after it. One Saturday it was so cold that the scrum slipped on the ice and fell on me."

"Ha, ha, yeah I remember that," smiled Mike. "We thought you was dead."

"I thought I was dead as well! More people fell on me as they tried to get up. And then, we carried on playing in the snow. Bloody freezing," shivered Stan.

"I know, that was Thomas, evil bastard," recalled Mike.

"He was alright if he liked you," Stan corrected.

"If he liked you and saw you in the school corridor, he'd walk up to you, say 'hi', then give you a dead leg," remembered Mike.

"Great, yeah, I know, proved he loved us. Got more injuries from a sports teacher in the corridor than playing rugby," Stan laughed. "Used to see him chasing kids down the corridor trying to say 'ello'."

Stan stopped walking. He thoughtfully announced, "He gave me the slipper once."

Mike turned his head to question, "Yeah? Reeeally?"

"Yeah. When I was in the First Year." Stan explained as he caught up, "Only been there a few months, you know, in the communal showers after sport. The teachers would make everyone get under the shower, then turn the water to cold?"

"Yeah," confirmed Mike.

"Well, it was winter," Stan continued. "It was freezing, and we'd just come in from playing rugby. We were all in the shower, about three to four of us standing at each shower head, fighting and wrestling to actually get wet. That's when Thomas turned the shower on cold. I screamed and pushed to get away from the freezing cold water. 'COME here, boy,' he bellowed at me. I walked naked out of the showers to where he was standing. 'Bend over and touch your toes'. Silence, then whaaaack, a size thirteen plimsoll exploded on me bum."

"Whoa, did it hurt?" enquired Mike, grinning.

"Naaa. Course it didn't. What do you think?" replied Stan sarcastically. "I wasn't going to cry, you know, with everyone watching. But my eyes watered, and I think tears came out of my ears. Then everyone came out of the showers to have a look at me bum. 'Cor, you have a great big red slipper impression on your bum,' they said, as if I didn't know."

Mike jumped high to look over the arched brick wall which edged the road bridge. The front of a tube train was just below them entering the station, "Quick, here comes a train," he warned Stanley.

The boys dodged the traffic as they raced across the dual carriageway. Hurdled the metal fence on the central reservation, then turned into the Tube station ticket hall. They squeezed through the mass of people at the entrance who were not yet aware of the incoming train and flashed their weekly season tickets at the uniformed ticket inspector. At the green painted iron stairs, they skipped two steps at a time, the handrail loosely providing support and direction down onto the westbound platform.

TRAIN

As usual, the boys met on the tube platform at Dagenham East, having a smoke while waiting for the train to London and work.

They waited where the double door of the second from last carriage would stop. This would be one of the only two smoking carriages now provided on tube trains.

The second carriage from the front, plus the second from the rear, were now always so crowded. There were now more people in these two carriages than the other six added together. The friends wouldn't miss a smoke; sometimes they chose to let a train go through because they wouldn't be able to enjoy a ciggie when they got on it.

Roy, Pete and Glyn bent their heads over the railway lines to view the incoming train. Joe Law stood back for safety. Head on, the three friends could see the train's motion swaying from side to side. They watched as the incoming tube train's clunky, clunk noise echoed louder then deeper as it moved under the bridge and into the station. This change of noise acted as an alarm call to fellow passengers in the ticket hall and street above.

The boys heard another deeper sound: a hollow rhythmic drumming noise came from the stairs.

Mike and Stan stumbled as they miscalculated the number of pairs of steps by misjudging a single step distance for a twin step leap. Out of breath, their overstretched legs crumbled and leading ankles twisted as they hit the floor at speed. Roy rushed forward and wrapped an arm around Stan's chest to save him.

The Tube train pulled in. As they looked back, behind it they could see another two coming from Elm Park. Everyone squeezed on. The boys tried to manoeuvre to get a space together, or at least within talking distance of each other. All the seats had been taken long before they stepped into the carriage. There was hardly space to strike a match.

The signals changed from amber to green; the guard in the last carriage put his mouth to the wall microphone, "Mind the doors." He pushed his 'go' button; the driver eight carriages in front set the train in motion. As the train gathered pace, the guard leaned out of the open doorway watching for hazards until he was clear of the station. The lads often reasoned why the guard's hat never got blown off, which usually ended in a series of bizarre opinions.

"We were just talking about Thomas at school," said Stan, "and how evil he was."

"Yeah," joined in Glyn, "he was. They all were, really." He paused, "What about in games when one team had to play in 'skins?' Playing football or rugby topless, wearing just a pair of oversize shorts for over an hour? Especially in the winter - brass monkeys, everything went numb or shrunk."

"And the school annual cross country?" added Pete. "Everyone, all the school had to run the same, topless, no socks or pants, remember?"

"That was so you had to keep running to keep warm and didn't walk," smirked Glyn. "Mark Burns and a few others would run to the bushes near the Beck Lodge to hide. They'd have a fag, wait until the mass of runners was coming back, then join them. It's a bit cold, having a fag outside in November wearing only a pair of shorts and plimsolls. I think I'd rather run."

"A bit cold for your dangly bits," Joe grinned, "where did they hide the fags and matches?"

"Up their arris, I suppose," suggested Glyn.

Four stations further, time for a fag. As young sixteen- and seventeen-year-olds, they earned enough to smoke and go out drinking Friday and Saturday nights. But there was a rule, 'everyone shared, everything'.

"Who's turn to flash the ash?" asked Roy.

The boys had been smoking for about three years. It started when they would share ciggies that Glyn nicked from his three brother's cigarette packets. The friends would smoke over the park, in the bin stores near the flats or Jon's mum's front room.

Without prompting, Stan took the packet of ten Embassy from his coat pocket while pushing the cigarettes out of the top of the pack. Joe was first to move his hand towards the irregular line of exposed filter tips. He received the usual taunts referring to his inability to spend money.

"Come on, Joe, you skinflint," angered Roy. "It must be your shout." Roy hovered a hand over the open packet then shook his head. Stan pulled the packet back.

"It's mine next, honest. I have got some today," Joe promised.

Stan took the initiative by slowly sweeping his arm in an arc towards his friends, each in turn took a cigarette. Once all the others had a cigarette, he wafted the packet in Joe's direction.

"Okay, go on then, take one and none for ron, please," Stan warned. He continued by slowly pushing a filter-tipped cigarette with his thumb towards the tightwad. Joe removed the cig from the pack with two fingers and placed it in his mouth.

Someone struck a match, ciggies were lit, the conversation continued.

The train pulled into and out of another station, it continued with even more people crammed into the tight space of the carriage. There was nothing for the commuters to hang on to; conveniently, the people were so cramped together no one could fall over anyway.

Joe Law took another lug on his cig, 'bang', 'whooosh'. The thing exploded, a foot-long flame shot from the end. Passengers jumped away from the flame, but couldn't move. They squeezed even closer together. Joe panicked, causing additional alarm and crush by throwing the flaming object high into the air.

The boys laughed out loud, the scrounger had been done, well and truly done.

Stanley had set up the booby trap the previous night. He had replaced half of the tobacco from the cigarette with scrapings from the heads of three live matches. The exploding cigarette had been identified with a small ink dot on the filter.

Still laughing, the pals recalled the time a couple of weeks previous when Joe had lost his balance.

As usual, the six of them were on the District Line train on the way to work. They were smoking and chatting as the train headed towards Bow. As it swung right, dropping down a gradient towards the Underground, it suddenly lurched violently sideways. All the overhead handles swung around in circles, as did the people holding on to them. Joe lost his grip and fell forward facing the seats. In slow motion, Joe tried to gain a foothold; somehow with an ice skater's pirouette, he managed to balance on the toes of one foot. Abruptly the train jumped again, with arms searching in thin air for a hold, he crashed to earth.

Unfortunately, he didn't quite get that far. Halfway down, his hand hit the seated passenger in front of him.

Intensely embarrassed, Joe's hand burst through the centre of the man's open broadsheet newspaper. His palm narrowly missed the commuters face coming to rest on his groin.

Joe's full weight was supported by the man's lap. With a shy 'sorry', Joe managed to manoeuvre his second foot into the only free floor space available allowing him to remove his hand. Body hunched hands free, he balanced against the motion of the train standing between the man's knees until people alighted at the next station.

Typically 'British', the man never moved, looked up nor spoke. Remarkably, even after his newspaper was shredded with a massive hole ripped through the middle, he continued to 'read' until his destination.

01-03

DREAMING

Some of the group alighted at Mile End to change Tube lines, others remained in the carriage to travel to onward stations. Pete was the last to alight, leaving Stan alone as he travelled the last eight of the twenty-seven stops from Dagenham East to Gloucester Road.

Today the carriage was quiet, Stan closed his eyes taking advantage of it being deserted. As usual he would be ten minutes late for work. He hoped someone in front of him would leave an empty 9.00am time slot on the office attendance sheet.

Stan was the first person in his family to work in an office in London. He had been reticent about the prospect.

Generally, it was thought, well, he thought - that everyone who worked in London spoke and dressed like the presenters on the BBC. Speaking like an east Londoner from Dagenham, he was the opposite. When he first began to work in the metropolis, he was surprised by the number of people in his office who didn't speak or act 'posh'.

He was grateful to Brian and Oliver who had helped him settle. The two plumbing design engineers, both from south London, had started out working on the tools. They could be brusque, they told it how it was, no flannel. These engineers had been friendly to Stan supporting him to boost his limited self-confidence. Oliver, the older one aged about 40 had told Stan to 'always be yourself'.

One day, Oliver had planned to 'accidentally' bump into Stan while leaving the office for lunch. He relayed a story from years ago when he was a young man to illustrate a point.

"Stanley, I was the same as you. Finking people don't understand me. That I was lower class and less important than the ones who speak proper in high places. I was talking to this architect on the blower, you know putting it on. 'Yes, of course, I do not believe that to be a problem'. I was saying. 'Oh, yes that would be fine, golly good'.

Stuff like that, you know, what I fought was posh. Then, the architect asked me another question about something else. It caught me off guard. I said, 'Na mate, I don't fink so that ain't gonna appen'.

Blown out the water I was. I was so embarrassed, angry with me self. I would now have to face this architect at meetings and that, what was worse all the people in my office had heard me make a right prat of meself - S***."

"Stan," he emphasised. "Be proud of yourself. Learn to be happy with who you are, don't try to be someone or fink you're someone you ain't. Fink about this, you come from your parents, rite? So, it stands to reason if you don't like yourself, you don't like your parents."

'Thank you, Oliver', Stanley pondered his wise words. He started to daydream, 'What if?' He remembered his date last year with Amy, a Dilys Watling lookalike.

She was way out of his league. His school friend Alan had still managed to arrange it through his girlfriend. The four of them went to the Odeon pictures in Heathway. Stan had always fancied Dilys Watling on Crackerbox, and he had a date with a girl just like her. After the pictures at about 6.00pm on a sunny afternoon, he walked Amy the short ten minutes to her home.

Holding her hand, they stopped together on the tree lined pavement outside her mum's house. Before he could stammer any daft words or do anything foolish, she moved close and put her arms around his neck. Pulling him close she played a love song on his lips and mouth with hers. He felt like he had had the life sucked from him, floating, numb with a warm glow all over.

As he stood rigid by a tree in Hedgemans Road, he heard her quietly say goodbye. By the time he regained the strength to open his eyes, to move his head, Amy had gone. After walking along her front garden path, she stood at the opened front door waving.

Stanley slowly waved back his arm gently moving a short distance. Amy waited for him to depart before she stepped inside and closed the door. He knew there was no point in pursuing another date. What passion she had shown him, did she understand how gorgeous she was? No vanity, no arrogance, just a normal sweet young lady. Different class, never to be forgotten.

Now, sitting on the Tube again he wondered. At the time she was working, Stan was still at school earning just £2 2s a week from his paper round.

Perhaps, now that he was working and earning £8 10s a week,

would she go out with him again? No, probably not. Money was irrelevant; he was not in her league; nothing would change.

02

DUCKLES

Chapter Marker

02-01

CURTAINS

Stan got off the Tube at Gloucester Road and walked the short distance past the Tobacconist, he turned the corner housing the Post Office into Harrington Gardens then entered the 19th century four storey building. It was 9.08am as he climbed the side stairs to the first-floor reception adjacent to the main office of G.H. Duckle.

He walked as if on eggshells into reception, trying not to draw attention. Jill was sitting at the reception desk sorting the day's incoming post with Sheila. Jill looked up and smiled.

In front of him were two people queuing to enter their names on the office attendance sheet.

He was in luck! One of them was wearing red and blue tonic trousers supported by narrow red braces. Underneath, the young man wore a checked Shen Berman shirt with a button-down collar. Brogues on his feet, with a black Harrington jacket tied around his waist by its sleeves meant it was his mate, Jim.

Jim turned his head and grinned as he saw Stan trying to look even smaller. He signed his name in half of an empty 9.00am slot of the form. When he was finished, Stan crept forward, he had just enough room to add his name in the same slot. Together the young trainees walked from reception into the main drawing office. Stan turned down the aisle to his drawing board, Jim went to the toilet to put on his tie.

In 1969, it was an unspoken requirement that all males had to wear proper trousers, shoes and a tie. Jim couldn't understand, always smartly dressed he took a special pride in his appearance. He was better dressed than some dozy hippy with long girl's hair or a leather clad Greaser.

How could he buy a tie to match his shirts and still remain within the dress code? The boys did enough to keep them out of trouble, they rebelled by wearing unconventional style ties. Stan was wearing a bright red and blue 'splodgy bubble' patterned kipper tie. Jim came back from the toilet wearing a super skinny plain black bootlace tie.

Midway through the morning the pair were summoned to John Endsley's Secretary's Office. Every trainee was given tasks to 'help the running' of the office. Jim guessed it was their turn to 'clean out the khazi'.

Maureen greeted the boys from her large, extra tidy polished desk. Leaning forward onto her elbows she very softly explained that what she was about to tell them was in confidence. 'There had been an unfortunate incident, a terrifying ordeal for one of the trainees. The police had been called. Stanley looked horrified, he looked at Jim for support. His friend was mesmerised, watching a window cleaner up a long ladder working on a building opposite'.

Maureen looked up at the two boys. Seeing them both looking out of the office window, she raised her voice.

"Ahem," she regained their focus, "a short time ago, Trevor Tufnell had gone to the bank to collect the office petty cash money. On the way back, he had been accosted and threatened by two men. The gangsters told him to hand over the money or they would kill him, he decided to dodge and swerve around them then ran back to the office." The lady now had the two boys' attention.

Maureen continued, "The Directors and myself were worried about this, we informed the police. After consideration, they have suggested that these people had been watching the bank for some time. Possibly observing routine collections and deposits. They may well have stood inside the bank before assaulting Tuf."

Jim and Stan were gobsmacked, both swallowed with dry throats. A robbery opposite the place they worked, S***. Stan peeked out of the window again, checking to see if the window cleaner man looked like a criminal.

"We have now decided, with police advice on three actions," Maureen interrupted the boys' thoughts. "Firstly, two boys will always go to the bank together. This shall not be the same two boys each time. Next, we will now collect the petty cash at different times, on different days. Lastly, if you are ever threatened when you have the petty cash, give the money to the person then return quickly back to the office." Again, she asked them not to discuss the info with anyone else.

"Now, on a lighter note," she grinned. "The task this time is light bulbs and curtains."

They were told to go to the old Stanhope Mews garage, collect a ladder from the basement and bring it back to the office. Using the ladder, they both had to take down the curtains around the office then fold them ready for the drycleaners.

The pair fetched the ladder. Trumping along the pavement, each had one arm through a rung with a ladder side rail resting on a shoulder. They played out old silent movie stunts, walking side by side along the path rather than one behind the other. When they reached a lamp post, they spun round it like a propeller. A car hooted them at a road crossing so they dropped the ladder then with exaggerated knee and arm movements ran in different directions.

Eventually, they dragged the thing up the stairs to begin their first chore on the third floor, fourth storey. Stan wasn't good with heights, he got vertigo standing on the kerb. Clinging onto a ladder with one hand while trying to unhitch curtain hooks from a rail with the other wasn't his idea of fun. His misery was compounded if he inadvertently looked out of the window or when Jim placed his foot on the bottom rung to bounce the ladder.

The third and second floors were complete, the boys carried the huge curtain parcels down the back staircase. As Stanley stepped onto the second floor, Jim threw a large curtain parcel from the third-floor landing. Stan staggered, a pile of unfolded curtains smothered him from a height, suddenly he was in total darkness. Laying on the floor beneath the curtains, he couldn't breathe for the dust. Giggling accentuated his problem. A voice next to him was hysterical, it had to be Jim.

"Jim, S***, get me out of here, I'm dying," laughed Stan, as he choked on the dust. He heard the noise of a door closing, had Jim abandoned him? Stan's ears strained, silence.

Minutes later a croaking, articulate voice enquired, "Are you agreeable under there?"

Stan laid silent. That wasn't Jim, the voice was old and posh.

"I say, are you well?" The posh voice again. Stan could feel the end of a stick or something prodding his legs, the curtain was moving, being tugged. Daylight seeped through a small gap, then an old whiskery face emerged at the gap. The man wheezed breathing heavily as his hands pulled at the top curtains dragging them to one side. Stan went to speak but sneezed loudly, causing the elderly man to totter backwards.

Mr Duckle, the owner of the company, grimaced as he straightened his back, then lifted a hand in response before gingerly walking down the stairs to the floor below. Stan wasn't sure if the hand gesture was a 'that's all I can manage', or a 'surrender and escape'.

The second-floor landing door cracked open, "Is it clear?" whispered Jim. "I heard his gammy foot dragging on the floor, so I scarpered." Jim helped Stan tidy the area, bundle the curtains and carry them to the first floor. Together the two boys completed the curtain task. Jim went back to his drawing board. Stan commenced the task of replacing expired light bulbs. It took a few hours, but he suddenly realised Maureen had made a joke.

Hours later, in possession of a small stepladder, he readied himself to replace the last light bulb. It was on the first floor where four doors opened into a tiny lobby. Stan held the new bulb between his teeth while squeezing himself with the ladder through the doorway into the space. He had to shut the door to open the ladder. His preferred technique when climbing a ladder was to go no higher than absolutely necessary. If his extended arm stretched high enough to unscrew the old bulb, he remained on that step.

No sooner was he up the ladder than a door swung into it nearly knocking him off. It happened a second time, but this time he could hear a noise on the other side of the door. It was Jim giggling. Stanley was not amused. Hanging onto the ladder with both hands while holding a light bulb in his mouth was a difficult operation.

It went quiet for a while, then the door slammed into the ladder again. Stan was scared, Jim's mucking about was getting on his wick, "F*** off," he shouted in a loud voice.

A posh, old person's raspy voice replied, "I, err, I say...W, W, WHAT is going on?"

"S***!" Stan recognised that voice, it was the same man who had helped him earlier. Old tin head, Mr Duckle. Could it get worse?

The lobby was outside Mr Duckle's office, Stan's ladder was blocking access to his room. "Holy S***!" Stan, red faced, shouted an apology.

Back on terra firma, he closed the ladder to make space. Then, holding the ladder in one hand with the light bulb in his mouth, he pulled the door towards him and squeezed past a mumbling owner.

02-02

BORED

A few weeks after the light bulb incident, the office was busy but quiet; Stanley was fed up.

He had been at work now, his first real job for about six weeks. Training as an engineer in the construction, building services industry he had a massive drawing board, which was so high he had to stand on the legs of his stool to reach the top. There was also a three-drawer cabinet for his belongings with room for his ashtray and cigs on top. He sat with a group of four other trainees in a corner of the main office on the first floor of the building.

Even in six weeks, the five boys had formed a bond, they would usually go to lunch or for a walk together.

Stan and Jim had become good mates. Possibly because they were the same age, also as Jim was from the east of London, Forest Gate.

Jim was a skinhead, he always wore skinhead clothes and listened to Jamaican style Ska or Reggae music. Stan on the other hand, was more into Heavy Metal and Progressive Rock. However, he was developing a liking for Motown and Soul dance music which they played at the football club.

Jim's hair was as short as possible, just within office dress codes. Stan's hair was as long as possible, just within office dress codes. Despite the swinging '60s, the normal haircuts for most men were still the notorious, society preferred 'tuppenny all off' or the 'short back and sides'. With the exception of skinheads, young men wouldn't be seen dead with short hair.

Stan was fed up. Drawing in pencil at school was easy, but for the past two weeks he was learning to draw in ink. Dragging the pen along the side of a square on tracing paper to draw a line was difficult. Any ink mistakes had to be scratched off the tracing paper with the edge of a safety razor blade then smoothed over with a hard rubber.

There was now a new type of pen available which made it easier, but a Retring was so expensive.

The Graphis pen he was using was old style, Dev started a rumour that the Ancient Egyptians invented them. The top of the nib rotated so that it could be cleaned, but it was as sharp as a carving knife. Worse, if he pressed the nip down too hard it cut through the tracing paper which had to be taped back together.

Stan had just tried to draw a line, and had achieved a five-inch slit in the tracing paper. The ink had spread across his work, some seeped through the slit forming a black puddle on the underside of the paper. He could have cried.

He sat back, looking around. How he was looking forward to the boating holiday on the Norfolk Broads with three of his friends. It couldn't come soon enough.

The young engineer had noticed there was always a steady flow of people coming and going from the office, he needed to get away. Stan was so frustrated and angry with himself. He called out to ask if any of his friends fancied a walk. They all declined. With his jacket hanging on his arm, he left the building.

It was a bright day about 10.20am, not too busy as most people were in their workplaces. The London streets were strangely quiet and relaxed.

'Hmm,' he thought to himself. 'I do like this being at work, if I was at school, I could never just walk out of class'. Stan took a slow walk, after twenty minutes he found himself at South Kensington Tube station. He had a look around the shops, enjoying the upmarket feel of the place.

Being Kensington, not only the lady's shops were called 'Boutiques' but so were some of the men's.

Most of the garment shops had amazing modern clothes, but were soooo expensive. They sold items in crazy colour combinations with strange patterns. Choose from ponchos, frayed bell bottom jeans, over-sized tie-dyed tops and dresses, Jesus boots.

Stan was captivated. One man stood inside a shop watching the world outside through the large shop window. He had a giant spiff protruding from his lips, a beard and wore a loose striped tee shirt. The thing that caught Stan's eye was the man's hair. It was formed of tight twisted braids with green, yellow and red beads at the ends. More amazing, his hair cascaded from a massive coloured sack like bobble hat on top of his head. Of the many different styles of apparel people in the area wore, some were 'mods' walking about in very 'now' clothes. Men with smart suits, tailored haircuts an abundance of facial hair. Ladies with bright make-up and very short mini dresses with either Flipped Bob or long hairstyles.

Others were hippies with long hair, moustaches, sideburns, bright beads and flowing clothes. He could see that everyone took a pride in their appearance, irrespective of their style they all looked so smart. Even the hippies had their own 'style'. The clothes and accessories were tailored, matched to each other, not just thrown together or shoddy.

He was there!

Stanley came to a bohemian stall on the pavement, he took time to examine the abundance of weird items hanging from it. In assorted bright colours were headbands, necklaces, bracelets, tie-dyed clothes, candles, incense, feathers. A bright shining square towards the back caught his eye. It was a magazine. Only about eight inches by six with an amazing shiny coloured graphic as the front page. Stanley couldn't make out the name, the wording was integral to the pattern.

The long haired, moustachioed proprietor looked over. "Can I help sir?" he offered. Stan pointed to the magazine, "What's that?" he queried.

"That's an OZ Magazine," the man answered as he bent forward to pick it up. He passed it to Stan.

"Latest edition," he informed him enthusiastically.

Stan looked through the pages. The whole thing was printed on glossy paper. Every page was in colour with a background pattern. There were psychedelic, erotic, photo negative or similar with the words in a different colour over printed. It was amazing, a work of art, he could frame the pages or hang them on the wall.

"How much is it," requested Stan.

"Two and six," replied the moustachioed man, "you can't buy it in conventional newsagents."

It took Stan aback. He could buy a newspaper and ten fags for less than that. But he'd never seen one before. It was so beautiful, the articles were 'hip', it excited him.

It was so 'now'. Why not? He paid the money.

"Can I get you anything else?" the vendor enquired, "something to smoke, perhaps?"

Stan declined.

02-02

From then on, each month Stan would pay the stall a special visit to buy the latest edition of OZ.

Many times when reading it while travelling on the Tube people would ask what it was. On a number of occasions, fellow commuters changed seats to sit with Stan, just to read or share the contents.

Stan rolled his magazine into a tube, a little later he looked at his watch it was 11.45am. 'Whoops,' he thought to himself, 'better get back quick before I miss lunch.'

CARPETED

Stan hurried back to the office. He passed the old lady tramp who regularly slept in the Tobacconists shop doorway. Laden with her belongings she carried half a dozen large heavy, dirty carrier bags. She trudged, her back bowed by the burden, moving to a fresh seat in the sun outside the station. Every few weeks she would vanish, then later resume her occupancy in the shop entrance. It was rumoured that she was an eccentric millionaire who couldn't tolerate people. During her absent days she was supposedly feasting and freshening up in a private suite at a top London hotel.

Stan wasn't sure if that could be true. The young man's alarm bells sounded, an orange covered figure with a shaved head, wearing sandals stood in the centre of the pavement before him. As he drew closer, he identified a tiny ponytail at the back of the man's head.

The orange cloaked man waylaid Stan. He chanted softly prior to producing a hardback book.

"If you give me ten shillings, I will give you this book," the man proposed.

"No, thanks," replied Stan, "I don't want to buy a book."

"I will gift it to you, you will not be buying it," the orange man gave Stan the book.

"Cheers," Stan was about to move.

"Now, you must gift me ten shillings in return," claimed the man.

For minutes, Stan tried to explain that swapping money for an object was called 'buying it'. But the man wouldn't agree, he insisted that Stan could have the book for nothing, as long as Stan gifted him ten shillings.

Having escaped the orange man Stanley returned to his drawing board in the office.

He felt so relaxed. He enjoyed the walk, the sun and amazing sights. The 'cool', diverse people. If he had worked in Dagenham rather than in London, he could have become insular, isolated from the world. Every day in this incredible City opened his eyes to new, remarkable things. The world was calm and soft, there was no aggression.

The young engineer thought the life differences of where he had just been, and the office proved everyone had the freedom to live as they wished. Although it was the same language, different nationalities and faiths there were no barriers.

He suddenly realised what the stall man had implied by 'something to smoke'. Stan now knew where to acquire 'weed' when he fancied smoking a joint.

Before he could sit down, John Smith came over to talk to him. John was a nice man, an engineer, medium build, short with ginger hair and freckles. He must have had a good relationship with young women. A few days earlier there had been a makeshift poster stuck on the wall outside the typist's office. It read: 'John Smith's Harem'. Now that was cool.

What had he been up to? The poster stayed there for a few days until the office manager removed it.

If it hadn't upset the girls, 'wink, wink'. Sam, the young petit Scottish typist was a cracker. Especially when she wore tartan miniskirts. Actually, he thought, they were all nice looking.

"Hi Stan," John called, "have you got a minute please?"

"Sure." Replied Stan, as he followed John to the stairs.

"Stan? Where have you been?"

"Er, I went for a walk."

"Why did you go for a walk?"

"Er, I felt like it."

"Okay, I see. But you can't just walk out of the office when you feel like it, you supposed to be working."

"Oh, sorry, I saw everyone else going out so I thought I could just do the same."

"No, I'm afraid not. They are going to meetings, surveys and things. Please don't do it again," implored John. There was a pause, then, "Why are you here? What made you want to come here and work in this business?"

"Well," said Stan "I liked maths and TD at school, I just thought engineering would suit me."

"I can warn you Stan, this is a horrible industry to work in. There is so must stress with deadlines and things. This industry has the highest level of ill health with many people dying from heart attacks. If I was you, I'd try something different. Go and work in a bank or something," John suggested.

"Er." Replied Stan. He didn't have an answer, his main priority was to earn money.

"Now, please don't disappear again without telling someone first. Only leave when on office business or to grab a sandwich or bite to eat. Please think about what I have just said." John affirmed.

Stan had well and truly been warned of his future conduct. The meekest man in the office, other than himself, had 'pulled Stan over the carpet'. What a contrast to his morning, he walked miserably back into the office where the other trainees were waiting for him.

"Come on," shouted Dev, instant energy. "Where have you been, it's Friday we are all going to Luigi's for a Fricadelle and rice."

"And chips," smiled Stan.

02-04
CABINET

Tuesday morning, Stan was on time for work. He signed in and walked into the main drawing office moving slowly towards Franie and Ron. They were next to his board. Were they up to no good? Why were they there so early, cackling?

The pair heard him coming and looking up, Ron put his finger to his lips, "Ssh."

"What are you doing?" whispered Stan.

They explained that Franie had brought some glue with him, they had got in early and were gluing Jim's three drawer cabinet together. They had glued the inside front of each drawer to the main body, now they were gluing his ashtray to the top of his cabinet.

"F*** off," an agitated Stan half whispered, "I'll get the F*** blame for that."

"No, no, don't worry. Don't tell him it was us, though will you," pleaded Ron.

The deed was done. The boys were in their seats failing to supress expectant sniggers very effectively. Their strange noises drew the attention of colleagues entering the office to start work. Some gave the trembling boys strange looks as they arrived at their work stations.

The door opened in walked Jim. From his facial expression, he was not a happy bunny. He was late because the Tube had signalling problems. No one had left him a blank 9.00am space on the signing in sheet. He was definitely going to give someone earache.

"Morning," he greeted the boys.

"Mormah, phleew," Ron squeezed out his reply through tightened, smiling lips.

Jim looked at him quizzically, he looked at the others with a frown. Next, he took his cigs and matches from his coat pocket then balanced them on the tee square on his board. He went to hang up his coat and fasten his tie.

Stan ignored everything in the room, he kept his gaze looking straight ahead. The other boy's expectations were uncontrollable, grunting muted sounds intermittently broke the silence.

Jim came back to his drawing board. His expression was of someone who thinks they should know why everyone is smiling but just can't put their finger on it.

Still angry from his journey, "What's up?" he commanded with a half-smile, half glare.

The furore started as Jim stretched from his chair. He tried to move his ashtray to position his cigs and matches on the cabinet. Jim pushed the ash tray so hard he nearly overturned the cabinet. Stumbled sideways off his stool he fell to the floor. His friends belly laughed, totally losing control.

Jim's eyebrows knotted he looked at them with a dark stare. The hassle of his Tube journey evaporated, he saw the funny side of the prank and joined in the laughter. At least, he knew why the 'idiots' had been so excitable. Finally, as he was in on the joke, he could start work.

Relaxed, ignoring his ash tray he repositioned his stool to make room to sit. About to open the top drawer of his cabinet he stretched his arm while bending to his right side. Grasping the drawer handle Jim pulled hard. Tug, tug, "The F*** thing is jammed, S***, S***, S***, what's going on?" For a second time, he erupted with rage.

He then tried the second drawer; it was the same. Then the third.

Now the secret was out, the boys were beside themselves with laughter, tears, snorting. Stan moved away from Jim for safety. He took up a position behind Ron and Franie.

Other people in the office wondered what was going on. Some stood to get a better view, others bowed their head to escape watching any forthcoming violence. There was so much noise. Jim was shouting and swearing, the other three now joined by Dev, cracked up. Fran went in search of a tissue to wipe his eyes.

Jim gripped the sides of the cabinet with both hands, lifting it above his head his cigs and matches fell pass his left ear. Steadying himself, he slammed the cabinet into the floor. Office good nature with self-control was abandoned, the volume of laughter increased, it became extreme. Some colleagues laughed; others took cover.

Jim tightly grasped the handle of the top drawer. He slammed the cabinet into the floor again, and again. The back of the cabinet was

02-04

breaking up. Pens, pencils, rubbers all types of drawing equipment spilled onto the floor. The drawers were stuck solid.

At this point, the door from the stairs opened. In walked Mr Duckle the owner with John Endsley, the most powerful person in the Company.

The owner was known as 'old tin head' because he walked with a limp with his head parallel to the floor, at right angles to his chest. The sports trophies in the Board Room were thought to belong to him. It was rumoured he had won them when racing at Brooklands.

As a pioneer racing car driver, he had been involved in a horrific crash, as a consequence part of his skull had been replaced with a metal cap.

At the sight of the opening door, most of the onlookers silently dropped into their seats. The boys were the only ones left standing.

Supressed laughter is no substitute for silence, but that was as quiet as the young trainees could achieve.

John Endsley walked slowly to Jim. "What is going on?" he asked quietly.

"My cabinet is glued together sir," gasping for air, a very red-faced Jim replied.

John Endsley was a big, big man, aged mid-forties over six feet tall, built like a heavyweight boxer. Always in control. When discussions at meetings got out of hand or rowdy, he would talk very slowly and quietly. People needed to reduce their own volume to hear what he was saying so the meeting became quieter. Respect.

He surveyed the mess on the floor, the wreckage that was once a three-drawer cabinet. Without irritation, he looked Jim in the eye speaking softly, he commanded, "Well, please address the problem quickly and quietly so that everyone can get back to work."

He then prowled slowly around the drawing boards to the four trainees. "Please tell me what is going on here," he asked them.

The boys were initially red faced from laughter, but it was now with fear. Barely raising their voices above a squeak. "Don't know sir," they replied in unison.

Without speaking, John Endsley with Mr Duckle left the boys. They walked slowly together, further away from their entry door around the silent office. Moving like an enquiring military patrol they ensured everyone was aware of their presence. After what seemed a very long time, they left the main office through the door into reception.

Jim gave the bosses five minutes to move on before he went outside to calm down. The colour of his complexion matched the red Post Office telephone box that he leaned against. He was seething. Worse, he was going to have a fag but, in his anger, had forgotten to pick up his matches, "Aaargh." Inwardly, he wanted to spank someone.

After giving all parties time to calm down, Jim went back into the office.

Gathering his pens and equipment from the wreckage on the floor he noticed a new three drawer cabinet by his chair.

"B***," someone either cared or knew they were out of order. Subsequently, Jim took the remains of his deceased cabinet to the old Mews garage. Away from the office without managerial interruption, he could continue to dismantle the cabinet to salvage the rest of his belongings.

The four boys kept their distance from Jim for the rest of the day.

02-05

BOARD

Stan met the boys at Dagenham East station as normal, it was a long time after the glued cabinet incident. They fidgeted on the platform together waiting for the next westbound train. How they wished for a vacant seat.

Did their feet hurt? Yesterday, 13, they had taken part in the OXMAF charity walk. They had walked from Upminster to Wembley Stadium, thirty B*** miles. Walking with 50,000 other like-minded people had been an inspiration. But the pain. There was no skin left on their feet just broken raw blisters.

As the train came into view, "Come on Joe, your flash," cried Mike, "you only have them bloody 'No.6' things anyway, just half a fag two drags and it's gone."

Joe took a small white box from his pocket, keeping his hand over the logo he passed the cigarettes around the group.

Each took one, suddenly, "What the F*** is this," shouted Mike, looking at the small white cylinder in his hand. "Half a fag, let's have a look at that fag packet," he demanded.

Joe reluctantly showed him the packet.

"F*** hell, number B*** 10, you tight sod. 'No.6' are small, but 'No.10'. S***, you are so tight," moaned Mike.

Glyn refused one of Joe's ciggies in favour of an Embassy from his own packet, "At least this will last me to Barking," he announced.

They lit their cigarettes, boarded the Tube train, just to be squeezed into a small area against the doors where the glass divider protected the end seat.

At each station, more people clambered onto the carriage. At Barking, only one person, an Asian man with a full beard wearing a loose 'one piece suit' managed to get on. He stood 'nose to nose' against Glyn. It was hard enough to smoke with so many people crammed together, but today it was impossible.

Glyn had one more drag left on his ciggy. He couldn't move it up to his mouth because of the closeness of the Asian man's face. He gradually lowered his hand between their two bodies, keeping the lighted end turned towards himself for safety he gently dropped the dogend onto the floor.

Roy, a few feet away watched through a narrow gap between two people's bodies. Glyn's dogend dropped but settled gently on the top of the Asian man's shoe. The raised edge around the man's loafers had trapped the dogend. The man seemed calm, looking ahead with his eyes focused into space. 'Surely, he must be feeling the heat on his toes?' Thought Roy.

Roy attempted to get Glyn's attention.

Glyn tried to ignore Roy, he hadn't a clue what had happened. He could see Roy winking, screwing up his nose, nodding his head at him but guessed Roy was being a twonk to set him off laughing.

The dogend was still glowing on top of the man's shoe, rolling to the movement of the train.

There was no alternative. Roy coughed to clear his throat, in a quiet controlled voice so as not to alarm the man, he said "Er, er mister there is something on your foot." The man snubbed him. Glyn whispered, "What?" Roy repeated his warning. Glyn winced.

Holding back a giggle a tear dropped from Glyn's eye. He took a deep breath, trying to gently kick the man's foot and dislodge the dogend. He missed, tried again, missed again. Luckily, as the train pulled into the next station the man moved to make space. He looked down to sight a bit of clear unoccupied floor and saw the dogend. A shake of his foot as he left the carriage solved the issue. No one spoke.

Arriving at Gloucester Road station Stan took his usual route to the office. He walked past the Green and spotted one of the 'three cups n' ball' tricksters standing outside the newsagents. They were out early today, must be chasing the morning tourists.

Next, he passed the old lady tramp with her many carrier bags as she sat in a doorway eating a bacon sandwich.

He arrived in reception again Jim hadn't left him a clean 9.00am space on the signing in sheet. Jim had the right A*** ache about his deceased cabinet. He would not believe Stan hadn't done it; his mood wouldn't let him leave a blank space on the sheet. Stan signed in at 9.10am before entered the drawing office.

All seemed quite normal. A low buzz of conversation, one of the three drawing office phones was ringing. Stan walked towards the boys. Looking at them he became apprehensive; he had a bad feeling. Something was wrong, the boys were smiling but not at him.

He turned off the aisle towards his board. His drawing board wasn't there?

"What?" Nor his cabinet? "B***, F*** what the F*** was going on?"

As he got closer, he could see a large flat object on the floor where his drawing board should have been. Jim was at his board ignoring him, apparently working with great concentration on a drawing.

Stan spoke to him, "F***, Jim, do you know where my board and cabinet are?"

Jim didn't speak but half moved his head towards Stan, then nodded at the object on the floor. He looked away and continued working.

"No way, what! S***." Stan looked at the tangle of wires, metal tubes and weights arranged on top of the wooden sheet on the floor. It was, it was a deceased dismantled parallel motion drawing board, Stan's.

He set to work rebuilding it. No one offered assistance, "B***." This had to be Jim's revenge.

Stanley would have to hammer the metal frame together with the ball of his hand, screw the wooden board to the frame, then restring the parallel motion tee square with its guides and counterweights. He needed a screwdriver, he needed help.

Before he could start the rebuild, the door from the back stairs opened. How the F***, did they know? Some type of intuition had caused Mr Duckle with John Endsley to pay them a visit. The whole office noise hushed.

'Again? No way, F***, F***, F***', thought Stan. There he was, next to a pile of rubbish, pushing two pieces of metal tube together. He was in deep S***, now. All around him was quiet the sight of bowed heads represented 'extremely hard working' people.

He stopped fiddling with the metal tubes and half turned his back to the two bosses, not knowing what to do next. Praying seemed top of the agenda. If they hadn't seen him? 'If you close your own eyes when you are young no one can see you'. Stan gave it a try, it might work. He didn't want to bring attention to himself, standing there like a spare 'one' at a wedding.

He felt the presence of someone slowly walk up to him, it stopped behind him. A quiet voice spoke in his ear, "What is happening today? Are you having problems?"

'B***', Stan just couldn't think.

He blushed deeper red by the second. He was a shy person by nature, lacking self-confidence. These encounters with the top management were not helping his nerves. 'Slowly', he thought, 'take a deep breath, no err please'. Turning his head slightly, softly he replied to the voice, "I'm building my drawing board, thank you sir."

"I see," said the voice, in a puzzled manner, "can you manage on your own?"

Stan turned his head a bit more as John Endsley's face appeared twelve inches from his nose. "Yes, thank you," croaked Stan. He thought, 'Please don't get into a conversation, the sooner the bosses walk away the better'.

"You?" summoned John Endsley, "help this man build his board." Stan turned his head in the other direction to see John Endsley commanding Jim to help him.

"Okay," whispered Jim.

The two bosses turned, walking slowly they entered the reception area.

Jim under orders silently helped Stan put his drawing board back together. He found a screwdriver which increased Stan's suspicions. Jim never, ever took responsibility for the prank. Perhaps it was someone else? There were enough jokers in the office.

Later, Stan did a search over the three floors of the office and the two staircases. He found his three-drawer cabinet under the back staircase on the third floor. Thankfully, it was in one piece with nearly everything in place. His ash tray was missing, so he later sneaked into an empty office on the second floor to 'borrow' someone else's.

02-05

02-06
CARDS

The months passed. Jim again became friends with Stan.

They had both joined the Duckle's football team which played on a Sunday morning. This had brought them closer together, also it helped them mix with work mates who played in the team.

The office football team played in a London business league with venues at Regents Park and Wandsworth. Stan's journey to GHD's home pitch at Wormwood Scrubs took more than two hours from his home. It was worth it as he loved football.

The work day finished, Stanley left the office alone at 5.30pm. Jim had sneaked out ten minutes earlier as he was off to look for a new jacket at a Skinhead shop in Piccadilly. Stan ran down the office stairs then walked to Gloucester Road station.

He bought an Evening News at the station entrance before waiting on the platform for the train home. When it arrived, he quickly identified a carriage with empty seats and shuffled to the side frame of the train doors. This allowed him to slide sideways through the edge of the crowd onto the train when the doors opened. Hopefully he would nab a vacant seat.

He took a vacant seat opposite two men in their forties. Wearing site boots their clothes were grubby and stained, Stan thought they were probably building site workers. Despite looking tired with heavy eyes, the pair were loud, in good spirits they joked and laughed with each other.

It seemed the newspaper articles were always about misery and despair, unrest in Northern Ireland, two million people dying of starvation in Biafra, the war in Vietnam. They often made him feel low and helpless. During the boredom of the journey he needed something that wasn't so sombre. Stanley didn't want to hide from the agonies of the world he just wanted control when he learned about them.

Being timid he also needed something to hide behind if he felt nervous or frightened while travelling. Perhaps, if he bought books in preference to newspapers, he would feel better and may also save money.

A raucous noise brought him back to the real world. The two builders opposite were talking to another man sitting in the seat next to Stan. The three were laughing while 'wink, winking' to each other.

"Oooh," the man next to Stan enthused to the two men opposite, "where did you get those from?"

"From an Italian tiler working on site," replied the first builder, "you know what those Italians are like, they can't leave it alone, I bet they get blisters."

He placed an index finger against his nose as to reveal a secret, "It's all that Latin blood."

"Yeah, I can see that from the cards. Strewth, never seen anything like that before. Mind you, wouldn't mind seeing it again," the man adjacent to Stan giggled.

"I know, and they are all lovely looking as well. No rough, just proper classy."

Stanley could not ignore their conversation. He tried very hard to look at his newspaper, to purport disinterest. Each time he read a word or two, more appealing words jumped the queue to his brain. The expression the builders could see on Stanley's face was a blank stare, red cheeks with listening ears.

The man next to the young engineer bumped Stan's elbow. Stan looked up, face turning redder by the second.

"Did you see what he's got?" enquired the man, pointing to the one sitting across the carriage.

"Aah, no," replied Stan.

The second builder leant across the carriage towards Stan, "Would you like to have a look?" he asked Stan with a broad smile.

"Err, what is it?" enquired Stan, a little bit redder, speaking through a quickly drying mouth.

Beads of cold sweat emerging on his forehead.

"Show him," ordered the man next to Stan. "He's a man of the world, knows all about that sort of thing and the ladies."

Stan put his newspaper on his lap and looked up. The second builder stretched his hand towards Stan's face showing him a box of playing cards. Stan focussed on the box. On the front, he saw a coloured photo of a naked lady. He didn't know what to do, where to look next. He could feel his face glowing even brighter.

"Want to have a better look?" whispered the second builder with a big grin.

He moved the box even closer to Stan's face, "Go on, have a look, we don't mind," he enticed him.

The second builder twisted the box in his hand, revealing a second naked lady picture on the back. He extended his arm making the prize available for Stan.

The young man overcame his dread, moving his hand towards the card box he grasped it between finger and thumb. A massive surge of electricity run up his arm, hitting his elbow.

"Aaaargh, F***, hellllll," he shouted. But his finger and thumb could not release the box, "Aaaargh."

The electrical charge subsided. Deeply embarrassed, Stan smiled with a gentle uncomfortable laugh. His elbow hurt like hell, it felt badly bruised. He needed to shake it and massage the joint but not while a train full of commuters were observing. The three men with shoulders jiggling were in stitches, bending at the waist they raised their arms to high five each other.

The young trickster joined in their laughter; he embraced their humour as something he would have done. 'If you hand it out, you must also accept it'.

"Thanks for that," said the man next to him. "Best one yet, can we have our cards back please?" He giggled.

Stanley looked up. His shouting and swearing, plus the loud chortling from the three builders had not made a good impression on the other travellers. The passengers had no idea why the builders including Stan had been so ill mannered? Despicable, on a Tube train at six o'clock in the evening.

The rest of the train journey home was a lot more sedate. Stan nursed his arm and elbow. Alighted the train at Dagenham East station he made his way along the platform towards the stairs.

As he ascended the stairs a middle-aged man raced pass him. The man's upper body twisted backwards, turning his head towards Stan he smiled then raced on. 'Queer! He must have enjoyed the builders tricking me', he thought.

Stan walked through the ticket hall, showed his ticket and waited at the bus stop outside. Within five minutes, the 103 bus arrived. Stan fought with the other passengers to climb onto the platform at the rear of the bus.

Some people in front of him moved into the lower deck, others climbed the stairs to the top deck. All the seats were quickly taken, the aisles on both decks were soon full of standing passengers. People were also standing on the stairs.

He heard a cry of 'waaaaiitt' come from more passengers stampeding out of the station to storm the bus.

The Clippy raised her arm to jerk the ceiling mounted bell cord, the bus pulled away. Stan was standing on the rear platform hanging onto the handrail below the rear window for dear life. Gradually the bright red bus gained speed outpacing the outstretched hands of the chasing crowd. Most of the abandoned commuters turned to walk solemnly back to the bus stop. Others thought better of it and started to walk home.

"Fares please?"

The Clippy collected the fares from people close to her, but as it was so tightly crammed, she couldn't move around the bus to collect distant ones. The lady asked these passengers to deliver their fares to her by passing them through the hands of closer passengers. Their tickets with any change were sent back in the reverse journey. It was only after travellers alighted that the Clippy had enough clear space and freedom of movement to walk around the bus.

As the bus parked at the fourth stop Stan stepped down onto the pavement. He walked slowly towards the traffic lights, ensuring he was out of the Clippy's eye line he concealed himself within the group of disembarking passengers. 'Ding, ding', the bus pulled away.

Sixpence better off Stan was very happy, he hadn't paid his bus fare.

The walk to his home in Hawthorn Road took him five minutes from the bus stop.

He always felt a bit happier when he turned into Hawthorn after a day at work. He had lived in this turning since he was three years old. It was a nice place to live with his loving family.

He opened the front garden gate as a small boy walked past. "Ello Bobby Moore," chuckled the youngster. Stan stopped; he looked around to see who else was near him. No one was? Puzzled, he watched the boy continue on his way then opened the front door and went in.

His mum greeted him, "Welcome home Stan, are you okay, love," she asked.

"Yeah fine, thanks," he replied.

"You look a bit concerned love?" she worried.

"No, no, I'm okay, thanks, fine."

"Okay," she accepted his words, "I'll make you a cup of tea."

"Stan?" called his dad, "what's that on your back?"

"Nothing," retorted Stan, then having second thoughts, "I don't know Dad? What could it be?"

"Take your coat off son, what's that, let's have a look?" His dad pointed at the coat.

Stan took his coat off, twisting it over his outstretched arm to have a look. Pinned on the back, positioned just below the collar was a large piece of white paper.

It read, "I AM BOBBY MOORE."

02-07

COLLEGE

Part of Stan's initial training was to attend a weekly Day Release Course at Beckvale Technical College to study engineering. This comprised a whole day followed by an extra evening of attendance and lessons.

Unfortunately, although he had achieved ten top grade 'O' Levels at his secondary school he didn't have a science subject qualification. His school had never retained a proper science teacher. Only one had ever been there for a short while. The rumour was that the science teacher had given a disrespectful disobedient pupil the stick. Subsequently, on an evening shortly after the boy's brutish Dad visited the school and threaten the teacher. The science teacher was never seen again.

Stan started higher education shortly after joining G. H. Duckle in 1969. Because he had good 'O' level grades he was allowed to join the Course at second year level. He whizzed through most subjects in the G* Course but due to his limited experience at school he struggled with Science. This was compounded because in the office he was being taught to use Imperial units, while at college he was being taught to use the new SI metric units.

Because he failed the science subject exam, he failed the Course. The Course could not be retaken so he couldn't re-sit.

In 1970, on receiving Stan's exam results John Endsley called Stan to his office. They talked through the problem and Stan was given a second chance.

Now a year later, Stan was called to John Endsley's office again.

In 1971, Stan enrolled on the only alternative course which would replace his failed Course G*. Course MT2 was more a craftsman's course than an engineering design course.

He hated it. Of the twenty-six students in his class, he was the only one who didn't work at Wade, Dagenham. The only one training to be a design engineer. The other twenty-five worked together in the same factory as turners and millers. They were friends. The Wade bunch were loud both in and out of the classroom. Some teachers struggled to be heard, some were ignored completely. Stan was ignored by all of them plus most of the teachers.

Over the weeks he crawled further into his shell. Timidly sitting in lessons, red faced with a dry throat, in a cold sweat. He was learning nothing and felt uncomfortable. The feeling of being useless and afraid made him angry with himself.

It took all of his inner strength to attend classes.

At first, he would leave the office and travel to the college for the evening lesson. But self-doubt made it easier to go home rather than to the college. He started missing evening lessons.

Stanley hated himself for being weak and not fighting his lack of confidence. He told himself the excuse that even if he had attended lessons, he would have learned nothing. It signalled the end of his career.

Later, on college days when he was on study leave away from work to attend college, he couldn't build the courage to leave the house. Sometimes, he would sit wearing his coat unable to open the front door. He knew he had to make things happen, to get qualified, but he couldn't move. On those days, he did nothing other than sit indoors. He felt that if he did an activity, he would be cheating his employer even more.

He couldn't tell anyone. It was his secret. He learned how to disguise his fear of failure by appearing funny and happy. Now and then a thread would tug his conscience, the deceit pushed his self-confidence to rock bottom.

Stan knocked on John Endsley's door and waited, quaking. He had received a call from Jill asking him to visit Mr Endsley's office, but she didn't know the reason. A cold shiver ran down his back.

John Endsley called Stan into his office. Without ceremony he sat forward in his chair and passed Stan a pile of postcards. "Do you know what these are?" he asked Stan.

"No, noo," replied Stan.

"These are college attendance cards," John Endsley answered for him. "You haven't been attending school."

The trainee didn't even know these things existed.

"What do you say? What can you tell me? Do I believe what the college is telling me, that you haven't been attending college?"

"Yes, sir," stammered Stan.

"Why not? Do you have a good reason? You have been defrauding the Company. You have been putting 'college' on your timesheet, but not going."

"The Company has been paying your wages along with college expenses, but you haven't been attending?"

"What have you been doing?" demanded the most powerful man in the company.

Stan stuttered, "I am afraid I have been unable to attend college and have been staying at home."

There was a pause.

John Endsley sat back in his chair; he spoke softly. He realised that there was more here than just playing truant. "Take a seat Stanley, explain to me why you couldn't go to school. I shall listen."

The conversation continued for another hour. Gradually, Stan opened up and told of his fear, guilt, helplessness. John Endsley was not critical but sympathetic. He listened quietly.

Finally, John Endsley told Stanley of his decision.

He would give the young man a third, last chance. Stan's work in the office was very good and he was an approachable, willing young man. Duckles would not claim back the college costs and expenses, nor the wages Stan had fraudulently claimed. But there would never be another offer of education. The current circumstances meant he couldn't promise a pay rise. As Stan wouldn't become qualified there were no pay increases for additional responsibilities.

Stan thanked John Endsley, quietly he left the room closing the door behind him.

He didn't go straight back into the main office but walked up the stairs to the top landing. It was quiet. He stood there for many minutes preparing the face he would wear when he eventually walked back into the main office.

He was shaking. He knew the result could have been twenty times worst. He would have to learn to be stronger. Most importantly, when he had a problem, he would have to learn to share it.

02-07

02-08

MOLLY

It was about 10.15am, Stan was sitting at his board in the office eating his lunch of ham and pickle sandwiches.

He never had time for breakfast before leaving home for work. He stayed in bed for as long as possible. Then, after his dad and mum but before his two brothers got ready for school, he would nip into the bathroom for a wash. Anyone going to have a wash or bath in that house had to shout, "Anyone need the toilet?" Before the door was locked.

10.15am was a good time to eat half of his lunch. It gave him enough time before Molly brought the tea trolley around at about 10.30am. Molly had her own small office. She was in charge of the post, in and out correspondence and filing for the office. She also had to find time twice a day to do the tea round.

Molly was a 'proper' Londoner. She was a slim chirpy lady, about 5'2" tall, around sixty years old. She had lived through the London Blitz and was thankful to be alive. Never had a great life but enjoyed what she had. Got on with things without complaining.

"Allo daaling, how you doing?" she'd ask Stan. Since the office furniture incidents with a knowing smile she would now add, "Anymore tricks or funny fings happened what I should know about?" Stan's face always reddened.

She walked through the office pushing her trolley handing out cups of tea and arrived at Stan's drawing board. "Milk and two sugars for ya daaling? I see that Sheila in the typists is wearing another short skirt, nice colour. Course, she has got lovely pins. Show them off I say. Cor dear, if I was young again? I tell you, I 'ad good legs, still 'ave for a lady me age."

Molly grasped the bottom of her skirt making a motion to lift it. Stan looked the other way. Jim choked on a laugh. Molly stopped, "P'haps not," she decided. "I'll tell ya. I was sitting on me fortune when I was young, could ave made a mint. But you don't realise till you're too old."

The two boys didn't know what she was talking about. Suddenly, the penny dropped. 'Ewww', they shared disdainful, unbelieving looks.

Molly passed the tea to Stan then turned to Jim, "Allo daaling, you okay?" she asked. "Wat you want? Milk and two sugars?" Jim nodded.

She made the tea and moved closer to Jim to pass him the cup. As she entered Jim's comfort zone his confident smile evaporated. Then, standing a few feet in front of Jim she gave him the cup of tea, "I just told him," she said, nodding towards Stan, "I was sitting on me fortune when I was young and I didn't know you could get paid for it," she smiled.

"I'll tell you," she carried on talking to Jim, "not in bad shape am I, really? There's nothing wrong with these either, look," she compelled him. Without realising he looked, following her hands as she put one on the outside of each of her breasts, she pushed them together and upwards.

Jim had unthinkingly watched the spectacle. 'For crying out loud, F*** what the F*** is she doing?' He screamed in his head. Jim was dazed and speechless. Stan sat motionless. Both mortified.

"Okay boys," smiled Molly as she turned to collect her tea trolley, "see ya later this afternoon."

She turned back to face them. Pushing her left breast up with one hand Molly gave the boys a smile and a wink, then pushed the trolley towards the next tea drinking customer, "Byyeee for now."

"Bye," the boys murmured back.

"What the F*** is she on?" whispered Jim. "I tell you what, better not go in the filing room alone while she's feeling fruity. Could be dangerous."

Dev's head jumped above his drawing board, "I don't know about that, but she sure has the hots for you," he roared in a south London-Jamaican chuckle.

"Ha! Ha! Dev, will you change seats with me at about quarter past three," pleaded Jim.

Suddenly, Franie's head appeared above his drawing board. "I'll swap with you James, always fancied me chances with a mature woman," he grinned. "Experienced, know what I mean?"

Dev laughed, "You call that mature, I bet it smells like Gorgonzola," another roaring cackle.

"Watch out, look." Franie whispered as his arm moved to point to something behind Jim, "She's coming back!"

"Yeah, yeah, 'cos she is. If she is this time, I'll give her a snog," bragged Jim defiantly.

Worryingly, Jim watched as Dev's and Franie's heads quickly dropped below the top of their boards.

Jim braced himself.

He tensed even more as he felt a hand softly touch, then caress his left shoulder.

"Allo daalingk, how are you, big boy?" spoke a whistling but deep voice.

Jim laughed as he turned towards the voice to see Ron standing behind him with his hands high on his chest, imitating Molly's earlier hand motions. "Yeah, yeah, okay Ron, never fooled me. Look at you, you tart. At least, you're better looking than er," he laughed.

"That's hurtful," replied Dev, "you are talking about my future wife. I think Molly's a lot better looking than you," Dev boomed. "Can't wait for quarter past three!" Another roar, "better get a paper bag."

"Yeah," agreed Ron, laughing. Then looking at Jim, "so she can put it over your head when you're at it, you ugly plank."

02-09

RICHARD

Thursday night, 'Friday Eve'. Stan smiled. He had finished work and managed to leave the office dead on half past five. As Jim was on day release at college, he made his way to the Tube station alone.

As Stanley entered the station, he felt the rushing movement of air on his face as a train entered a platform. He skipped down the stairs two at a time onto the platform. Arriving at the doors just as they opened without breaking step, he was through them and sitting in a previously vacant seat. Phew. A bit red faced, out of breath but delighted.

He no longer bought newspapers to read on the train, now he read books. He saved money plus he could lose himself in the plot for the whole sixty-minute journey.

In the office, sometime before, Stan had mentioned his plan to start reading books on the journey to and from work. It was meant to be a passing comment but became an in-depth conversation. Archie, a Senior Engineer was chatting about Stan's interests when always helpful Brian eavesdropped. The three-way discussion intrigued Stanley. He hadn't realised the number of people who read, nor their enthusiasm. Utilising euphoric tributes each engineer suggested or recommended books they had enjoyed.

Stan was at a loss. As usual, he didn't want to offend anyone. Astutely, he noted he would sample different novels to 'get a feel' for his preference. As soon as Stanley tried Science Fiction type novels he was hooked. He had read a few, and was currently halfway through the first book in Osimov's *Fundamental* trilogy.

After settling himself in the Tube train seat, he shyly looked around the carriage. It was peaceful, he took the book from his bag.

A man about four seats away to Stan's left sat forward then smiling at him. As their eyes met the man gave Stan a slight nod. Stanley recognised him instantly and smiled back. They had had a painful but electrifying experience together on the train a while ago.

The young man cautiously looked back to the older man, checking if his builder friends were about. Sure, the other two were sitting on the same side of the carriage as Stan about three seats away. Having already been the fool guy he would enjoy the drama. Someone else was going to get caught with the nudie playing card trick. Just to check Stanley searched around for any visible clues of another prank.

There was one empty seat opposite Stan. 'Perhaps that was the snare seat', he thought.

At each station, people would stream onto the carriage, race to the snare seat, slow down then walk away. Stanley was confused, why would they rather stand holding onto the overhead handles?

Each time this happened the builders sat forward in anticipation. They would grin, then disappointedly sit back again. The train had gone sixteen stops without anyone taking the seat. Expectations grew, the next stop was Mile End. Because people changed lines and trains here there was a lot of potential.

As the carriage emptied, Stan stood and leaned to get a closer look at the empty seat.

"F***," there was a richard on the seat. No, it couldn't be. A fat richard about six inches long. No wonder no one sat on it. He couldn't stop smiling. One of the building workers winked as he caught Stan's eye.

A flood of new passengers charged into the carriage. Their bounty, a vacant seat. Bizarrely, they rushed into unoccupied spaces, they twisted and grappled with the carriage fittings but never once touched each other. The 'snare' seat remained vacant. In turn, as before, each commuter walked to the seat then continued walking.

Suddenly, there was a bit of a scuffle by the door.

A young man had squeezed through the door to claim a place next to the internal glass seat protector. He opened his newspaper, leaned back and with a controlled scream fell backwards through the opening. Completing a double pike dive onto the man sitting in the seat next to the richard his newspaper flew into the air. The commuters in the area gave muffled screams as they stepped away.

A man adjacent to the doors shouted that he had been kicked. A lady stooped to pick up her hat. Stan checked for the glass in the frame!

The train pulled out of the station.

While giving his profound apologies, the young man slid down from the other's lap and managed to stand in front of him. He apologised once more. Bending over to gather his paper from the floor he saw the adjacent vacant seat, then without hesitation he slammed his bum into the trophy.

Gasps. So many passengers took a deep breathe it caused a vacuum in the carriage.

Initially, there was a false silence. Everyone standing or sitting near that seat knew its contents. They bit their lips while looking the other way, but gradually people's smiles developed into sniggers.

The young man was not initially aware that he had a squashed richard on the back of his trousers. However, something made him uncomfortable because he started to fidget. A pair of schoolboys were in stitches which promoted more laughter. The crash-landing man became more and more embarrassed.

He couldn't have known what he was sitting on, but it must have felt slippery and cold.

Luckily for him, he had been reading The Evening News, a broadsheet newspaper which gave him a degree of isolation. A larger page to hide behind. All that was visible were two bunches of fingers, one each side of a large open newspaper. Every person in that part of the carriage was looking at the young man. Some smiled or nodded knowingly to each other. The builder across the carriage to Stanley sent him an 'eeek' facial expression, then grinned.

Suddenly there was movement, life. The young man let the top of the newspaper gently fall and rest against his forehead. This allowed him to release his right hand which he slowly relocated behind his back. The man's arm thrust and pushed backwards. Then he brought his right hand back to the newspaper and repeated the same action with his left hand. He repeatedly swapped arms. Suddenly, calmly, still hiding his face he sat in a normal posture and began to read his newspaper.

It wasn't until the train had travelled eight stops to Upney that the young man left the train.

Still hiding behind the newspaper he sat curled like a spring. As the guard's voice warned 'mind the doors' the young man threw his newspaper into the air and quickly escaped between the closing train doors.

Minutes after the young man had gone the three builders grinned and cackled as they examined the snare seat. To their astonishment the richard was nowhere to be seen.

They smiled at Stan, "Did you enjoy that?"

02-09

"Cor yeah," he replied. "I can't believe he kept putting his hands on it. Was it real? He kept pushing at it behind him with his fingers."

"Yeah, yeah, of course it was," replied one of the builders, "got it from the khazi on site," he grinned.

"Do you think he's taken it home with him?" The four men all laughed. "In his pocket?"

Eventually, one of them wedged his hand right down the back of the snare seat to locate the toilet object. He tugged then pulled, eventually out popped a flat misshapen richard.

"He must have been ill to do one like that," the man grinned. Everyone chuckled.

The builder looked at Stan to explain, "It's putty and some pipe compound, looks real though, don't you think?" He giggled.

02-10
DECORATION

Wednesday afternoon, a couple of days before Christmas 1971.

The main reception area had a nice Christmassy feel. It was swamped in ceiling hung decorations that Sam, Sheila and Jill had stuck together to produce chains. They had made 'Chinese Lanterns' by cutting slits in sheets of paper and gluing them as tubes, then pushing the ends to form a bulge in the middle. To allow the beautifully decorated tree to be squeezed into a corner the table had been replaced by a smaller one. Cards from clients and suppliers stood on the windowsills and reception desk.

To buy the new decorations the ladies in the typist's office had taken a train together to the large Downworth's store in Oxford Street. They were happy with the result bought with the petty cash money Maureen had donated. Their office was now as brightly bejewelled as Oxford Street itself. To complete the Yuletide atmosphere a large sprig of mistletoe hung over the office door.

It had been noted that John Smith seemed to need more typing done than ever? The boys considered that he was standing outside the girl's office much more than was necessary. Every time one of the gang looked up, he seemed to be hovering outside.

The boys stayed well away; they had previously chatted about it while eating in Luigi's. It would be too embarrassing to have to kiss one of the typists, or worse, let a typist kiss them! Yuck! Maureen? Double yuck! But what about Sam? Uhh, perhaps Sam. They agreed Sam could kiss them.

What if Molly was hiding close by 'in ambush?' She might be hiding under a desk and as the teenage male walked past, suddenly "allo daaling", bosh. Before they knew it, like a king cobra she would be hanging off your lips by her teeth. And then her teeth would fall out?

Just too mortifying for a seventeen-year-old boy to even consider.

There was an increase in anticipation and excitement in the main office of G.H. Duckle. As Christmas Day was on Saturday this year, they would have an extra day's holiday. Pack up on Friday not to return until the next Wednesday, a full four days off work. And it meant the week back would be only three days. Yeah!

Just after lunch people began to trickle from the other two office floors above into the main office. They slowly entered the office to join friends or stood around waiting and chatting.

Tuf from the Barbican Project and Will from the Benghazi Project entered the room to meet up with their mates. They made their way behind the boys' drawing boards to greet them.

Tuf sat on Ron's stool. "What you doing here?" complained Ron.

"Sitting on your stool," Tuf smiled. "We've been told by Maureen, John Endsley's Secretary to come down here and wait."

"Oh," replied Ron, "I wonder what's going on?"

"Well," continued Tuf, "we heard a rumour that someone was leaving, because it's nearly Christmas they have a small presentation for 'em."

"Mmmm," thought Ron aloud, "wonder who that is? Haven't heard anything."

Will moved closer to Ron, lifting his first finger to his lips he leaned forward to whisper, "We think it's Fran."

"What's Fran?" Earwigging Franie jumped in. "Come on, tell me what you know." Franie was agitated.

"We know you're leaving," replied Ron, "that's what this do is all about. It's your leaving do, could be you might even get a leaving present."

"I ain't going nowhere," exploded Franie, a bit louder than he had meant, "I'm staying here," he whispered.

"How long have you been here now Fran?" Will asked.

"I ain't leaving," Franie insisted, angrily. His voice choked.

Jim winked at Will, "Maureen was looking for Franie a couple of days ago." He turned to Franie, "I think it was the day you was on Day Release. She had a letter for you, but she couldn't find you. She said it was too important to be left on your board."

Will moved closer to Tuf and spoke in a feigned whisper so that Fran could hear, "Perhaps that letter was his termination letter. He's been sacked, got the elbow and he don't know yet?" He grinned at Tuf.

"He will in a minute," Tuf smiled.

Franie was again about to argue when the door to the main office opened. This time it was Maureen. She entered the room closely followed by John Endsley with Mr Duckle third.

They turned left and took up a position at the side of the office which ran along Gloucester Road.

John Endsley took a step forward to address the gathered colleagues.

Franie's heart was in his mouth. 'Had he been given the sack? What had he done wrong? How had he missed the F*** letter? All these people were here to watch him get dismissed, S***'.

John Endsley spoke, "We have some news which we would like to share with you all. Maureen has been very busy. As the person most involved, she shall explain."

Franie felt worst, the torture was similar to waiting to being executed. The colour drained from his face.

Maureen stepped forward.

She explained that all of the offices were going to be redecorated. The number of office telephones would be increased from one per floor to two. Those people with just a drawing board would now also have a desk and chair. Also, this part was very exciting, the Directors had agreed to have the current dark blue lino replaced with new grey carpet tiles. She held up a sample.

There was a murmur of appreciation from the colleagues.

Maureen spoke again, "And, the best till last."

She continued, "We will be having a hot drinks machine installed in the main office. You shall now be able to have a hot drink at any time. Each drink will cost 2p, and the Directors have decided to give everybody a very generous allowance of three free drinks a day. Molly, shall come around every Monday morning to give everyone their 30p allowance, in 2p coins."

Stanley muttered to Jim, "Molly will have a problem with that, still thinks it's not proper money. It's been nearly a year since decimalisation, and she still talks in £ s d. Because they are the same size, she thinks a 1d and a 2p coin are the same thing. Pennies is old and Pence is new, but she don't understand."

Franie relaxed a little. 'Okay, nice', he thought, 'but who's leaving?'

Maureen carried on, "After Christmas when the new drinks machine is installed, we shall have a specialist come here to teach us how to use it." She smiled with pride.

She took a breath and spoke quietly to Mr Endsley, then she engaged with the crowd again.

02-10

So as not to disrupt the office the works would be undertaken in two phases. Half of these works would be carried out over the Christmas break; the second phase would take place in January.

To facilitate the works, furniture in each room would be moved and squeezed into one half of the floor space of that room. Stacked were possible, but surplus items would be moved to the old Mews garage. When this work was complete, the furniture would be repositioned by the builder.

The storing of the old furniture would start on Thursday afternoon and finish on Friday morning.

"Brilliant, another Chrissy present, that's tomorrow," a relieved Franie declared in hushed tones.

Maureen continued, "The Directors understand it shall be hard to continue working during this time. They would appreciate it if everyone could work for as long as possible into Thursday evening. Please only start to pack your personal belonging with your project material after you can no longer work.

Once the moving is complete everybody is invited to join the Directors at the Hereford Arms for Christmas celebrations and drinks.

We shall need the trainees to help with the move so they will not be available for normal duties. If you require any trainee to help you, please see me."

She looked towards the boys, "Boys, can you please come to my office at 11.45am before lunch tomorrow, as I need to explain your duties."

Maureen addressed the room, "Any questions?"

No questions, but lots of smiling faces. More time off work! Great!

LICENCE

Later that afternoon Archie came to visit the boys. Archie was posh he was exactly what Stan thought people working in London looked and sounded like.

He was always very smartly dressed. His clothes just 'looked' expensive, something you would see in an Aquascutum shop window in Knightsbridge. He had black hair cut as a mop, a small black tailored moustache and heavy black glasses. He was a lady's man. Archie wasn't attracted to ladies like the ones in the typist office, but Ladies he could meet in Sloane Square.

"Hi," he addressed the boys in his quiet well-spoken voice. "As tomorrow is going to be a wash out a few of us are going to The Stanhope tonight after work. If any of you are interested, please join us, it will be fab. We will be in there from about six o'clock."

As he walked towards reception, Archie continued, "Hope to see some of you in there."

He was only a few yards from the boys when he swivelled, "Oh, Stan have you got a minute please?" He waved his hand. "Can you just come over here a minute?" Stan placed his drawing pen on his cabinet and followed.

"Stan, I'm sorry, I nearly forgot," he admitted, "I have been talking with John have you got your draughtsman's licence yet?"

Stan was bemused, "Ah, no, what's one of them?"

"Well," Archie continued, "as you have been training for over a year now you need to get a licence so that you can work. You need to be registered."

"Okay," accepted Stan shyly.

"Be an idea to get one prior to the New Year. Why don't you go to the Post Office just ask for a Draughtsman's Licence Form," suggested Archie.

Stan agreed. On hearing that these licenses didn't cost anything, he immediately set off for the Post Office. Since the shop on the corner of Harrington Gardens below his office was a Post Office he didn't have far to travel.

He entered the Post Office and queued. After waiting for about forty minutes, he got to a counter cashier. At the booth, he calmed his nerves then requested a Draughtsman's Licence. The smiling lady clerk searched through rows of drawers in her side cabinet, then away from her stool she rummaged through shelving on the back wall.

"Do you know what colour the form is," she shouted.

Stan shouted back that regrettably he didn't.

The lady returned to the counter, she expressed her fear that the form had a different name or code to the one he had given her. Stanley was asked to wait a minute while she concurred with her manager.

Another ten minutes lapsed before the lady returned. Grinning to herself, she advised that the Post Office didn't process those types of form.

Stan, confused, made his way back to the office. He bumped into Dev on the corner.

"Hi little man, where you been?" chuckled Dev.

"I was going to get a Draughtsman's Licence Form at the Post Office, but they didn't have any. Archie tells me I need to be registered." Stanley half spoke to Dev, half to himself, "Don't know where I'm going to get one now? Where you been? Eh, are you registered?"

Dev grumbled, "Ollie asked me to go the building supply shop down Stanhope Gardens to get a long weight. I waited about twenty-five minutes before the burke in there found that they didn't have one.

I think the shop bloke had the right ump. I was sitting there minding my own business and he like sauntered from behind the counter, like he was floating. He gave me the evil then opened the main door.

I glanced up at him. He said something like, 'There you go, times up, you've had long enough, bye'.

So, I walked out, he shut the door right behind me. Just going back to the office now," established Dev.

"Eh, Dev, what did Ollie tell you he wanted?" enquired Stan.

"Well, he said to go to Plumbplus in Stanhope Gardens and ask for a long weight," replied Dev.

They both looked at each other as smiles gradually filled their faces. The penny dropped.

"I think you did have one," laughed Stan, "you got done Dev."

"Yeah, you and me both, Bro," chuckled Dev. "That, there Draughtsman's thingy, I believe that's probably the same. Two birds in one bluff."

JOHN

Maureen had announced the office redecoration plans the previous day. The trainees were committed to complete any outstanding project work before mid-afternoon, then start to shift office furniture to make room for the decorators.

Stan bumped into Jim while walking from the station to the office. Stepping out of the bakers eating a bacon roll Jim had nearly knocked him over. By chance, they had both come in early because of the extra work that had to complete. It was 8.30am as they entered the office signed in then went to their drawing boards. To benefit friends who might arrive later, both signed in on the 8.20am slots of the attendance form.

A couple of minutes later, Will came into the office from the back staircase. He walked up to the lads in some excitement.

"Hi," he spoke rapidly. "Just had a funny phone call. Someone phoned up and asked if we have a John Smith working here?"

"Who phoned?" remarked Jim.

"They said they was the Police," answered Will.

"What did you say?" questioned Jim.

"Well, I said I would have to check." Will replied.

"You dipstick," interrupted Stan, "you know he does. Why did you say that?"

Will stammered. "Well, after the Tobacconists robbery a while back, I thought I best be careful. You know, the police told us not to talk to anyone. The caller did give me his number and asked me to call him back. I'm going to tell Maureen when she comes in."

A few months prior, someone had broken into G.H. Duckle's offices and robbed the Tobacconist shop below. They had removed floorboards in John Endsley's office then cut a hole in the shop's ceiling to gain access. When John Smith arrived in work on that day, the place was in a mess. The burglars had broken the lock on the office door and there was a rope ladder nailed to a desk hanging into the Tobacconist shop. They had got away with expensive lighters, cigarettes and valuables. Everyone at Duckles had been under suspicion of collusion.

Jim was just going to ask if either of them had gone to The Stanhope the night before when a disgruntled Brian trekked into the office. He plodded over to the three young men, "Can one of you please make me a drink?"

"How are you?" enquired Will.

"Not good," an exhausted, peeved Brian replied, "had a S*** night. I left the pub at about half ten. We had had a good night, about ten people turned up.

When I got to the station, there was no ticket collector so I just walked straight through. Got all the way home, went to open my front door and couldn't find my keys. I had to walk a mile to me mum and dads. Got them out of bed and slept on their settee with the dogs.

This morning, no change of clothes. I feel dirty. I couldn't find my season ticket, keys or wallet so I had to borrow money off me mum. Maybe, I was robbed, I can't remember we had a skinful. Perhaps I fell asleep on the train and someone rifled through my pockets.

Unless, I have lost my keys and wallet in here or in the pub. I need to have a look. Be grateful if anyone can help me find them."

"Have you seen John yet today?" Will asked Brian. "We've had a phone call, someone's looking for him."

"No," replied Brian, his croaking voice matching his crumpled appearance. "Was it one of the typists who phoned?" Brian probed.

Stan arrived with a cup of hot coffee.

"Thanks Stan." Brian kept talking, "John was bladdered last night, left before me. He was with the typists most of the time, drinking dark stout with whiskey chasers. Maybe, he went home with one of them?"

Will left the main office to visit Maureen. Not certain if he had done the right thing, he uneasily informed her of the phone call from the police and left her the contact phone number. She said she would follow it up, then asked him to go back to work.

Maureen never got back to Will, but at about 11.00am when Brian was talking to her, a very weary looking John Smith limped slowly into the office.

A crowd gathered to enquire after his health, waiting to hear his story. Stanley nipped to the kitchen for a black coffee.

"As far as I can remember. I think I left the pub at about quarter past nine." A few eyebrows twitched.

John lit a cigarette, a full column of smoke left his lips as he spoke, "On the way home, I got on the westbound train at Gloucester Road, I must have fell asleep. When I woke up, I was still at Gloucester Road station. Being wasted, I thought it must be a signals problem or something, so I closed my eyes again.

Next thing, a guard woke me up at a station only to tell me to get off. He said I was on the last train which was about to terminate in the sidings. Somehow, I was at Southfields my station. The guard told me the time was gone twelve, I'd lost more than two and half hours.

Anyhow, I was so pissed at the time I didn't realise. Sadly, I fell asleep on a bench on the platform."

John took the coffee cup and swallowed the contents in one. His head was spinning.

"The station man must have called the police, cos they woke me up. When they asked for my name and address, I told them. Unfortunately, when I showed them proof of ID, I gave them Brian's wallet. First, they thought I was being sarcy by giving a false name. Telling them I was called John Smith didn't help. But luckily, I found my wallet in my jacket, so they half believed me. I thought it was okay then.

The copper said, 'Are you John Smith who has robbed Brian Taylor, or are you Brian Taylor who has robbed John Smith?' They arrested me on suspicion of robbery. I spent the night in the cells."

"I'll tell ya, a cold night in a cell helps you think things through. In daylight, I looked at my overcoat which is not mine. I think it must be Brian's. I think we got them mixed up in the pub so I'm hoping he has mine."

"How did you get out?" asked Archie.

"The police said they had a telephone statement that I was John Smith," he replied.

"But where did the time go?" queried Jim.

"All I can think of, is I'd fallen asleep on the train going west, stayed on it all the way to the terminal, then travelled all the way east. On the second trip going west, I woke up for the first time at the same station I'd got on it."

Brian returned from Maureen's office, he hadn't heard the tale but was pleased to see his mucker.

"Well, Dick Turpin," Brian, greeted John, "I think you must have my coat. How are you now?"

"Oh, not to good, I need a livener," replied John.

"Okay," proposed Brian, "we'll take all our stuff over to The Stanhope and sort things out."

Off they went.

"Shall I water your horse, while you're away Dick?" shouted a bright spark, as the pair left through the reception door.

02-13

PANIC

As agreed, the seven trainees met on the back stairs of the office just before 11.45am on the Thursday. They all stood in scrum formation each with an arm extended like commandos synchronising their watches.

"Right," dictated Ron, "quarter to, let's go."

He pushed passed Tuf and knocked on the door to Maureen's office. As instructed, they entered, shutting the door behind them. The boys stood in two rough lines around her desk, fidgeting as she talked them through the redecorating plans. When Maureen stopped to refer to the notes on her desk, Tuf stealthy raised an arm to flick the bottom of Ron's ear.

Maureen heard a whimper, from the corner of her eye she saw a flurry of movement. Possibly arms flying around.

John Endsley's Secretary briefed the boys.

Everyone in the office had been given large waste sacks. As soon as these staff members had put everything that was no longer needed in these the boys would take them to the basement of the Stanhope Mews garage.

Anything that needed archiving would be put in a sack with a labelled luggage tag tied round the top. The boys would take these to a different garage in Queensberry Mews, which Duckles had just started to rent.

Any drawings, documents etc that were to be kept would be stored in furniture after it had been moved. The gang would transfer half the office furniture on each floor to one end of the room. Then the remaining furniture was to be stacked on top. New mops and buckets had been provided for the boys to swab clean the floor spaces.

Dev, Jim and Stan would work in the main office. Will, Franie on the second floor, Tuf with Ron on the third floor.

All information had been passed on, Maureen excused the boys. As it was nearly Christmas, they decided to eat lunch at Luigi's.

Most engineers were working to meet deadlines or to complete their work to a point where they could leave it until after the Christmas Break. At the time, it was good news for the boys as very little was available for archiving or storing. However, normal to the industry it meant the actual time available to complete their clearing up tasks was gradually diminishing.

After a sixty-minute lunch followed by a look at the albums in the local record shop, they just sat at their boards chatting. Stanley examined the cover of the 'Yeah' album he had bought himself for Christmas.

Molly was buzzing around to ensure all the post was ready. She didn't want to be the only person left in the office on Friday afternoon. She had one and a half days to despatch a huge issue of drawings going to Libya for the Benghazi Project, but to date had received nothing to send.

If it came to it, she was quite happy to hide the filing, but she had to get these drawings and documents to the Post Office on time.

Will came down to speak with Stan and Dev. His office was struggling to finish the Benghazi drawings, could they help?

Polly, Colin Parrat, his boss, had sent him. He couldn't remember the whole story, but it was something about people in Benghazi don't have a Christmas Break? The drawings had to get there 'tout de suite'. The drawings must be in the post tomorrow at the latest.

"Watch out lads, here comes Dick Turpin," laughed Dev.

John Smith called the boys to join him as he walked to Dev's board.

"Lads, it's okay, Polly asked me earlier. James, can you keep working on the move please. Dev can you work with Will and Franie on finishing the drawings please, Stan can you sort out the printing, docs and stuff for the project issue. Thanks, I'll leave you too it." He returned to his desk.

"How many are there?" Dev asked Will.

"Hundred and ten masters, with six off each," replied Will.

"How many already finished?" Dev grilled Will.

"About sixty masters done, probably fifty copied," replied Will, "OK, let's go."

Dev and Stan followed Will upstairs to his office where they were briefed by Polly. They then set off on their individual tasks.

Stan went to Molly's office to agree a plan.

"You've come to see me, ave ya me luv, what's occurring then?" She was always happy to see Stan. Sometimes she would be naughty just to watch his face glow.

He disclosed his strategy. As drawings became finished, he would take them to the printers to be copied, once folded he would bring the copies back to Molly. Stan would collect and take any new masters to the printers. She would add the drawing information to the issue sheets as she sorted the copies into sets. At intervals, Molly could parcel the items ready for the Post office.

Molly digested the information the boy passed on, she agreed with the idea but informed him of her concern.

Her worry was that they would miss the deadline leaving her alone to sort out the mess.

It was the first time he had seen her as vulnerable. The cocky, bumptious lady wasn't as self-assured as she would like people to believe. She needed help. Stan gripped her gaunt mottled hand and while squeezing it gently reassured her that she wouldn't be alone in office on Friday evening.

Gathering a batch of master drawings into a large roll Stan made his way to Cromwell Road. It was a short walk of around fifteen minutes. He passed the station, a right into the dual carriageway, another fifty yards down the stairs to the basement and entered CromwellRepro. Instantly, his nostrils rebelled at the ammonia filled air generated by the large, noisy dyeline copying machines.

Bizarrely, the smell eased his worries, it signalled that he had reached his bolthole. He knew the crew and Manager well, a place he could relax away from the troubles of the office.

Here, Stan was trusted and allowed to produce dyeline copies while putting the world at rights or listening to the radio. Although slight, the physical activity with the change of surroundings calmed him. He was always offered a hot drink with a biscuit.

The trainee engineer stopped at the counter to greet Bill, the man in charge. Stan explained the panic in the office.

"That won't be a problem, as long as we get all the drawings by 9.00am tomorrow morning," assured Bill. "Off you go Stan," Bill pointed him to the print room, "we are busy with other jobs, you can do those on number two."

Standing at one end of the large machine he unrolled the tracing paper masters onto the table behind him. Next, he took the first drawing and laid it onto the start of the hanging roll of yellow copy paper, then he fed them together into the rollers. As the front edges entered the machine Bill called him.

"By the way," he announced, "we have a sale on for Christmas. You might be interested. Please tell your bosses and everybody back at the office. We have some good deals."

From experience, Stanley turned his attention back to the copier and pinged the sprung wire, paper cutter with his forefinger. A section of the copy paper matching the size of the master separated from the roll as the pair disappeared into the machine.

Once the first sets of copies had come off the printer and were folded, Stan inspected the shelves on the back wall. There was a set of Retring drafting pens in a case, a complete set of eight. They were reduced from £8 to £4.

"That's what I would really like," Stan told Bill, pointing at the pens. "But I can't even afford four quid. Shame."

He rushed the copies back to Molly. A race upstairs to collect the next finished masters from Will then back to CromwellRepro. Close to 5.00pm he had made four trips, ahead of schedule all of the masters were now with CromwellRepro.

Bill asked his crew to work a bit later to complete the order. He advised Stan that all the remaining copies would be delivered to the Duckles reception at 9.00am the next day. Stan thanked them all. They were in front of programme, he couldn't wait to get back to pass the good news to Molly.

As he was leaving, Bill called him to the counter. "Stan, just a minute. That was a big job, and you have helped us a lot over the year. I would like to show my thanks. Would you really like that pen set?" He pointed to the Retring pens on the shelf.

"Not 'alf but I can't even afford the case," Stan despondently accepted, "my weekly train ticket costs me £3, nearly the same as the pens set. I can't even afford two quid, really."

"Well," continued Bill. "There is a way, not a right way. But I could hide the cost of them in your company invoice. How about, I add them to this order for all these drawings and you can take the pens with you?"

"I don't know, do I have to do anything?" asked Stan sheepishly, he was scared of doing something illegal.

"No," assured Bill, "honest it won't be an issue. I'll write out the invoice for printing with added pence to the price of each copy. The invoice will still be just for copying, no problem."

"But don't take the pens into the office till after Christmas," Bill grinned.

The manager of CromwellRepro took the pens from the shelf. Tempting Stan, he physically wafted them in Stan's face, "You know you want them?"

"Okay, and honestly thanks, what a Christmas present," Stan was over the moon.

Bill smiled, "Let's just tell everyone that they were a present from your girlfriend." Despite his reservations, Stan took home a nice new set of drafting pens.

02-14
TRANSITION

This morning Stan had missed seeing Bronwyn on the Tube, the first time they hadn't met since he saw her at the Bomb in May. It was Christmas Eve, he had made the effort to get to work early so that he could concentrate on his office move tasks. He also had to help Molly with the Benghazi drawing issue. Hopefully, all the drawing prints would arrive as promised at 9.00am.

He was looking forward to having a Christmas drink with his work mates. Boxing Day he would spend with his sweetheart and her family.

Stan arrived in work at 8.40am. Jim, Dev and Ron were already in the office working hard. Their task was to move the furniture as directed by Maureen.

Ron had decided to work in the main office to help Dev and Jim catch up on the lost hours of yesterday. He would work on his designated tasks on the third floor from 10.00am. By then, Stan should have finished the Benghazi duties and could work on the main office removal as originally planned.

The prints arrived from CromwellRepro at 9.00am as promised. Stan collected them from reception and took them to the post room to help Molly. She was brighter today, the dark mist had gone, she was looking forward to drinks with the girls.

In truth, Stan was a bit scared of being dragged under the mistletoe by Molly. She kept cornering him, standing 'too' close or making rude remarks. The teenage boy just didn't think it was possible for a lady of her age to actually have the wit to wind him up with touch and innuendo. Everyone knew that sex stopped at forty?

He worried that she had hidden mistletoe in her office before he went in. The room 'seemed' clear, but he didn't let his guard drop, ensuring Molly never stood between him and the door. Every now and then he could hear the faint laughing, noises being made by Jim, Dev and Ron in the main office. Probably, at his expense.

In the main office, the other staff were milling around, filling sacks with rubbish and belongings. The task was to install the existing amount of furniture in half the floor space. Periodically, squabbles broke out among work mates. One person would move their desk and chair into an empty floor space, then another person would push it back. It was comparable to riding on the Dodgems at the funfair. Soon it became apparent that most of the types of furniture were indistinguishable. Once an item had been moved a few times its owner could no longer identify its location.

"Er umm," the mechanical engineer Mick 'Spud' Murphy (being Irish) coughed.

Gaining the office's attention, he precariously climbed on to the seat of a swivel chair. Holding the back rest with one hand, trying to reduce the spinning effect of the seat with his feet he bent double to balance. He probably would have been just as tall if he had stayed on the floor, "I have asked the ladies in the typist's office to label stickers so we can put them on our belongings."

"Unfortunately, they are very busy. So, they have given me a lot of blank sticky labels for us to complete. We can write our names on them before attaching them to our furniture. I'll leave them on this desk." "Wow, aah!" Spinning to his left, he dropped a foot to the floor to control the chair. The airborne boxes of labels missed the desk and landed on the blue lino.

Initially, there was a fight for the labels, steadily the chaos calmed. People went about their business more sedately, even pointing out each other's furniture to help.

It was after half past ten when Stan left Molly in the Post Office and returned to help the boys. No one had realised that the Post Office would be heaving on Christmas Eve. It was rammed full; people were queuing outside onto the pavement. He had stayed with Molly to help carry the heavy parcels. However, once they had actually got inside, she urged him to go back and carry on with his other duties.

'I will be able to push the parcels along the floor', Molly had convinced him.

Typical Molly, as he left the Post Office she waved and shouted, "Bye luuuvly, fanks for all your help, big boy. See you in the pub later." Stan's face flushed.

Stan made his way into the main office where the barracking started.

"Got lost did we or have you just escaped from Molly's room?"

shouted Jim. "We tried to get in, but it was locked. Wink! Wink! We heard someone moaning and groaning inside, we thought you might be too busy to open the door."

"Did she chain you up Stan? Give us a groan," added Dev. "Let's have a look at your wrists?"

"It ain't his wrists she was interested in," laughed Jim. "Look how red his face is, he's still out of breath, look. Been at it for hours poor boy. Dev, check his neck for luuuv bites."

Stan ignored them, the three boys got back to work. It didn't seem that they would get to the pub much before lunch.

They managed to stack single desks with chairs on top, desks two units high, the planning chests three high. Gradually, the empty space in the centre of the room grew more lino blue as the furniture was cleared. They worked their socks off, lifting, carrying, bending and stretching. It got to 12.00pm. A message came via Jill in reception, the second and third floors had been finished.

Tuf and Will were summoned to Maureen's office. Sulking that there was more work to do, they mooched down the stairs and knocked indifferently on her door. To the pairs surprise she gave them an envelope containing luncheon vouchers to pay for their lunch meals.

They fought over the envelope on the landing outside her office. Both pulled against the sticky seal. It ripped, Tuf grabbed the booty. Two LVs each, "That's 30p each," they cried in unison.

"Blowout!" shouted Will as Tuf waved the LVs in the air. Excitedly, they told the other boys of the booty. Together they sat to have a LV Meeting.

Once the meals were decided Tuf and Will sprinted to Luigi's to purchase everyone's special sandwiches, cakes and cans of drink. Ron and Franie started to transfer the filled sacks to the mews garages.

When the food arrived, the boys moved to the back stairs away from the seniors. Settled on the steps to eat and chat maybe they became too full of festive joy.

They resumed their tasks at 1.00pm. By 2.00pm, everything had been moved, stacked or stored away.

The boys sat in the main office chatting while Stan finished mopping the floor. Clowning around, Stan started pushing the dripping wet mop closer and closer to Jim and Ron's feet. He then splashed it all over their shoes, "To give them a good clean," he claimed.

All six boys rose to grab him. Stan kept them at mops length. Most of them were wet, they advanced on him.

With cheers and chuckles, they cornered him. "What shall we do with Molly's boyfriend?" bayed Franie.

Tuf pointed to the space between the ceiling and the top of a stack of three planning chests. The others nodded in agreement. They evaded the swinging wet mop. Jim took a position behind Stan to trap him in a bear hug. Still whirling the mop, he was lifted about eight feet above the blue lino floor. Mop and all they then threw him on top of the pile of furniture, triumphantly squeezing him into the two feet high space.

Stan screamed with laughter. He had to lay on his side to fit in the space. Before the boys could retreat, he successfully swung the wet mop and hit them with it. Water everywhere.

Everyone in the main office was enjoying the spectacle, it was a great send-off before the Christmas holidays. The boys were splitting their sides.

The door to the back stairs opened. In walked Mr Duckle, John Endsley and Maureen.

02-15

ADJOURN

Mr Duckle looked at the strange young man with contempt. It beggared belief. What was he doing laying in a tiny space above him between the office ceiling and the top of a pile of office furniture? Why did he have a wet mop?

There really was nothing he could say in regard to their deplorable actions and high spirits. He thought it best to ignore the idiot and his moronic friends. It was now five times that he had walked in on the manic trainees and each time none of them was working.

The drip, drip of water onto the blue lino caused a distraction but John Endsley ignored it. If he had a sense of humour, he may have smiled at the small young man, above and behind him, laying on top of a pile of three planning chests.

He addressed the office. "On behalf of the Directors, we would like to thank everyone for their hard work during the past year. This includes of cause the work over the past two days. We recognise the hard work you have all put in to complete the first stage of the office redecoration.

We shall reconvene in the Hereford Arms shortly hoping you can all join us for a seasonal drink and snacks. The office shall be closed until Wednesday the 29th.

In the next fifteen minutes, please gather all of your belongings and valuables that you are taking home. You will not be able to collect then later. Thank you."

Turning his back was like a signal, a starter's gun being fired at a 100-yard athletics race.

Before the Senior Officers had opened the door to the back stairs, some people had put on their coat. Picking up their bags they raced through reception. Then a charge down the front staircase to liberty! Not all would attend the pub. For some, it was just a treat to get home early. To buy that last minute present, a fresh turkey or simply to be with their family.

Dev and Jim helped Stan down onto the blue lino covered floor. Aiming to win the race to the pub the boys frantically got ready. They stored the cleaning equipment away then tidied themselves. With quickly gathered belongings tumbling from their arms, the group finally made their way to reception. As Jim opened the reception door, he found himself the next person in a queue. His pals collided with each other as the door swung back into Ron's shoulder. Mumbling, they looked past him to check the holdup. Spud twisted his body to face Jim. "Decorators," was all he said, then looked forward.

The sound of a man's voice increased in clarity as it approached, "Excuse me, excuse me, scuse mate. Mind your backs folks please."

Everybody stepped aside.

The front end of a colossal ladder followed by a tiny man wearing bib and brace came into view through the open doorway. The decorator seemed to be hanging onto the ladder, it looked as if he was trying to stop it floating away. Behind him came a huge man with half a dead cigarette in the corner of his mouth. Last, was the rest of the ladder with a roll of canvas sheeting on top.

The lead person in the line waited for the ladder to pass then stepped towards the landing.

"Whoa, hold your horses," someone shouted. After the ladder came another two men in paint bespeckled overalls carrying an enormous paint splattered tarpaulin. Rolled and tied with string it sat balanced across each man's shoulders. They both carried a large tin of paint in their free hands. Amusingly, a single mistletoe branch projected from the top of a cloth cap over the second man's face.

"Had any luck?" shouted a voice in the queue.

"Twice," answered the mistletoe man with a broad smile.

"We know someone who would love to get under that with you," crowed another voice from the queue.

As soon as the workmen had moved into the main office the staff exodus continued.

02-16
DRINKS

John, Archie and Mick 'Spud' Murphy entered the packed Hereford Arms. Patrons squeezed together and held their drinks at a distance as the new arrivals made their way through the crowd to the bar where Ollie and Brian were waiting.

"Typical B*** plumbers," grinned John, "always first when there's a beer going."

Brian beamed and ignored the jibe, "What you having?" he asked.

"It's ok, thanks," replied Archie, "Maureen has given us some Christmas beer money to get us started. There should be enough for a few rounds."

Archie ordered the drinks and a spare pint mug. He took a few notes from the money Maureen had given him plus the change from the order then placed them in the empty mug. With the mug positioned on the bar, he placed an empty herbal cigarette packet on top. The mug would hold the whip. People could now buy a drink with the money, and he would not be tied to the bar. He did, however, keep an eye out to check who was dibbing in the whip.

Glass in hand each of the five formed a circle to chat.

There was a continuous flow of work colleagues arriving. In groups, they took money from the whip to purchase their drinks then added the change to the glass. Friends, generally from the same department stood in groups chatting. To protect the food fare, some ferried the buffet from the bar to tables in the back corner of the pub.

"Just seen your herbal cigarette pack over there," Ollie commented to Archie. "Do they really help stop smoking?"

"I believe so," replied Archie. "But if not, I have been told that they are still healthier than ordinary cigarettes. I used to get them for the trainees. You know. They all smoke too much. All day in the office they have a cigarette alight. There were complaints about the smell of the herbal ones, so the boys stopped smoking them."

"I heard," joined in Ollie. "They did smell, er, er, awful. Like a dung heap on fire."

"And the smell sticks to your clothes," added Brian. "I'd get on the train on the way home and people would walk away from me. Apart from the 'strange' ones that is who thought I was advertising," he twisted his head to one side and winked.

"Did I tell you about a few weeks ago, coming back from a site meeting? The train stopped at Earls Court for a few minutes. On got a woman who sat across from me. High heels, short skirt, know what I mean. Nice! I looked up, she had a beard. A full black beard. She wore an odd sort of hat too, sort of lacy. It had plastic daffodils stuck in a band around the top. There was no real shape, just like a piece of net curtain stuck on her head. As though she, or he, had just plonked it there."

"Well," added Archie, "that's Earls Court for you. But if you want to see some really strange sights, you should see what's going on around Sloane Square. They would make your hair curl."

"Another round? Same again?" interrupted Mick.

'Please', they all answered.

John changed the subject. "Where are the girls? I thought they would have been here by now?"

"I heard they were going up west for lunch," answered Mick. "I was talking to Molly this morning. She was all dressed up, so I asked her. They had a table booked for 1.00pm in a Covent Garden restaurant."

"Oh, okay," replied John. Trying to hide his disappointment.

"Missing them, are we Dick?" questioned Ollie. "Dick by name and dick by nature, hey." He sniggered. The others uncomfortably grinned at the snipe.

"Er, you know what?" Mick continued, "for someone of her age that Molly does have a decent figure."

Howls of derision slammed Mick's comment.

"You must be joking," shouted Brian. "How can you even think of that?"

"I didn't mean it like that," protested Mick. "I Just!" He was drowned out with sarcasm.

"Typical B*** Irishman," taunted John, his chance to get even. "Not like what? A couple of dark stouts, and you fancy anything in a skirt. Anyway, I heard she has a sweet spot for your trainee, young Stanley."

In the style of a Roman Emperor, he lifted a thumb from a clenched hand and rotated his hand to make the thumb point down.

"So, you're out of luck." Game, set and match.

"On the subject of women in the office Dick," Ollie grinned, speaking softly, "I don't think we should go any further?" He put a finger to his lips prior to speaking a bit louder, "Where are the Duckles posse? Are they here yet?"

Mick pointed to the back corner, "They came in a while ago. They are over there. Looks like they have got drinks so they must be buying their own."

"I'll nip over to see them. Give them some money from the whip," volunteered John, grasping the chance to distance himself from the current 'lady' conversation.

The boys had earlier arranged a whip round for themselves when arriving at the pub. They were more comfortable in their own little group away from the bar, away from senior members of Duckles staff.

John waded through the crowded pub to get to them. He asked if they were happy before informing them of the office whip on the bar. To cover what they had already spent and add to their whip he gave them £3. After a short awkward dialogue with the younger men, he turned to go back to the other engineers.

As he walked past the pub doors he could hear 'singing' of a sort, outside.

"Ernie, Ernie, Ernieee the fasteeest milkmaaaan in theee weeesst." He knew that voice. The doors opened and in staggered Molly in full flow, 'Ernieee'. Supported by Jill's left arm Molly careered towards the bar. The party girls Sheila, Sam, Maggie and Roisin followed.

Molly had a bunch of mistletoe around her neck. Three of the ladies were still wearing paper Christmas cracker hats, Roisin held an empty bottle of Blue Mun in her hand.

John smiled to himself. Pointing to the corner he welcomed them, "Hi, we are over there by the bar." He led the way, the girls followed giggling.

"I've had too much orange juice in me vodka and orangers," shouted Molly to everybody in the pub.

Time moved on. It was now after 5.00pm. A lot of Duckles people had left for home or private parties. Molly had gone home in a taxi, paid for by Maureen's whip money. Jim, Will and Stan were the only trainees still in the pub.

Noticing that the middle of the bar was clear Stan scurried to invest in another round of alcohol.

Archie noticed that the central part of the bar was clear and dashed across the room to buy some drinks.

They arrived at the bar together, one of those squirming moments when each wished they had made the decision one minute latter. What to say? "Hi Stan, how are you doing?"

"I'm fine thanks," replied Stan. "Er, how are you doing?"

Both offered the other a drink.

At the same time, both replied, "Thank you, I'll get one for you." They laughed together, the confidence of being intoxicated took control.

Stan ordered the drinks, oddly they stood at the bar gossiping.

"What are you doing for Christmas?" enquired Archie. "Do you have anything planned?" Over the past few hours, the beer had gradually reduced Stan's self-restraint and self-consciousness. He explained that he would be at home with his family on Christmas Day and at his girlfriend's home on Boxing Day.

"You have a girlfriend?" acknowledged Archie, "Fab, not Molly by any chance, is it?" He laughed.

"Not so lucky," Stan laughed joyously, real banter from Archie. But he didn't give anything away.

Archie continued, "I wondered if you did have someone on the go. I have seen you in the telephone box outside the office many times lately. Especially at lunch time."

"Oh," replied Stan, blushing.

"Come on Stan, do you call her at lunch time?"

Stan confirmed he did. He had been bursting to tell someone about her, even if it was Archie. Like an open tap his emotions streamed out.

"She is called Bronwyn. A couple of years younger than me, petit with long dark hair. We met at the disco in The Bomb, the Bombardier pub in Barham. I've been seeing her for eight months."

Stanley took a breath and reasoned, "Well, seven months and 15 days actually." He hoped he had retained enough control not to appear too enthusiastic.

Archie asked if Stan had bought her a Christmas present.

"A few really. Perfume and stuff. Tickets to see Stevie Wonderful at the Tammersmith Odeon in January." Stan announced proudly.

"Whoo, that's great, Stevie Wonderful, fab? Have you had many girlfriends?" enquired Archie, guessing the answer would be a big fat no.

"A few, but none lasted as long as this one with Bronwyn," Stan answered, smiling happily.

"Oh! Well, I can give you some good advice then," professed Archie. "If you are going on a hot date and will end up 'doing it'. It's a good idea to 'knock one out' when you are getting ready, before you shower. That way you will last longer when you get down to the real thing later on."

Stan was flustered. He could talk like this with his mates at home. But with an older man, about 30 years old in work?

Being close to inebriated he took it in his stride. "Thanks, Arch, is that what you do," Stan asked, his eyes looking up as his top lip felt for the beer in his glass.

"Oh yes," replied Archie, "always when I'm dating a hot chick, always!" he smiled, "and don't forget contraception you don't want to get tied down at your age."

Will came over and interrupted them. "I think Jim needs to go home," he advised Stan. "He's a bit worse for wear."

Archie and Stan followed Will. Jim assured them he was, 'Fine. Well, just a bit wobbly'.

"I think I'd better go home," Will confessed, "I'm going to the loo, then I'm off."

While Will was away, the others agreed that someone should go home with Jim. Stan volunteered. They would both be to travelling east. Stan knew Jim travelled to Forest Gate station, so it made sense. Will walked with them to the station, helping Stan chaperone and assist Jim, then Stan was on his own.

STAIRS

Everyone in London was a bit wobbly. Jim and Stan didn't look out of place as they negotiated the stairs, escalators and travellers of a similar disposition at interchanges on the Tube and Overground network. Luckily for them the exodus when people left their place of work had passed. Also the homeward journeys of the totally pickled was hours yet.

On autopilot, eight stone Stan with twelve stone Jim on his arm arrived at Forest Gate station. After fighting the closing carriage doors to exit their train, they meandered along the platform to climb the stairs. Two steps up and one down, sometimes one step up and two down the friends persevered. With the help of the handrail, Stan finally got them to the ticket hall at the top. The ticket collector wished them 'a Merry Christmas', he waved them through the barrier. The man had previously decided that as it had taken these two young men fifteen minutes to walk up a set of stairs, there was probably no point in asking to see their tickets.

The pair stumbled out of the station onto the pavement as Jim shouted, "I'm gonna be sick."

"Okay," shouted Stan, heroically struggling to control the human lump on his arm, "do it in the kerb."

"Nooo, there's a bin," Jim shouted, pointing at a waste bin fixed to a lamp post. It was about three feet above the pavement. With Stan supporting his arm, Jim lurched forward just in time he heaved into the waste bin. Stan released the arm, quickly stepping away.

"Eeer! Huey! Aargh!" Coughed Jim from the back of his throat. 'Shlooop!' His stomach exploded as vomit crashed through the bottom-less bin onto his trousers and shoes.

"Waaah, nooo. I'm all F*** wet, now," he wailed in despair. In frustration, Jim bent at the waist to sit on the floor.

"Nooo, you prat." Catching Jim's arm again, Stan tugged and

prodded to persuade Jim to remain upright. Shouting in the drunken man's ear Stanley coerced Jim to avoid sitting in the sick puddle by dragging him to cleaner spot against the station wall. "Have a sit down and rest here," he instructed, exhaustedly.

Shortly, the ticket collector appeared with a mug of cold water. Jim was very appreciative; he swallowed the refreshing liquid which began to revive him.

After another fifteen minutes, despite not agreeing to let Stan take him home, Jim 'looked' better. He insisted Stan left him sitting against the wall to enable his 'bestestish' mate to take himself home. After a loud angry discussion, the boys had a handshake to agree that Stan would escort Jim across Woodgrange Road only. No further.

The ticket collector watched in disbelief as the pair supporting each other stood swaying at the kerb. A concerned driver stopped his vehicle ten feet before them, he signalled to the traffic to stop. The ticket collector had to act fast, he hurried from the station to usher the big one safely across the road. He then returned and escorted the little one through the station forecourt onto the eastbound platform.

02-18

CHRISTMAS

Nearly everybody returned to the office on the Wednesday after the Christmas Break.

As programmed, the builders had completed half of the works. So, to allow the office staff to return to work they had positioned the office furniture to the plans provided by Maureen. One half of the office floor was now grey floor tiles, the other half was blue lino. The walls were different colours and contrasting shades of the same colours.

In order to meet deadlines and facilitate the office redecoration, a lot of Duckles engineering work had been completed before the break. With little to do, the atmosphere in the main office was relaxed. What's more, the main office closed at 4.00pm each evening to allow the builders uninterrupted space to work. Even better for the trainees, the plan was to close on Friday at midday.

Dev hadn't been in all week. They missed his chirpy sarcasm and chuckle. The trainees closest to him began to worry he was unwell. Usually, he phoned one of them if he was sick.

The six lads enjoyed sharing gossip, talking through their holiday experiences. The best scandal was the rumour made up by Will that Stan had taken Molly home after the Christmas drink. Jim was not able to refute this gossip. He had no memory of anything that happened on the 24 and swore he must have travelled home alone.

A vague story immerged about John Smith partnering one of the typists. Earlier, Ron had been in the typist's office collecting post for Brian when he overheard the girls whispering about a flirtatious encounter. At the interesting part, Roisin had booted him out before shutting the door. He stood with an ear against the door for five minutes then gave up.

The boys couldn't find out who was involved or what had actually happened. That didn't stop them guessing it was John Smith and exploring all the romantic possibilities. Each account developed more scandalous, bawdy details. The minds of a group of teenage boys could be much more inventive than the real story.

The group decided to have lunch in the Hereford Arms where the tales evolved to become even more fantastic and outrageous.

Afterwards, 'first day back' tiredness and alcohol numbed their zeal. The afternoon dragged. Stanley was so bored he wished he had some work to do. The only benefit when waiting for a 4.00pm home time was the ninety minutes before a 5.30pm one. Only one day back and they already looked forward to another long weekend. The group couldn't wait to hear the tales of Dev's holiday, they hoped he would be back on Tuesday, 4 January 1972, to complete the gang.

02-19
FURNISHED

First day back at the office in 1972, people greeted each other with a 'Happy New Year', and a handshake.

Their movement up the front stairs and into reception was slow. People looked at each other quizzically, what was the holdup. Perhaps a new 'signing in' procedure?

Maggie sat at the brand-new reception desk, smiling. Waiting to be taught how to use the new telephone exchange system Sheila and Roisin sat opposite her in fancy new armchairs with a new oval coffee table between.

Maureen stood in reception at the door to the main office with a drawing plan in hand. She directed incomers to a large drawing pinned to an easel outside the typist's office. "Please check your name against the plan location," she was instructing. "It will show you the new furniture arrangement with your seat location."

Stan moved through the queue to the main office door. He glanced through the open door towards his drawing board to check if his mates had arrived. There was no one there? His drawing board wasn't there? There were NO drawing boards there?

The office was shiny bright. Newly painted ceilings and walls with new light fittings made it look bigger. The furniture layout was different, it was unsettling as nothing looked familiar.

He entered the room, walked to the easel and studied the layout plan. His new location was at 'Desk 12'. Quickly, Stan took a minute to scan the plan again to check for his mate's new desk positions. Dejected, he couldn't find any of their names on any furniture near him.

Had the trainees been split up? They no longer sat together, misery. Stanley took a deep breath: from this moment he was on his own. His mood changed. Excitedly, he moved between the office furniture exploring the layout, checking the labels for his desk. He felt 'grown up', important, he'd never had a desk before. If nothing else, it was somewhere to sit and eat lunch, even a place to keep his cup.

He walked across the room to roughly where he thought 'Desk 12' was sited. There were numbered labels on each desk, but no names. He found his desk, next to it were his old cabinet, drawing board and stool. Each with his name label still attached. Then, he saw the telephone on his desk. 'Nooo!' He hated answering the phone.

As each trainee arrived the others acknowledged them as they searched for a desk location. The separation of their desks had been a complete surprise. The boys were not silly, each one was aware that the bosses had split them for a reason. Each one quietly kept their head down and played safe by staying away from the others.

Every now and then, one of them would catch another's eye and nod. Soon after, with an interval of just a few minutes, the pair would meet outside by the telephone box for a cigarette and chat.

Mick Murphy appeared about 10.00am. He took his place at 'Desk 11' then said hello to Stan. Within thirty minutes after organising his belongings, he sat on the corner of Stan's desk.

"Hi Stan, Happy New Year," he greeted the young man. "As you can see, everything about Duckles has changed. The hierarchy has decided that the office is to be set up as Engineering Groups.

It's going to work like this, each Engineer will be responsible for one trainee. Unluckily for you, I'm your mentor," he laughed. "If, at any time you get fed up with me or want to learn or work in a different discipline you can request a move to another mentor."

"When we have a panic, as usually happens on every project, you may still be asked to work for someone else. Just to complete that job. Is that okay with you?" he asked.

Stan nodded.

"Any questions," Mick continued.

"No, thanks," Stan replied. "Uhh, sorry, yeah. Not about that. About something else. Do you know where Dev sits? We haven't seen him since before Christmas. A bit worried he is not well, or something?"

"Sorry Stan. Didn't anyone tell you he left," explained Mick. "He got a new job for a company in south London, closer to home plus more money. Didn't he say goodbye?"

Stan shook his head, 'Dev must have had a problem? He would have told him, surely. They could have gone for a beer to say goodbye'.

At lunchtime, the trainees met around Ron's desk. Stanley told them the news about Dev, which they couldn't believe.

"Some mate, didn't say goodbye, just slide away," moaned Franie.

"Perhaps he had his reasons," retorted Jim, "perhaps it happened while we were away for Christmas?"

Ron collected the 'loo roll of remembrance'. Dev's name was the last one on the list with the date, 24 December 1971, it was official.

"Oh, well, it's done now," pondered Tuf. "I wonder if he emptied his cabinet."

"Good point," added Franie, "it might be like the Marie Celeste. Just an abandoned cabinet sitting in the office, and no one knows where the owner has gone. Just disappeared." He lifted his arms as high as his shoulders, opened his hands then pulled a puzzled face.

"Better than that," grinned Jim, "it might be full of buried treasure."

"Not buried treasure you numskull," egged on Franie. "It's not buried, it's in the office. Office treasure, our treasure. Let's have a look for it, quick?"

"Luckily, thanks to Spud's involvement before the break, everything has been given a label with the owners name on," cried Jim as they raced onto the back stairs.

All the furniture that was not used in the new layout had been stacked on the landings beneath each set of stairs. The boys ferociously pulled down the stacked furniture enabling them to check the owner's name labels.

"Got it," yelled Franie. "Here it is, this one, 'Deavan Abraham'." The boys pushed forward, closer, crowding around Fran.

Shrewdly, Fran kept the cabinet in its position under the stairs. Within the smallest of spaces, he managed to examine the cabinet while fending off the marauding hands of the other lads. He slid the top drawer open locating a scale rule.

"Anyone want a scale rule?" he cried.

"Ya, ya, please," requested Will. The scale rule was passed by hand to Will at the back.

"Thanks, brill," he said. Then, "it's an old imperial one, rubbish, that's no good." He placed it on a table in the alcove under the stairs.

Franie kept passing items back, a broken pencil, two razor blades, an old drinking straw. All were rejected by the others.

"Comics," cried Franie.

02-19

"What?" yelled Ron, "not *Awe*? Let's have a look," he pleaded. "I love *Awe* magazine, 'Fantasy Four' and all that."

"The Huge," shouted Will, excitedly.

"Na, nothing like that, one here called *Ebony Pumer*," announced Franie.

"Never heard of it," confessed Ron.

"Me neither," shouted Will.

"Yeah, its *Ebony Pumer*, it's not shiny," continued Franie. "Er, looks like a newspaper, not a comic, hold on, cost twenty-five cee."

"Twenty-five what?" asked Ron.

"Cee," repeated Franie, "I don't know."

The newspapers were passed to the back of the crowd. Will and Tuf studied them. "If these are American, the cee could be cents, 25¢," suggested Tuf.

"Good idea," supported Will, "American newspapers, from America?"

The boys laughed. Fran distributed the newspapers. Stan and Ron sat on the stairs examining one. Jim took one to his desk. The others stood around or leaned against the banisters looking over Tuff's shoulder at his copy.

The content of the papers shocked them. Most of the images, cartoon strips and messages were disturbing.

'OZ Magazine', targeted the hippy generation. It used bright, artistic graphics to generate its message of love and equality for all. It reflected the belief Stan and his mates at home developed during drunken nights after the pub.

At first sight, these newspapers appeared to campaign for equality for everyone, but the message from the cartoons and essays in *Ebony Pumer* was not equality, but Supremacy - Power. It seemed the ideology wasn't to suppress power and share it, but to reverse it.

They couldn't believe Dev would read anything like this and checked the name on the furniture label. Dev was their friend! Did the content of these papers illustrate his true feelings for them? Was that why he never said goodbye?

They returned the newspapers with all of the other items into his cabinet hoping that no one else would ever see them.

RAISE

When Stan arrived home on Thursday evening, his mum informed him of a franked envelope waiting on the mantel piece. A franked envelope, something official?

He stretched across his two brothers who were sitting on the cream tiled fire hearth in front of a roaring fire. The boys grumbled, John was reading the *Bandy*, Eddie the *Deano*. They shuffled away and closed their comics. Stanley reached out to pick up the envelope. He opened it to find a letter from G.H. Duckle. "Got a letter from work," he called out.

"Good news, we hope?" replied his dad licking the length of a cigarette paper with his tongue as he rolled a cigarette.

Stan quickly unfolded the letter, "They are pleased to award me a pay rise!" He called aloud, a bit surprised.

"Well done boy, good work." Dad praised Stan, he flicked the wheel on his Xippo lighter to light the cigarette.

"Oooh, wow," Stan was delighted, 'a salary increase'. After his college attendance history, he didn't expect that. He hadn't mentioned it to his parents.

"This correspondence is private and highly confidential," Stan quoted from the letter, "Please do not share this information with anyone."

He digested the wording of the letter. His new salary was £583. Not too sure what percentage that was, but after flunking college he was pleased to get any increase. It was a bit of a let off, his opinion of John Endsley rose. It seemed he did have a compassionate nature under the stern exterior.

"I'll just find an old pay slip to check how much," he told the family.

"Anyone got a piece of blank paper?" he sang, he was so happy.

"You can use, aaah! Cowson," Pete jumped from his cosy chair, flicking flaming strands of tobacco which had fallen from the cigarette onto his hand. "The back of the envelope," he continued.

Stanley hunted for an old pay slip. "Found one, £10 20p a week," he called.

He sat at the dinner table with the envelope and a pen. "Eh, multiply that, add that, equals that. My old wages were £530 40p a year," he called to his dad.

"What's the new one?" asked Dad.

"Hold on, let's see," Stan scribbled on the back of the envelope. "Now that's a year, so that divided by that, is er, er, that much more, so." He looked up, "Dad, it's about an extra pound a week, not a lot really, but about ten percent."

02-21

CRISIS

Stan was a bit early for work, it was 8.45am and he was already at Gloucester Road station.

As he'd finished reading his current book on the journey to the office, he took the opportunity to stop off at the tobacconists and purchase a new novel.

The trainee got to the office at 8.59am, just enough time to sign in the attendance sheet. He walked into the main office, squeezing through a crowd of people standing at the new green felt noticeboard. Choosing a hot chocolate from the new drinks machine he looked back at the impassioned people around the noticeboard.

'It had only been there a few days', he thought. Someone had put something interesting on it already. A rude calendar perhaps? He smiled, wondering what Miss March looked like. He decided to have a look later.

Walking towards his desk, he saw Ron wave to catch his eye. Stan joined him at his desk.

"Morning," greeted Stan.

"Morning," Ron replied, "have you seen what's on the new noticeboard?"

"No," answered Stan, "is it a rude calendar?"

Ron ignored the witticism, "Did you get a letter about a pay rise?" he asked.

"Might have," answered Stan. Remembering, 'it's private and confidential status'.

"Well," revealed Ron. "Someone did receive one, they have pinned it on the noticeboard."

"Nooo, F***, holy S***," exclaimed Stan. "What? No! They will get murdered, who was it?"

"Don't know, nobody saw anyone do it," replied Ron. "There's been people looking at it since I got here. I heard them saying that the

96

person's name and address has been cut off. No one knows who did it."

"That's clever," declared Stan.

"No, no, look." He was thinking. "It's clever if we all get the same amount, but if we all get different amounts the bosses will know who put it there."

"S***, you're right," agreed Ron, "someone could be in deep S***, unless they did it on purpose?"

Stan went to his desk to start work. He didn't have to worry too much about morning time keeping as Mick always came in a bit late, then stayed late. About an hour later, the phone on his desk rang. He picked it up.

"Ello?" he answered sheepishly.

"Is that Stan," Roisin asked.

"Er, yeah," Stan mumbled.

"Hi, I have a call for you, putting you through caller," she sung in her Irish accent, "you are connected."

"Ello?" Stan mumbled again.

"Hi, it's Jim, Stan, is that you?"

"Yeah, it's me, are you ok. I haven't seen you yet today?"

"No, no, listen, I have a problem and can't get into work," Jim replied. "I'll explain. Don't tell anyone, but I'm trapped in Stella."

"You are trapped? In what? I can't hear you," whispered Stan.

"In Stella." Repeated Jim.

"You are trapped? In a cellar? What you doing in a cellar? Do you want me to call the Fire Brigade?" suggested Stan.

"No, no, me and Sst-Ella are stuck together," repeated Jim.

"I thought you said Stella. It doesn't make sense," questioned Stan.

"Yeah, yeah, me and Sst-Ella are stuck together, one can't move without the other," whispered Jim. "Look, listen."

He spelled out his problem.

'He had stayed at his girlfriend's house the night before. They were in separate bedrooms, but when her parents left for work Stella joined him in his bed.

They were in the middle of some bedroom gymnastics, when they heard the front door open. Scared, they stopped and laid motionless, praying. Stella's mum shouted up the stairs. She had come back for her season ticket and was leaving again for work.

After the "all clear," Jim and Stella felt uncomfortable. Jim tried to get off the bed, but he was trapped inside her. Locked together, like two dogs you see in the street.

Stella got a friend to phone her GP. Apparently, there was nothing to worry about. The shock of hearing the front door had probably made Stella go into spasm and tighten. All they could do was relax; everything should slowly return to normal'.

Stan was gob smacked, he didn't know what to say or do.

"You still there Stan," called Jim. "We've been like this for nearly two hours but at least we have now been able to get to the phone. Crawling about like a spider, it ain't easy.

Hopefully we'll be alright soon."

"Yeah, yeah, that's amazing. Like a spider?" Stan chuckled, "never heard of that before, so sorry. I'll, er, I'll just tell Maureen that you've got a massive growth on the end of your cock, and it's so big you can't put your trousers on."

"Don't make me laugh you donut, it hurts," pleaded Jim.

"It only hurts when you laugh," chuckled Stanley. "If she's just hanging around, say ello to Sst-Ella for me. Okay, I'll tell Maureen you phoned in with an upset stomach, Okay?"

"Yeah, cheers mate, see you next week," thanked Jim.

UNEASE

The next week started quietly at Duckles. Not a tranquil quiet, but a silent aggression of unrest.

When Stan entered the main office that morning, there was a second pay rise letter with name and address removed, pinned to the green noticeboard. A group of people stood around the noticeboard talking in whispers.

More letters joined the protest. Comparable to the 'mark of a masked' man, no one was ever seen adding their letters of dissent. However, the number of letters increased so much that new ones had to be pinned on top of preceding ones.

Stan had previously been surprised, happy, that he had received some type of pay increase.

Alas, with so much discontent in the office he considered joining the revolt. He thought it through.

Conceivably, screwing up college twice and getting caught five times by Mr Duckle while skylarking about was enough to get anyone the heave-ho. Life had a habit of kicking him in the teeth. Not knocking them out, just loosening them a bit. He could sense an omen when things were going adrift. The warning wasn't a sign of panic, but of reform. It suggested there was a need to swallow, change direction then move on.

Perhaps he was learning something, no longer a child. Maybe, he should be thankful he had a job. When everything is stacked against you, cowardice is the better part of valour. He decided not to get involved, 'to protect his teeth'.

About 3.00pm the fire alarm sounded, "Rrrr*****."

On hearing the noise, Stan looked up surveying a sea of blank faces. No one moved. He decided to go with the flow and carried on with his work.

Ten minutes later the sound was still deafening everybody. Without warning the reception door flew open, two alert firemen raced in. Hurrying around between the desks and drawing boards they were 'looking' for something.

No one moved.

One fireman stopped to speak to Franie, "The fire alarm is sounding, can you smell smoke?"

Franie looked up from his drawing board, "No!" He retorted indignantly.

"You are in danger, why are you still here? Why haven't you evacuated the building?"

The fireman was becoming very angry. He confronted the people in the office, "There is a fire alarm sounding it means there could be a fire in this building, you are in danger, please leave the building now."

A third fireman entered the office from the back stairs. He walked to the others and shrugged, "They are just sitting working upstairs as well?"

The sight of the third fireman prompted people in the main office to evacuate. The lead group were just about to leave through the reception door when a tall, stocky fireman appeared. He stood in the doorway, purposely blocking their exit. Without any respect for the office workers, he sent them back to their seats. This man meant business.

The fireman stood, hands on hips and scowled. He remained silent, sweeping his head in an arch staring out the Duckles people. No one dared look up. No one wanted a face off.

It seemed like ages before he let rip. "I can't believe that the fire alarm has been ringing and when the Fire Brigade get here you are still sitting, working. It has now been ringing for twenty minutes and you are still here. Never, in my days as a Chief Fire Officer have I ever experienced anything like this. Each one of you is putting my men's lives in danger. I don't care about any of you, because you are all idiots. I care only about these brave men who are sent here to save the lives of idiots."

He strolled around like a teacher at primary school. "I have the authority to close this building, I will be speaking to your superiors about this in a minute. Now, get out of my sight, go directly to your designated fire assembly point - GO!"

As one, the office stood, picking up their belongings they moved towards the door. He now stood to one side of the door bogging out every single person as they walked towards him.

His face was pure loathing. Would anyone have the backbone to look up or ask him to move away from the door?

"STOP!" he shouted, "What are you muppets doing with your coats and bags? You are not going to a party. I know it is a cold and wet January afternoon, and you want to protect the nice presents you got at Christmas, but this is a fire drill. Take them back to your desks, now."

Meekly and in silence everyone returned coats and bags to their seats. They turned back to the door 'the Sergeant Major' had vanished.

With the aggressor gone, the feeble became strong. "Who does he think he is, lucky he left when he did, I was just going to..."

The Duckles staff quickly made their way to the assembly point before he came back.

After a while, people from the other office floors arrived to join them. At first, the gathering together gave them a tribal courage against a common grudge. But 'the Sergeant Major' left them in the cold and wet for more than forty minutes. Their bravado slipped away.

They couldn't even sit in a pub as they were shut until 5.30pm. In the end, soaking wet, cold and beaten they just wanted to be in doors, dry and warm.

Around 4.40pm, Maureen with John Endsley, both carrying an umbrella and wearing suitable winter overcoats appeared at the assembly point. They told the gathering that they could finally return inside. Firstly, they should congregate in the main office.

Once they were all settled, John Endsley told of the twenty-minute dressing down he and Maureen had received from the Chief Fire Officer. 'They were all in it together', he reiterated the words of the 'Sergeant Major' Fire Officer. It must never happen again.

Graciously, everyone was allowed to go early. The rumour instigated by a teenager trainee was that Maureen didn't want people dripping on the new grey floor tiles.

Stan left the office with Jim. As they walked through the door into reception Jim held his arm by his side pointing a finger upwards at the green noticeboard. It had been cleared of every scrap of paper. No evidence or indication of any office grievances remained. Never, was a word of the protest ever disclosed.

On the way home, Stan sat quietly on the train. He had his novel open, but the events of the day kept flowing through his head, he couldn't concentrate on his book.

The turmoil of the day made him appraise his life. At home, he had a loving girlfriend and a loving family. But what of work? Would he be at Duckles all his working life? Did he want to be at Duckles all his working life?

He had to consider the options. There was a lot of dissatisfaction in work. He really needed to go back to college to gain a qualification. Dev had left, his friends were talking about leaving. His journey to work was so long and expensive. He had to make a decision.

02-23

UNCERTAINTY

It took Stan a few weeks to decide if he should try to change the direction of his life.

He thought back to 1969. He had left school and was looking for a job. Circumstances, not choices had decided where he worked. Maybe, it could be called fate.

Stan had had an appointment with the government job finder agency, but they had not really been much help. As there were few job vacancies, he was advised to continue his education. He had taken their advice and started to study both 'A' level Pure Maths and Applied Maths at a different school. Stan couldn't settle, it didn't work out, he quit after a few months. In hindsight, he was full of education and consequently needed a change.

During the period after school, he was unsure of what to do next. He lived on his paper round money which meant he had a great social life. However, the future was a puzzle. Mentally drained, fatigued and lacking self-confidence he knew he would have to get a job. His parents must have understood as they supported him as much as possible without interfering. Irene and Pete left him to make his own decisions. They gave him 'me time' to clear his mind.

After three months of being inactive, he was ready. Finally, he started searching through copies of the News and Standard newspapers. As he delivered them every night, he had daily access to hunt through the Jobs Vacant sections.

Stanley applied for two situations that he favoured. Both these opportunities he applied for replied offering interviews. He was amazed that employers want to see him, his self-esteem grew or was he just lucky?

He attended the interviews two weeks before going on a boating holiday with his family. Bizarrely, he had enough confidence to buy beer in a pub but not enough inner strength to attend an interview. He didn't want to travel in London alone. His mum travelled with him; she sat in a café while he was at each meeting.

The first was at G.H. Duckle a building services engineers, the second at a giant Petrochemical company called Nurse Hooper based in Paddington.

NH was his preference. They would train him to work in the modelling room. He would become a 'modeller', designing and building miniature 3D oil refineries before construction commenced on site. His dream job, one of Stan's hobbies was making Aerofix plastic models at home. He had started to design a car for a Dauxhall Car Design competition. He really enjoyed woodwork and metalwork at school. This vacant position was ideal, also NH were paying more money than the engineers.

Within a few days of the interviews, he received a job offer from Duckles. He dallied, waiting to hear from NH. Daily, he checked the post. NH didn't correspond, his self-confidence slipped.

The day before his holiday came sooner than he had wished, he had to make a decision. Did he ignore Duckles, gambling a NH letter would be on the door mat when he returned from holiday? Was employment in the building services industry going to be his only hope?

It was now critical, he had had the offer from the engineers for ten days without replying. The opportunity may have already been lost? He needed a job accepting the offer became his only choice.

A week later, when the family arrived home from their holiday there was a letter on the door mat. To Stanley's disbelief, it was from NH requesting Mr Paterson attend a second interview. He was so disappointed. His hands were tied. Duckles was reality, NH was no longer a possibility.

Now, again in the real world three years later, Stan sighed. He understood that only he was responsible for not making the best of his opportunities at G.H. Duckle. He had failed, if anything relating to his working life was going to change only one person could make it happen.

02-24
INDICATOR

For a few months, Stanley had been looking for opportunities to change his work situation. He sometimes remembered and pondered on the earlier advice given by John Smith, 'to get out of the industry'. It seemed a long time ago.

Things were changing. Ron had left a few weeks ago. He had started a new job in Insurance. Today, Jim had told Stan that he was also leaving. Stan was gutted, he's mucker was leaving. The Duckles posse was finished.

Jim was moving to a Local Authority in east London, actually changing disciplines from Engineering to Civils. As he was getting married to Stella later in the year, they would need the extra money. Jim made Stan promise that he would go to the wedding. There was no way Stan was going to miss that. They agreed, when everything had been finalised Jim would send Stan and Bronwyn an invitation with a map on how to get to the church and reception.

There were two job adverts in the evening papers that interested Stan. They both intrigued him, but neither was in engineering. Then again, back to John Smith's suggestion that Stan should work in banking. More an instruction than suggestion, perhaps Stan was more suited to banking or insurance. He needed to find out before making a decision. The vacancies intrigued him. One position was as a 'Trainee Bank Teller', the other for an 'Apprentice Millionaire'. He applied for both.

Once more, in spite of currently working as a Trainee Engineer both businesses offered him an interview. He was astonished. Perhaps his 'O' Level passes from so many years before gave him an edge. He must have something that employers wanted?

The first interview was at the Centafield Bank in Fen Street, near Bank Station. Stan was asked to wait in the banking hall when he arrived. While he sat there, he noticed the strong smell of polish. Every solid surface was highly polished dark wood. The circular columns, wall panelling, the floor. The counter and the chairs. Everything was reflective surfaces, like a house of mirrors at the funfair. The smell made him uneasy, he had no idea why, but he knew then that he couldn't work in a highly polished room. At the interview, Stanley was forthright, rather than waste time he immediately informed the interviewer that he couldn't work in the building.

The second interview was near London Bridge. If someone was bonkers enough to advertise for an 'Apprentice Millionaire', Stan was mad enough to see the joke. He considered the potential income on offer, also working with a like spirited fun person as an employer would be brilliant. He had nothing to lose. If he earned a £1M, he could accept some hardship.

The trainee engineer entered the building and made his way up the stairs to the floor of the address he had been given. A short time after he rang the doorbell a smartly dressed middle aged man answered the door. After inviting Stanley in, he escorted him to a private office. The man introduced himself as Mr Charles Prenton Smith, a Senior Manager at Equity Life Reserve or ELR.

Charles was very polite. He talked Stan through the company history, the enormous client base, funds held at international level. The company had been dealing and based in North America since 1890. Now was the time for it to expand into the UK and Europe. It was a 'unique opportunity for the right person'.

Charles explained how the organisation's pay structure worked. For the first month, ELR would pay him £50.00. For the next four months, he would be paid £60.00 a month plus commission on his sales. After that, he would be paid only commission on his sales. Charles agreed that this didn't seem like a Millionaire creating process, but ELR only targeted the top 10% of highest earners in the world. Commission was very high. He would be paid a monthly commission for each client he brought to the Company.

Stan agreed to sit two tests, one numeric the other English Language. He was taken to a small desk at the side of the room to perform the exams. With zeal, Stan raced through the papers scoring 100% in each.

Charles appeared very happy with the results. He then clarified how contact would be made with potential clients.

The office retained many books, brochures and magazines with links to the elite, famous and wealthy. There were also telephone directories for individuals and companies. Each day for the first three weeks Stan would sift through these to build a directory of potential clients.

Charles articulated, "You search in a society magazine to find Sir X and his daughter xx at a function. You arrange a page in your personal client directory for them. Add their names and relationship, the function, the date. If it's a birthday, add that then calculate the people's ages.

Next, check the telephone directories, locate the phone numbers and home address of your targets. Check Companies House for Company Directorships. Do you comprehend Stan, you build a bibliography of each person together with their family and friends."

Stan nodded, "Yes, like a secret agent," he inferred.

Charles smiled, "Exactly, good, but we do them no harm, we help them and their families."

He continued with his briefing. "You telephone them and try to speak to them, but only for one minute. If you can't speak with them, ask the person who answered the phone to give them your name. Make sure you tell someone your name. Tell everybody your name, you want it to be subliminal. Mention something you know about them, the party perhaps.

You repeat the same process a month later. Only disclose what you do for a living after they have trust in you. Working in finance if you are pressured. Leave it a while, but once you get on speaking turns after a few telephone conversations arrange a meeting. Buy them lunch, a drink in a local pub, or a meal. Don't scrimp, go big. A top London Hotel or restaurant. What you spend will have a relationship to the business you bring back. After a meet or two, you can dig around start suggesting financial services. They are your friends, if they don't have a need ask about their friends. Seal the deal.

We can go through this once again after you have joined us. We will sit with you to help through the first weeks. As a privilege, we shall pass three current potential Client contacts to your account when you start. All the leg work is done, you will just need to seal each deal and take the commission."

Charles pressed on, "Stanley, I think you may be suitable, you are the type of person we seek. There is one last thing we need to do."

Searching in his desk drawer, Charles took out his diary and telephone book. "We know that this type of work requires a certain type of personality profile. Therefore, we employ a specialist in Harley Street to undertake some tests for us. We consider 'Psychological Testing' a more neutral and credible method of assessing an applicant. I would like to arrange a testing study."

He fingered through the dates in his diary. Then picked up his telephone.

Stan had realised for some time during the interview that this type of work wasn't for him.

This was worse than working in the bank. Cold calling, harvesting details of people's private lives. He hated making phone calls, even at Duckles. Charles was a nice man, he seemed to like Stan. It looked as if Charles would be offering him the job, but Stan didn't have the self-esteem to refuse the offer.

"Do you pay for these tests?" enquired Stan.

"Precisely, we do," replied Charles, "no need for concern my boy. They are all part of the interview. We need to know that the candidate is a perfect match with ELR. From my experience, I would think you are a fit."

"Well," confessed Stan. "Before you make any arrangement for tests, I would like you to know that I'm not so sure about this job. I wouldn't like you to lose money on tests that I don't take."

Charles' face dropped.

"I need time to think about this type of work," Stan lied. "It is very different from engineering."

"Well, Stanley my boy." Charles proposed, "I can see you have a point. How about you sleep on it. You have my number, please telephone me in the next two days and tell me your decision."

Stan thanked Charles, they shock hands and he left for home. The nervous engineer knew that he would never have the courage to phone Charles and turn him down. He didn't want to disappoint him. He wondered, hoped that Charles also knew.

Stan sat on the Tube on the way home. He felt worn out, the interview had been absorbing, full on. Although he wasn't really interested in the job, he found it fascinating. He had listened to every word. He wondered just how many people knew about this cloak and dagger business of selling. Selling what? He didn't even know what ELR actually did. He didn't know what they sold.

His mind drifted, 'Did they actually sell anything? Was ELR a cover? Perhaps, it was a clandestine operation? He may have just been in a MI5 cell which investigates rich and famous people. Charles could be codenamed "M," the Harley Street specialist may be "H"?' He would never know.

The two interviews he attended proved one thing. Of the two industries - finance and engineering - he was more cut out to work in the later.

Stanley enjoyed engineering work. He relished the drafting, calculation and design challenges. He could lose himself so deeply in a task that the day would pass 'in minutes'.

Also, he took great personal satisfaction that what he drew and designed would become a tangible, functioning product for the community.

It would be easier now to pick a path to shape his working future. It would have to be in engineering.

02-25

ONWARD

Archie entered the main office holding his lunch. A sandwich in a brown paper bag in one hand with a cardboard cup of soup and Aztec bar in the other.

Stan was at his desk checking through yesterday's evening papers for job vacancies. He hadn't had time the previous night as he had seen Bronwyn. He always tried to catch the last bus home at 00.15am which got him home around 00.40am. If he missed the bus, he walked, which meant he got home an hour later.

There was a vacancy for a trainee working on the London Underground. 'That may be interesting', he thought. Marking the bottom of the page with a red pencil he turned the page.

Archie walked up to the coat stand a short distance from Stan. He placed his lunch on Mick's desk, removed his double-breasted sheep-skin overcoat then hung it on the coat stand.

He gazed over to Stan. "How are you, Stanley?" he asked.

"Fine, thank you," responded Stan.

"And your girlfriend? Briony was it?" Archie continued.

"Yeah, she is good as well, thank you," replied Stan.

Archie moved to Stan's desk shuffling around he looked down at the newspaper, "Is there anything of interest in the paper?" he enquired.

"No," replied Stan. He looked up, candidly he spoke, "Ssssh, I'm looking at job vacancies."

"For you or Bronwyn? I remember," Archie probed. "Or for both of you?"

Stan confirmed he was looking for himself. Not necessarily to move on, but to check what was available, he lied. He told Archie that he had just seen the London Underground vacancy.

"Why not go for it?" submitted Archie. "Even if you don't want the job. It will be good experience. People don't do many job interviews in their whole life, they don't learn the art. You need to develop a way of projecting yourself. You have to learn to make them want to employ you, not the other way round."

"Okay," whispered Stan. "I'm not too sure if I know enough to work somewhere else, just yet?"

"How long have you been here?" asked Archie.

"Nearly three years," revealed Stan.

"Look Stan," Archie continued, "you know and have learned lots of things that other people don't know. It's just that because you do it every day, you don't realise. You do things now that you didn't even know existed when you first came here.

If someone off the street came in here now and was asked to design a frictional pressure drop pipe or ductwork system, they wouldn't even understand the words. Does your dad know what that is?"

"Er, no," smiled Stan.

"That's it. You need to gain some confidence, but you are a good hard worker. Don't be afraid to branch out. If you can earn more money, give it a try.

Oops, soups getting cold." Archie finished chatting, picked up his lunch and made for his desk.

Taking Archie's advice, Stan applied for the London Underground job and another position with an engineering construction company, HWB.

Both interviews went well. He was not offered the LUL position as the interviewer was looking for someone with more experience, but he was offered the other position with HWB and accepted.

He felt quite emotional when he left G.H. Duckle. He had made some good friends along the way, been given tons of exceptional advice.

Things never stay the same it was his turn to move on. His name was added to the 'loo roll of remembrance' to join those of all past G. H. Duckle employees.

03

BUTTONS

Chapter Marker

03-01
START

Stan started his new job at H.W. Button. He now journeyed to St James Park station, three Tube stations shorter than before. He would never be late for work again?

He walked the short distance to Victoria Street before entered the old white stone and red brick building. It was next to Coutts Bank, near the corner and easy to find. Inside the double doors was a white stone spiral staircase with black wrought iron spiral formed railings serving the four floors. An old matching wrought iron cage lift for about four people operated within the staircase.

Stanley wasn't keen on heights, an 'operate it yourself cage lift' wasn't his preferred method of vertical travel. He took the stairs to the third-floor suite of offices. The third-floor landing opened onto a tee shaped corridor with separate rooms on each side. All the rooms on that floor were leased by Button's. As the stairs and corridors were accessible by anyone in the building each room was individually locked when unoccupied.

He made his way to reception where he introduced himself to Sandie, the receptionist, telephonist and typist. She was very smiley, a good looking blond over six feet tall.

Presently, Mr Willis entered reception cigarette in hand. Stan noticed he used a cigarette holder. Other than in 1930's black and white movies, it was the first time he had seen anyone use one. Also, he had a very strange way of smoking a cigarette. He always held them in two fingers with his thumb on the bottom. The cigarette pointed upward sitting adjacent to his right ear, just away from the side of his face. When he moved the cigarette to his mouth, he would use an exaggerated looping arm motion away from his face then back to his mouth. The movement, like a salute was reversed when he took the cigarette from his mouth to his ear. This was done whether standing, sitting or while walking.

He greeted Stan, shock his hand and escorted him to the office where he would be working.

Terry Willis, the Managing Director, was the person who had inter-viewed Stan for the vacant position. He was well spoken, a bit plumy who tended to hang onto words as he spoke.

Stan guessed the man with thinning grey hair was about fifty years old. He remembered his humiliating faux pas when they first met. Walking through the corridor as he arrived for the interview he bumped into a man and asked for 'the writer'. The man calmly explained that 'the writer' was the person who sent the letter. By chance, it was him.

They entered the office. Two men in deep conversation stood in a small glazed and panelled inner office. Mr Willis interrupted them to introduce Stanley. One was Harald Theobald Fitzpatrick the Site Engineer and Contracts Manager; the other was Charlie Atkinson the Company Accountant. Mr Willis departed the room and 'left them to it'.

Harry pointed Stan to a desk with a drawing board adjacent in the larger office area and told him to make himself at home. He would be with him shortly.

The office was in need of decoration, it had bare wooden floorboards coloured with age. There was a tall open stone fireplace with a large mirror positioned above. High windows with low sills ran along one side looking onto Victoria Street. What appeared to be the bottom half of an ancient gas fire sat in the hearth. It was just a few pipes assem-bled as connected loops with small holes in the top. Stan guessed it was a fire because one end was connected to the gas cock sticking out of the floor. The first time he lit it he used his lighter and suffered singed eyebrows and lashes.

He later developed the art of lighting it. He learned to turn the gas cock on, stand back, wait a moment then strike a match and throw it at the fire. An enormous flame would explode eight feet into the room them small flames lit along the holed pipes.

The majority of Button's projects involved the installation of systems within buildings. Areas of Stan's duties were similar to those at Duckle's, but parts were more hands on. He would now be involved with the actual 'nuts and bolts' of the industry. Able to become involved in solving site problems. He would be able to see and touch the finished items, flush a toilet connected to a pipe he had drawn, stand in a building his design had heated or cooled.

03-01

Stan sat listening to the two in the small office. Charlie reminded him of a vampire. He was tall and skinny in a navy suit with a grandpa vampire hair style. Harry, or Harry TF as he was sometimes called was like Archie back at Duckles but with nobs on. He was extremely tall and skinny, sophisticated, incredibly well spoken. His clothes were amazing. They had 'expensive' written all over them. He wore a large gold ring on nearly every finger. A thick curb link bracelet around each wrist with a matching necklace worn outside his shirt.

Stanley later discovered that as well as working at Buttons he owned a small building company plus an upmarket trend setting boutique on the south coast.

Stan thought to himself, If Harald is called Harry TF, then Archie - Archibald Fortescue Jones - would have been called Archie FJ. He would have to tell Jim when he saw him.

Sometime later Harry sat with Stan. Firstly, he explained his conversation with Charlie.

A building company had not paid Buttons for works they had done. The same builder had done it before under a different company name but with the same Director. Charlie was distressed, he felt he should have spotted the Directors name on the Contract Documents.

As with the first time, if the building company declared itself bankrupt Buttons would get nothing. If it went into administration as well as not receiving payment for works, all of their vehicles, equipment, materials etc that are on site would be confiscated by the Administrator.

"Sorry to advise you Stanley, but you may not be working in your new job for very long," apologised Harry. "Best keep an ear out in case you need another job."

Harry got them both a coffee from the machine then talked Stan through his first duties. He gave him a program of when each item was required and pointed to the cardboard boxes in the corner where all the project files and drawings were filed. Stanley was working on his tod! He would quickly find out how much he had learned at G.H. Duckles.

03-02

CHARLIE

Charlie paid Stan at least two visits a day. He would plant his right buttock on the corner of Stan's desk with one leg swaying, coffee in hand, cigarette in the other. He loved a chat.

Watergate, the Rate of Inflation, Olympics, Terror Attacks, Cod War, Space Travel. It was as if he read or heard some news then made his way to Stan for a discussion. Most of the time Stan was alone so he indulged in the gossip. Participating in the discussions did break up his day.

One day, Stan was busy working to meet a deadline. Charlie's rear end dropped on his desk, cigarette in mouth.

"What do you think this is Stan?" questioned Charlie, pushing his open hand towards Stan's face.

Stan looked, it took a moment to focus, "I don't know," he replied.

"Look, I have the same on the other hand," added Charlie, swapping hands.

Stan looked again, "No sorry, I don't know."

"Can you see the purple stain?" Charlie continued.

Stan could see that both hands had purple stains on then, but he didn't know what had caused it.

"I'll give you a clue. I have had these stains since Saturday when I was gardening. Tried everything, can't wash it off."

The door opened. Sandie walked in. Seeing Charlie's back, she speeded up. Charlie heard her and stood, turning to face her.

"Sandie!" Charlie called, "look at my hands, what do you think made these stains?"

The door closed. Too late – Sandie had gone. Charlie turned back to Stan and continued his guessing game.

"I've tried soap, paraffin, petrol, nothing washes it off. What do you think this stain is?"

Stan shook his head.

"Cola, disinfectant, everything," Charlie added to his list.

Stan shook his head.

"I'll tell you, shall I, I'll tell you. These stains, the ones I can't wash off are the stains of a, I'll tell you is that okay, the stains of a Royal Sneezewort."

Stan suppressed a giggle. Lucky his Duckles friends weren't listening.

"Well Stan, the real reason I nipped in," Charlie changed the subject, "is these English Football Pools numbers." He pulled a dirty, scrunched up slip of paper from the 'lucky' pocket inside his jacket.

Stan moved his head for a closer look at the piece of paper. Like a naughty schoolboy hiding a bawdy photograph the accountant moved it behind his back.

He explained that he had been using the same eight number selection on the 'Pools' since 1961. He assured Stan, that as every possible scenario in the universe would eventually happen at some point these numbers would one day win the top prize. Only recently a man in Hampshire had won a record £512,000. It was guaranteed! So, because of the principles of probability and destiny Charlie's numbers had to be more valuable than other numbers.

"So, Stan," he enquired, expectantly, "would you like to buy these lucky numbers from me?"

Stan thanked him for the offer, but declined.

"How about £12 for the lot?" he proposed, "that's only £1 50p each?"

Stan rejected the offer again. He wasn't interested, even if it was only £12 that was a week's wages.

"Thanks for the offer, but I couldn't afford them even if I wanted them," he smiled. "If you don't mind, I best get on with this." He turned back to his work.

Charlie returned the crumbled piece of paper to his dirty pocket, "Thanks for the chat," he cheered, opening the office door to return to his office.

About 12.00am the office PA system crackled. "Could Stan Paterson please come to reception." It was Sandie. 'Cakes?' Wished the young engineer.

He hurried to reception hoping for a chocolate éclair. But when he got there, he had a surprise.

"Hi," Sandie greeted him. "Are you very busy at the mo?" she enquired.

"Enough," answered Stan, "but I'm going to site later, what is it?"

Sandie continued, "Terry and Kathy think that we need a back-up for me on the telephones. You have been voted the lucky person. What do you think?"

"Err," Stan's usual reply when confronted with something that made him nervous.

"Kathy has asked me to teach you how to use the switchboard?" Sandie smiled.

"Err, okay then," a despondent Stan accepted. It was worse, he would be trapped at a switchboard for hours.

"Come round here then and sit on my lap," enticed Sandie. Stan stood rock solid with an ever-blushing face.

"Come on Stan only joking, you know me by now? Get yourself a chair, I'll show you."

For about an hour, Sandie showed Stan how to operate the switch-board. There were grimy white revolving ping pong balls wearing jaded black numbers, with cables, sockets and extension ping pong balls. Then, the dreaded PA system!

"Just hold this button down, lean forward and speak normally, calling Mr Willis please, telephone."

They finished, Stan left his first lesson to have lunch.

He was really glad it was over - for now.

QUIET

A nice bright day in June: 10.00am, coffee time. Charlie pushed the door open with his shoulder to enter Stan's office. He was excited. He had earlier received some vouchers for free chocolate bars.

He placed his coffee cup on Stan's desk. Sat on his usual corner, then lit a cigarette. For effect before speaking, the showman bent his head back then blew a long chain of smoke rings into the air.

"Stanley, have you seen the competition to name a new chocolate bar? On the form, you have to record the name you suggest and complete a four-question quiz." Slowly, he stood up, walked forward then stood on tip toes to see out of the window. He turned and went back to Stan's desk, a puzzled look on his face.

"You can win £100," he resumed. "If you get all the questions right, you win free vouchers for any chocolate bar they make. And," extra pleased with himself, "I know all the answers." Charlie stood up again, he moved closer towards the windows. "Can you hear that?" he asked Stan.

"Hear what?" queried Stan.

"That's it," continued Charlie walking to the windows to study the street outside. "There's no noise outside." Generally dismissive of the rumble, peep and brum brumming of the constant flow of vehicles along Victoria Street, the silence caused his senses concern.

"There are no cars, no traffic. Only a few people."

"Could it be a major car crash, somewhere?" suggested Stan, rising from his seat.

"Doubt it? Woohoo, come here Stan, quick, look, look." Sliding the bottom half of a sash window up Charlie encouraged Stan. He thrust his head through the opening then rotated it left and right.

Stan raced over, "What?"

"Look," Charlie pointed to the street below, "no one."

"Hold on," Charlie was bouncing off the walls, "listen, a squeak? Hear it?"

"Nah," confessed Stan.

"Wow, look," the accountant pointed to the right.

Stan squeezed his head through the opening alongside Charlie's, "What?"

"Street cleaners, hundreds of um."

"I can't see, your heads in the way," joked Stan.

Stan saw them. The scene reminded him of Pary Moppins. There were two columns of street cleaners pushing their trolleys along the pavement, one cart behind the other. One line on each side of the street. About every fifteen yards, with military precision the one at the back would stop. Eventually, they were standing equally spaced along the length of Victoria Street.

Charlie leaned so far out of the window Stan thought he would fall out. On a signal, each cleaner swept the area around them. When they had a pile of waste, they brushed the sweepings onto a shovel and placed them into their cart.

Sandie excitedly came into the office, "Have you seen outside?" she asked.

Charlie's stare followed another signal? The street cleaners dispersed in groups disappearing down side roads off the main thoroughfare.

"Yeah, the street cleaners, they are going now," Charlie answered Sandie.

"No, no, the soldiers? There are hundreds of them marching along the road. Listen, you can hear the trump, trump of their metal stud boots rapping on the road. It's growing louder, they are coming from the Abbey."

Stan and Charlie stuck their heads out of different windows. Two lines of Guards in full dress uniform with shouldered arms, matched along the street. The red tunics were visible yards from the viewers, polished belt buckles reflected sunlight in every trajectory. The troops separated in pairs at intervals. Without any command the rear pair stopped, wheeled then marched arm swinging to opposite pavements. With exaggerated knee lifts, they turned to face each other.

Kathy, the Office Manager entered the room followed by Dyfed and Barry. She made straight for an open window to share her knowledge with the others.

She had heard on the radio that, apparently Grand Duke Jean and

QUIET   123

his wife Princess Josephine Charlotte of Luxembourg were coming to the UK on a Royal Visit. They would travel on a train from the airport to Victoria Station.

There were now people hanging out of windows on all sides of the street. Strangely, there were very few people actually in the street. 'Not like you see on TV', thought Stan. 'There were no cheering crowds here, or flag waving'.

Guardsmen were collapsing in the heat. As one fell to the floor, a couple of medics rushed out from their hiding place, they resussed him before carrying him back with them.

Instantly, a substitute Guardsman would appear to fill the vacant position.

Charlie started to give the people in the office a history lesson. "Isn't it strange how history is always alive," he proclaimed. Sandie made for the door.

"Perhaps the ancestors of some of these very Guardsmen stood in this room. The building was constructed in 1870 as apartments for Guards Officers stationed at Buckingham Palace. How about that?"

A few low groans slipped from the congregation's lips.

"Believe me," Charlie continued, "that is why the mirrors in these rooms are so high. It's so that the Guardsmen could adjust their Bearskin Cap before attending the Palace."

The phone rang, incoming calls at reception had been diverted by Sandie. She answered it. The caller was Harry TF for Stan.

Harry informed Stan that there was some important work to be done the next evening, Wednesday. It would be after work so he could have Thursday off as a reward if he helped.

Stan agreed to help. Harry instructed him to attend work as usual, but tell his mum that he would be home late. He was to bring in some old clothes, jeans, sweatshirt, shoes, gloves and a hat. If he had one, also a torch. They would get changed before they left the office.

There was a slight murmur from outside the window.

Stan concurred with Harry, put the phone down then went straight back to the window.

An unfamiliar noise was increasing in volume, puzzled he listened for a clue. It was the sound of horse's hooves clipping on the tarmac road surface. The procession was coming from Victoria Station on the left, moving towards Westminster Abbey.

In the vanguard were mounted Household Cavalry, their polished silver breastplates matching their equally reflective helmets sparkled in the sunshine. Groomed horse's tails danced to the rhythm of the trot. Three magnificently ornate ceremonial carriages followed, then more cavalry. The Queen was seated with her guests in the first of the three carriages.

There was a rapid volume increase in the loud thundering noise as the entourage passed below, the high speed of the horses meant it lasted just seconds. Onlookers witnessed the last horses leave towards the Abbey then became aware of a drawback. There was tons, mounds of horse S*** on the road. The minute the horses passed under the windows, up came the aroma.

"Ewww! Peew!" howled Kathy, pulling back from the open window, "that will clear your sinuses."

It reeked. Everyone hastily slammed down their windows, 'whiffy'. At least, it stopped Charlie talking.

"How can they run and S*** at the same time?" asked Stanley. Hoping Charlie didn't hear him.

"To get away from their own stench. F***, as quickly as possible," chuckled Dyfed. Charlie coughed with laughter, "Look, look," he pointed outside, into the street.

The moment the procession passed a road sweeper's hiding place, the man raced to the nearest pile of horse muck. As quickly as physically possible, holding their breath, they shovelled the 'manure' directly into their trolley. Job done, many of them abandoned their trolley by the nearest kerb so they could take 'odour refuge' against the closest wall.

Everyone in the office laughed, what a job? Minutes later, a large road washer lorry drove down the street cleansing the road.

When Stan arrived home after work, he told his family about the Parade. They gathered around to watch the TV news to check if they could spot anyone but it only showed the Queen.

As directed by Harry, after tea in readiness for the morning he packed a sports bag with the old clothes and things that Harry had mentioned.

PLANNING

When he arrived at work on the Wednesday morning, Stan's office was quiet. But there was lots of toing and froing between other office rooms. He couldn't see anything through the frosted glass door of his office, just hear the perpetually opening and shutting of doors along the corridor.

Around 3.00pm everyone was called to Terry Willis' office.

The assembled were told of Button's financial problems involving unpaid fees. Basically, confirming what Harry had told Stan.

The contracted builder on the Caletonia Gardens Project had not met its commitment for three months. The builder had gone into liquidation owing Button's a large sum of money. The site with all its contents had been seized by the Court to 'safeguard' Creditors. H. W. Button would probably not get paid, at risk of losing all of its site equipment and more.

Like a Commanding Officer, direct from a war movie Terry Willis' plum voice briefed them on the proposed approach to recover at least some of the assets.

Cigarette, standing to attention by his right ear he stood to address the room, "My thanks to the people here, who have agreed to help us recover our property."

'Have we', thought Stan, 'I thought I was going to start working on site?'

Terry Willis continued, "We are going to enter the site at 9.00pm tonight. When we arrive, the gates will be open for us. The last one in is to fit the new padlock we take with us. This shall make the gates appear secure and keep unwanted meddlesome, busybodies away.

Stanley? That will be your duty. It will also avert any security or law enforcer getting suspicious."

'B*** H***', fretted Stan, 'a few months ago I thought I was going to be 007, now I'm going to be a B*** burglar. Law enforcer? He can't even say the word 'policeman'.

"Kathy and Sandie, thanks for your help." Terry clarified, "if you could man the telephones here, please. Harry TF, you don't dress like a man working on site so you shall take up a position by a public telephone box in the vicinity. Any messages will be transmitted between the office and Harry. Ladies, you shall have a different line each so that one shall always be available."

"That's all for now. We shall leave the office at 7.30pm please have something to eat before we leave. You should be changed and ready to go. Thank you." He closed the meeting.

"Hey, and be careful out there," added Dyfed chuckling.

After official office hours, Stan sat quietly reading his book. A new science fiction novel, *The Indromeda Strain*.

It was about 7.00pm. He tucked into the extra sandwiches brought from home that morning. After sitting on his desk for ten hours, they were a little warm with turned up corners, but he was hungry.

The call came at 7.20pm. Sandie spoke on the office public address system. "Please meet in the ground floor lobby in ten minutes."

Stan quickly got changed into his 'burglar outfit', checked he had his train ticket, keys, money, then took the stairs to the ground floor.

Dyfed, the Labour Manager was waiting. Shortly, John arrived, he had travelled from the company stores in the railway arches at Peckham.

John moved to Stan and offered his hand. "You must be Stan, I imagine. Nice to put a face to a voice. How are you getting on? Writing out materials lists and placing orders?"

"Fine thanks," blushed Stan, "enjoying it, are you er, John from the stores?"

John nodded.

Harry arrived in the lift, pushing the cage doors apart he stepped out.

"Where's Willis?" probed John.

"He's decided not to come," answered Harry, "decided he's needed here at 'Command Central'," he grinned.

"Good F*** job, an all," joined Dyfed in his Welsh brogue. "Stick out like a pork chop at a vegan picnic. The way he dresses, people would think the Prime Minister had turned up. What now?"

Harry took control, "Okay, let's go through it? John first?"

John started, "Yeah, Barry, and Tom are driving our lorries to site now. They left the stores about sixty minutes ago. They are going to park up a few turnings from site, then phone in Kathy when they get there."

"Right, Dyfed?"

Dyfed lifted his right hand to his mouth, mimicking a microphone. "Dyfed to control," he started, "Zak, Kevin, Jon and his boy, will gain entrance at twenty hundred hours."

Stan laughed.

'That's soon', he reflected, 'it's started already, S***'. 'My first robbery', his face drained of colour.

Dyfed persisted, "They will collect our two-way radios from the site caravan and charge them. Any ready ones will be left in a box just inside the gate. Over and out, out."

"Lets' go," commanded Harry. "Wait! First, remember. Every single thing on site, even the office cat and S*** paper has been confiscated. So, no one owns anything. If you see a drill or something expensive, it's fair game, load it onto our lorries. I have something for you Stan." He passed Stanley a supermarket bag containing a brand-new padlock, chain and two pints of milk.

"Remember the route back from site to the station, don't get lost."

"And please, as its June, don't put your gloves on until we get there."

They set off. Stan worried about having his fingerprints on the padlock.

03-05

PLUNDER

Harry and his crew started their journey. On schedule, they left the office at 7.30pm and walked to St James Park station. Aboard the north bound Tube train, they made their way to Kentish Town station.

Barry and Tom had been driving the two drop sided lorries from the stores at Peckham. The lorries arrived first. At that time of night, they had missed the rush hour, only taking about an hour to get to Kentish Town.

They drove to the Caletonia Gardens site, first they needed to establish the best parking locations that wouldn't cause local residents irritation. As they parked up, Barry worryingly saw a few curtains twitch. He signed across to Tom with a finger across his lips, holding up five fingers on his second hand. Five minutes to let any prying eyes withdraw. Both men sat quietly in their cabs.

Time up, Barry dropped down from his cab then went to find a telephone box. He called the office to confirm the lorries had arrived.

While Barry was away, Tom removed a holdall containing bolt croppers and a battered old red 'Keep Out - Danger' sign, from his cab footwell. He made his way to the site entrance where Barry joined him.

To conceal Tom cutting the old padlock chain Barry held the sign against the gate making exaggerated movements, pretending to be unlocking the padlock. The action gave Barry the giggles, "We don't have time to play charades you wally, you know, er Clockwork Orange?" He snorted.

They fixed the sign to the gate.

"Can I pretend to lock the gate, please?" Barry asked, grinning as they entered the site. Tom serenely ignored him.

The gate was left ajar, they went to the caravan to check the walkie talkie radios. All green lights, luckily the last person out had returned them to the charging bank.

Zak, Kevin, Jon and Bal, had been watching in a parked van in sight of the front gate. Now, at minute intervals they left the vehicle and slid through the gate opening. Once in the site they grouped behind the caravan. As the four of them had been employed here, they knew the site. They were aware of a couple of expensive machines they wanted for themselves, plus sanitaryware they could stack in the van.

Phase one, four of the craftsmen combed through the buildings collecting Button's property, plus equipment. Everything including expensive building items was transported to the open yard where Tom and Barry loaded the caravan.

The Victoria Street crew arrived at Kentish Town Station.

Harry reached pavement level with the team in single file behind him. He made for a telephone box on a street corner. The crew followed.

Harry stood in the kiosk, head down under the dim yellow ceiling light, sorting out a handful of coins contained in a fist full of rings.

Adding coins to the top of the telephone directory book compartment, he spied a moving shape by his head. Anxiously looking up, outside the kiosk he saw Dyfed's smiling face with a raised thumb by his eye, "Do you know the number?" he queried.

"Of course I know the F***, number, I've worked there for eight years," cried Harry.

"Have you got enough change?" was Dyfed's second question.

Harry TF twisted his head, there was also a face at each of the other three sides. He cracked the door open, "Get away, we are not supposed to know each other?"

The crew split, they stood around looking conspicuous while Harry rang the office from a telephone box.

He was delighted to hear the other members of the 'dream team' were in position. Harry led the way, as a disguise he decided to take off his fashionable black rimmed glasses.

Unfortunately, this meant he couldn't read the names on the street signs. The next chaotic moment was after he walked into someone's front garden and stood sixty centimetres from the side of the house to read the sign.

After hearing a Welsh voice behind him giggle and comment about a blind bat, Harry opted to replace his spectacles.

Harry made off down the street. Stan followed, then came Dyfed and John together.

In this formation, they did a recce of the streets adjacent to the site. The two lorries were a hundred yards from site, the drivers had gone.

The team slowed as they came to the site. Harry removed the fractured padlock chain from the gate and entered with it in his hand.

Stan took the new chain from the supermarket bag and positioned it on the gate. Dyfed and John squeezed in as Stan locked the padlock then moved into the shadows. He placed the old padlock with the chain in his bag.

John and Dyfed assisted the others by the caravan.

Tom came over with two radios. "These are for you. One for you Harry, one for Stan."

He passed them the radios. "The call signs are 'Danger 2' for Harry, 'Danger 3' for Stan. The drivers are 'Danger 4 and 5, the yard is 'Danger 1'. Do you know how to use these, Stan?"

Tom gave him a quick refresher instruction.

Stan unlocked the padlock so Harry could leave via the gate. The senior engineer returned to his position a short distance from the telephone box. He reported back to 'Mission Control', he would now loiter there for the next few hours.

When the caravan was nearly fully laden, Tom backed his lorry into the yard.

Barry hitched the caravan as the others worked tirelessly, loading the lorry. When it was complete, Stan opened the gate and directed Tom onto the road. Tom drove off back to Peckham, Stan returned into the site and locked the gate. It was 10.00pm, the first part of the robbery was finished.

Stan felt so proud, he was beaming. The young man could also feel the relief and energy from the others.

"Danger 3, calling Danger 2, over," he called Harry.

A few minutes, a sheepish response, "Danger 3, receiving," answered a baffled Harry.

"Danger 2," replied Stan, "first vehicle has left." He knew Harry had the call sign wrong, but there was no point in arguing. Nerves? Harry didn't acknowledge the information, perhaps there were people near him. Perhaps he'd been arrested? The Sweeny?

Barry waited fifteen minutes. Everyone had a breather and a hot drink, then he went to collect his lorry.

Stan, remaining in the shadows, turned to have a pee while he had the chance.

An elderly man trundled along on the opposite side of the road, crouched over with a walking stick he moved painfully while his small old dog sniffed the fence panels. Stan hoped the man was hard of hearing.

Barry reversed his lorry into the loading area, adding the plunder to the second lorry commenced. It was easier without the obstruction of the caravan. Someone had found a brand-new cement mixer, a big one. The tradesmen argued whether to take it. Eventually, they agreed, it took four of them to roll it up a makeshift ramp onto the lorry.

Sometime later, the old man with the dog came back. He had changed pavements. The man was now on the same side as the site, walking at an angle to the fence which exposed Stanley's whereabouts. Stan whispered into his radio, "Ssssh." The 'ssssh' was passed around between the others.

The dog walked, sniffing the ground. It came to the site entrance, cocked its leg then looked up. Eye to eye with Stan its tail started to wag. There was a moment where Stanley had to decide if he was visible to the man. If he was, his position may give the old fellow a heart attack. To remove any suspicion that he was hiding, Stan needed to speak first.

He pressed the 'push to talk' button on his radio, "Nice dog," he said, "taking him for a nice walk?" He took his finger off the button.

"Aye," replied the elderly man, "get some fresh air before bed. You are working late, sonny?" he quizzed Stan.

"Aye," agreed Stan, thinking feverishly for some words.

"I watched some other workmen fixing this 'Danger' sign to the gate, are you with them?" the old man posed.

"Yeah," answered Stan, "what's the dog's name?" He played for time.

"Simon," answered the old man.

Stan held back a chuckle - Simon, the dog?

He took control. "That's a nice name for a dog. You see, because of the danger, only a couple of us can work here together at one time. We have to work late so that local people are not put in any danger."

"I see. Is that, that asbestos stuff I've read about, then?" the old man questioned.

"Yeah, exactly," confirmed Stan, while thinking 'what the F*** is asbestos?'

"We have to be careful. Good night, I may see you tomorrow same time," the young man waved.

The elderly man took the hint, Simon escorted him home. Once Stan witnessed the old man had crossed the road, he gave the 'all clear'.

Loading the second lorry was completed at 11.10pm. Dyfed and John joined Barry in the lorry cab, Stan saw then safely onto the road. He quickly removed the red 'Keep Out - Danger' sign from the gate. As the lorry pulled away, Stanley passed the sign through the open cab window to Dyfed.

Stan called Harry, "Danger 3, calling Danger 2, over."

Harry responded, "Danger 1, receiving."

"Danger 1, mission complete, over. You may leave to go home, over and out." Stan signed off.

"Received Danger 2, hallelujah, my back is killing me, over and out." Harry made his way to the telephone box and passed on the news to Kathy in the office. There was rejoicing in Victoria Street. This was a massive economic rescue.

Stan went back into the site, he needed to lock up. The other four couldn't be found. When he radioed that the second lorry had gone, they appeared, three carried bags of loot.

Zak zipped pass him to collect the van. They had been hiding in a room adjacent to the yard, acting like so many pirates.

The four of them took an additional fifteen minutes loading their loot, Zak blew Stan a kiss he waved and gently eased the heavily laden vehicle into the road.

Stan padlocked the gate then walked to the station.

RECOGNITION

As proposed by Terry Willis Stan had taken the day following the 'raid' as leave. He had used the day to surprise Bronwyn on her way home from work and go for a few drinks.

Friday morning he was back in the office. He sat at his desk playing 'cops and robbers' with the walkie talkie radio from the night before - "over, ten, four."

When Stan had agreed to help, he hadn't realised that he would meet the people he spoke to every day. The ones needing materials ordered or drawings sent, information clarified, delivery times agreed, roads closed.

Charlie pushed the door ajar as a single eye peeked through the crack. All clear, he was buzzing as he strolled in for a chat. He couldn't control his excitement. Before he reached Stan's desk, he was speaking aloud, "Did you see that Skylab on the news? Amazing."

Charlie changed tack, "Oh, sorry first, I keep forgetting to ask. How is the training going for Alberta? You only have a couple of years to go?"

Stanley, had wound up Charlie that he trained with 'Dicky' Tonovan at a club in Dagenham. The ruse was that he had been chosen for the preliminary karate squad for the 1978 Commonwealth Games in Alberta, Canada. When Charlie pooh-poohed the idea, Stan had cut out symbols and logos from sports magazines to falsify his letter of selection.

Terry Willis entered the room, pulling up Harry's chair he sat with Stan. Stan tensed.

Charlie snuck out.

"Good morning, Stan," Terry beamed, "things are looking good. Thanks for all your help on Wednesday. John Herbert is going to produce an inventory on everything we secured from site. We are sure it shall help us financially.

Now, we have news on the office refurb project in New Bond Street. You produced the tender submission." Terry smiled, "Your first tender submission? Well, well done, we are the lowest."

Stan smiled, 'Whoo!'

"Our tender is only one percent lower than the second lowest. So, our price appears to in the right area. I am very pleased," he continued, "could you please have a quick check on our materials, the cost figures, before end of play Monday."

Stan nodded.

Terry continued, "Lots of things today, Stanley. At your interview, we spoke of your professional education. I have had a word with old Mr Button and he has agreed to fund your college. So, please see Kathy next week as she will provide you with the college information.

Next, we are engaging a new draughtsman to help you. You shall still be undertaking all tasks, but fewer drafting duties. He starts on Monday.

Oh! Also. As you shall not be in the office when you are on study leave, old Mr Button feels we need to employ another intermediate engineer. He shall be advertising the position soon.

Finally, young Mr Button, is very appreciative of what we achieved on Wednesday, so he will be 'in the chair' at the Feathers from 3.00pm today.

Stanley, here's a point with regard to the intermediate position, if you know of anyone looking to move from their current position, please tell them about us.

Thank you, Stanley," Terry Willis rose from his chair and left the room. Stan sat quietly, trying to take it all in. His face ached from smiling. He couldn't concentrate on his work. He decided he would take a walk at lunch time. Get some air. Stop smiling, for a minute.

The office PA system crackled, "Could Stan please come to reception." It was Sandie. 'Bad news?' Thought Stan.

"Hi," Sandie greeted him. "Have you got a minute please?"

"Err," Stan's usual nervous reply.

Sandie explained, "Do you remember that I have a Spanish boyfriend, well fiancée?"

"Yeah," replied Stan. He had heard the gossip from Charlie, no surprise there?

Apparently, about three years earlier while she was on holiday, Sandie had met the son of a Spanish millionaire and fell in love. She would visit him a few times a year. Charlie was sure his dad's private plane collected her at Rydd Airport, near Dover.

"Well, I am going to see him in six weeks' time, in Spain for four weeks. We are going to plan the wedding."

"That's nice, congratulations, I hope everything goes well." Smiled Stan.

"Sorry, Stan, I know how much you like doing the switchboard. June will cover my normal time, but Kathy needs someone to cover my breaks. Mr Willis said that as you are now trained on the phones there is no reason why you can't help."

"No problemo," replied Stan, "I would be happy too, I hope all your arrangements work out well." Inside he was going, "Eh? Aaah, nooo."

Stanley walked back to his office along the corridor, a cog in his head slipped into place, 'college'?

Trying to hide a huge grin he returned to reception, he apologised, "Sandie, I'm really sorry, but I will be in college in six weeks' time."

Later at 3.00pm the office gathered on the pavement outside, Mr Willis led them to The Feathers a five-minute walk to the Broadway.

The group entered the black painted pub to the sound of loud funk, jazz Go-Go music. It was dimly lit, made worse by the thickness of the smokie atmosphere. Spotlights hung over the bar and above four large gilded hooped bird cages. The bird cages, one in each corner hung about four feet above the floor. 'Shaking it' inside each cage was a Go-Go dancer.

Attractive young blond-haired women, wearing short, very short white mini dresses, a loose 75mm thick red PVC belt with knee boots.

Stan followed the person in front through the crowded dance floor to the bar. Some girls were dancing along to the music, all the men were transfixed on the dancers. Harry was beside the bar taking orders and passing back the drinks. He had been born for this; he was in his element. His clothes, hair style, moustache, jewellery, way of speaking. Standing there, over six feet tall, super length cigarette in one hand with a wedge of £1 notes in the other. He was a pale version of 'John Shaft' from the film, and he loved the attention.

Better still, young Mr Button was standing next to him at the bar, passing him more money to spend.

Stan watched as Sandie moved onto the dance floor, as she started to gyrate to the music a gallery of young men formed. Just behind her, he saw four familiar smiling faces watching her, Zak, Kevin, Jon and Bal.

Zak saw Stan, he lifting his hand and blew him a kiss.

The 'Buttons party' continued, it was just like Christmas. Within a few hours of alcohol lubrication, the group were facing each other, dancing in a circle with the girl's handbags piled in the middle, singing their hearts out. What a day.

ISSY

After the weekend, back at work.

Stan was introduced to the new draughtsman called Isaac Newman. He was a hippy, but not the sort of Posh Hippy Stan had previously seen in Kensington. 'Issy' was fresh from the Squat. Scraggy, shoulder length wavy hair parted in the middle with a full beard. In amongst all the hair was a small face with tiny eyes wearing John Lennon, 'lovin' spoonful' glasses. He wore a faded baggy 'V' sign sweatshirt with a cravat tied around his neck. Red corduroy trousers and Jesus boots, no socks, finished the mode. He looked, as Stan's friends would say 'soapy', meaning he looked like he needed a good wash.

Stan showed Issy around and got him started.

"How long have you been drafting?" Stan asked.

"About six years," answered Issy, "I now work as a freelance. Save enough money to live for a few months, you know, food and grass and that and then I hang out. I find a commune with some good vibes, stay there for a few months and chill."

"Oh, okay," replied Stan. "Where did you work before you came here?"

"I was at University in Admaston, studying Sociology," informed Issy.

To the point, "What is Sociology?" enquired Stan. "Is it a type of engineering?"

"No, no," explained Issy, "it's about people and their lives - rich and poor. About how society works. How one type of society interacts with other different societies, work to life balance."

Stanley was confused, he wondered how the new man could produce ink drawings?

"Aaah, are there a lot of jobs available in that field, then? Ones that deal with that sort of thing?" asked Stan.

"No, not at the moment. That's why I'm here. I'm designed to be in the future, when the world cracks. As societies break up and crumble, big organisations or governments will come to me to ask what is going wrong. Then I will tell them how they can put it right."

Shortly, Kathy called Stan to her office. She explained that the college enrolment for his new course was next week, on a Tuesday. She gave him the Course information pack with some money for travel. It was a sandwich course, not day release. So, Stan would be away from the office for a period of six weeks, twice a year. Thankfully, it was a specialist course related to his employment.

Lunchtime, Stan sat and thought about what Issy had told him. He decided to keep an eye on the hippy's work. Mr Willis wasn't stupid; he must have interviewed the man?

He ran over the previous conversation in his mind. If it was true, how could Issy with no life experiences, tell others how to live? He even confessed that he 'drops out' of society when and if he wants just to spend half his life spaced out on drugs. Surely, it would be better to ask the thoughts of people who were better placed. Say, a widow with three young children, balanced against those of a 'self-made' entrepreneur? Issy ran away from life, he learned about life from books, whereas the other two had real life experiences.

During the following weeks Issy and Stan worked and played hard together. Irene, always said that Stan was like his dad, "He would talk to anyone."

The two young men frequently played elastic band fights. It started as a one band ping, then became the whole box. One protagonist at each end of the room, they would lock the door and fire salvos. The invention of flicking them along the end of a wooden twelve-inch rule gave better target success with a more painful ping.

During the next weekend, as usual Stan met his friends in the Golden Hind in Romford. He mentioned the job opportunity that Terry Willis had mentioned two Fridays previous. Ken Cole was interested so Stan gave him the address to send his details. Perhaps he would be teaching Ken how to use a switchboard soon.

That Tuesday, Stan left home at the same time as usual but travelled directly to the college to enrol. He had to travel by train from Dagenham to Wandsworth in south west London, which took him two hours each way.

When he arrived at college, he made his way through the large building, noting the course number with the associated location of the enrolment desks. Then he returned to the large entrance area where he observed the comings and goings of the teaching and student societies.

One gang of about twenty or more young people stood out. They were very loud and appeared to know each other. Not again. If he hadn't believed in déjà vu before, he did now. He moved closer to the group, listening. He could not believe what he heard. The group were apprentices at the same company, also they were on the same course as him. His previous experiences came flooding back. At least, now, he was prepared.

He walked slowly through the crowded room, listening to conversations, trying to hear who was on which course. He hoped that he would hear other voices speaking about his course so he could mix with them. He was out of luck. If there was only one class of students, he would be with the loud people.

A while later a smartly dressed man carrying a large folder, holding a folded A3 sheet appeared.

He made an announcement. The man called out the reference of Stan's course number then asked for attention. He declared that there were more than fifty student names entered on the course application register. The college had therefore, decided to create two separate study groups. Stan's expression changed. Fingers crossed.

The man asked for twenty-five of the students to register as one class in the room to his right. The other students would follow the speaker.

Stan watched. He couldn't believe it when Mick 'Spud' Murphy came out of the door on the right. Mick was now a lecturer. Stan couldn't let sentiment confuse the situation and trip up his plan. He watched as the group of loud students filed into Mick's room. Stan's chance, he didn't want to attract attention so moved discreetly. He wasn't going to be press ganged as student number twenty-five in that study group, he shuffled as far away from them as possible.

Directly, Mick shouted that he had his quota. The first smartly dressed man waved his folder in the air, the remaining students followed him along a corridor into another room. Stan was very happy, his experience at Beckvale College a few years earlier had taught him that even when undertaking a simply activity he needed to be aware of his surroundings. Even at a tender age he now understood it was better to have some control of his life rather than bounce from one misadventure to another. Based on past experience he knew he had dodged a bullet.

03-08
EPISODE

There was one episode the young engineer couldn't forget.

About a year before, Harry had annoyed him on a survey trip when they travelled to inspect a large carpet manufacturer's factory and offices in the Midlands. Harry's lifestyle meant he would only travel First Class or by cab, also he only stayed in 5-star hotels. This time he had instructed Sandie to book his preferred hotel in the Birmington Bullring.

On the morning of their journey, Harry directed Stan to purchase two First Class return tickets to Birmington. He gave him cash for his own, Stanley needed to buy his with a credit card.

The night they arrived, he informed Stan that after the evening meal some of his friends would meet them in the hotel bar for drinks. Stanley was apprehensive eating in the posh hotel restaurant where even the staff looked down their noses at him. He was nervous and didn't enjoy the food, preferring to eat little to quickly remove the snobbery and his own discomfort. When two young women sashayed into the bar, everyone's jaws dropped.

Implausibly they waved to Harry then drifted along a 'catwalk' to speak to him. Stan was numb. Harry TF's friends were amazing looking dolly birds, perhaps actresses or super models. The clothes they wore looked expensive. The garments weren't really dresses, but pieces of scalloped tiny bright coloured reflective beads or sequins. They acknowledged Stan, then openly flirted with Harry.

Stanley sat with them in the bar, the egotistic trio gushed, holding another's hand one lady gently groomed Harry's thick moustache. Harry called to the bar for a bottle of champagne. Stan collected himself, he much preferred being ignored. He uneasily looked around the large hotel bar. No one was looking at each other, they were all looking at Harry and his friends.

Stanley didn't have the wit to chat to them, discreetly he inspected

140

the girls' faces. It struck him that make-up was hiding a lot of flaws. After inspection, he guessed they were aged in their forties, not twenties. Then a terrifying thought gripped him. If they were on the game, had Harry booked one for him? The idea was repellent, his face bright pink he decided to evade any possible torment. Stanley gave his apologies and retreated to his room.

At least, he could reclaim some kind of normality in his room. It enabled him to phone his beloved Bronwyn. Stan sat fiddling with the television, he wasn't tired or drunk but he struggled with the controls. He fought with the handset to reduce the volume. Changed channel, and had to increase it again. He looked out of the window at the lights of the traffic, occasionally a car hooter sounded. He wondered, did he say goodbye too quietly? Should he have been more polite? He wished he had been more polite.

The next morning at breakfast Harry appeared unwell. He looked like he'd been on the nest all night. He wouldn't eat anything, just drank black coffee, one after the other. Stan passed him a pack of headache tablets. He was certain Harry hadn't gone to sleep. They left the hotel. Harry hailed a taxi to the site which cost a fortune. Later they returned to the station in a taxi. Harry treated them to an evening meal on the train home.

Stan was happy with the actual site visit. He should have known Harry would grab the headlines. Although, he did wonder if the girls genuinely knew Harry, or if he had 'booked' them for the night?

The problems occurred later, back at the office. As normal, Stan handed his expenses sheet to Kathy for reimbursement. Dejectedly, the form was returned, he was hauled over the coals.

Kathy examined the documents and called him back to her office. In no uncertain terms, he was advised, 'Buttons would not refund him for any first-class travel, nor 5-star hotel fees.' He was told to establish the price of a second-class train fare and the cost of a night in a good quality 3-star hotel then resubmit his claim.

Harry's arrogance on that trip had cost Stan a lot of money. Money Stan didn't have. At least, Harry paid for the taxi fares.

03-09
NAP

Stan was back at work after returning from holiday with Bronwyn in Majorca. As she had travelled abroad with her friend just after the love birds met, she had promised Stanley that they would also have a holiday in the sun together. Stanley had completed his studies it was a good time to relax, somewhere the two of them could spend private time.

Stan had greatly enjoyed his time at Wandsworth College. He had had an experience similar to when he studied for 'O' levels at school. At Wandsworth, he had spent two school years with new friends inside the college building and socially outside.

Lunch was either in the pub playing darts or the refectory playing cards. One thing he fondly remembered was the card schools during break and lunch. The six close friends would race to the refectory to grab a table, not to eat but to play Nap for a small flutter. The first time they played the staff cautioned them that gambling wasn't allowed in the building so an empty matchbox became part of each game. Wagers were added to the matchbox as it was passed around the table, after all bets were placed it sat 'invisibly' on top of a cigarette packet.

Deep inside he still felt ashamed of failing previous day release college courses, now he accepted he couldn't take the stress. At Wandsworth, he had an environment that suited him. Stan never missed a day, he passed the course with good results, finally achieving the qualification he pursued.

He still kept in contact with some of the lads in his class to share gossip and meet up.

Stan also enjoyed working at Button's. As well as the skills he initially mastered, he would also attend site meetings with Harry and conduct surveys of existing installations. Added to that his friend Ken who he had introduced to Button's still worked with him.

Later, Stanley needed some 'first day back' air. He walked along

Victoria Street, turned left along Strutton Ground where all the cafes and food shops were then into the smaller more peaceful back streets. Walking past a small shopfront, something caught his eye. Turning his head, he looked then stopped. The shop window was nearly bare perhaps that was what gathered his attention. There were three small white plastic boxes on a royal blue velvet background, a tiny single white sign with black lettering sat behind the boxes. Stan looked closer, each of the white plastic boxes had a green flickering strip light along the top. He found the sign difficult to read, 'Pommodore calculators - the future'. Calculators? He had heard about these on the news. They would revolutionise engineering.

He was interested, but without money, back from holiday he was skint.

Stan walked away from the shop. Twenty steps later his thirst for new advancements in technology, a desire to move forward with mankind's developments caused him to stop.

'Um, why not?' He thought, 'at least I can have a look and play with them. If I see a different type next week, I can decide the one I want'.

Stan turned back and entered the shop, the bell on a spring above the door rang. A short tubby man in a white laboratory gown stood behind the counter, he welcomed Stan. Stan informed the man of his interest in the little white boxes and listened to the explanation. It was amazing, they were so easy to use, 'select a number, hit the function, select another number, hit equals'.

Currently, he was using an 'adding machine'. He had to punch in a number, twist and push the central joystick into a slot to choose the function. Punch in a second number, twist the joystick again, pull down on the handle at the side. Repeat. All the figures were printed onto a 50mm wide roll of paper, but he didn't see what would be printed until the next section of paper appeared. If he got one action wrong, he had to start again. The young engineer enquired after the price of the 'calculators'. It shocked him, it was £20, more than a week's wages. He thanked the vendor and glumly left the shop.

Stan loved new technical ideas and objects. He could not forget these little white boxes. Each lunchtime he walked to the blue decorated window at the little shop for another peek.

A few weeks later he went back to the shop with his credit card to buy a little white box.

03-10

TROUBLED

Stan left the office to attend the day's site meeting in Covent Garden.

He travelled by Tube and arrived in good time so he could visit Button's site office. There, he drank tea and chatted to Dyfed and Barry who had renamed him Simon. Harry and Zak entered the office.

"Time to go Simon," called Zak, "meeting is just starting."

Off they went. Stan had previously been told by Harry, 'Meetings were about programme and responsibility. Someone will want to blame you, you use everything to avoid it'. Unless Harry prompted him, Stan was to stay shtum. He was there to listen and learn, not to offer information or comment. There was always tea and biscuits so he could sit there quietly eating chocolate bourbons.

The meeting broke up about lunchtime. Stan was excused to return to Victoria Street.

Too much tea, he was bursting and made his way to the site toilet. The centre of the existing building had been removed. What was left was a scene from a war film. It was like the trenches at Passchendaele, wet mud with debris enclosed by the walls of the old building. Dead centre was a small wooden hut, about eight hundred millimetres square - the toilet.

He could hear loud laughter and obscenities directed at 'Simon' from Zak and Barry as he stumbled through the swamp. Finally, trying to keep his shoes dry, after trudging across the quagmire he opened the loo door. In the centre of the shed was an old battered galvanised dustbin. It was full to overflowing. The undersized wooden seat stood perpendicular, half submerged in the contents. Even without a roof it smelt bad enough to make anyone heave.

Gagging, Stanley choked, he shut the loo door then turned back to the building. He would have to go back to the office.

The young engineer made his way to the Tube station and took the westbound Piccadilly Line to South Ken. It should have taken ten minutes. It took thirty minutes. He was sweating with pee need.

The young man sat, knees together, trying to think of anything other than his location.

Stuck in a busy train miles below the ground.

The train would move, then wait outside every station for a few minutes. Stanley stood, he sat down, he walked slowly along the length of the carriage. He walked back to his seat. The four passengers in the carriage with him discreetly watched when he faced away from them. Such behaviour warranted caution.

The train pulled into Hyde Park Corner station, Stanley remembered there was a public toilet at Gloucester Road Tube Station, an extra stop, but it would be worth it. He hung on, the train pulled into Gloucester Road station then stopped. He had made it, relief, every part of him was ready to burst, just a few seconds.

The doors didn't open! At least one full minute later they did. Stan stepped onto the platform and calamity, he couldn't hold himself any longer. He lost control and warm water surged down his leg. He couldn't stand there in a puddle, people were passing along the tunnel. Stanley was so embarrassed he could have wept. For a person with low self-esteem, this was the ultimate embarrassment. Avoiding the lift, he made for the emergency stairs.

People in London rarely look at each other. However, when you are nervous, lacking confidence you assume they are looking at you. When you are walking around in wet trousers, you know they are looking at you.

Stan kept walking, he had to make a plan. There was no way he could travel on a bus or train while wet, plus he probably smelt of wee. Focusing on traffic route signs as he walked, his knowledge of the sequence of Tube stations helped him look for place names he knew would be to the east.

He found a telephone box and phoned the office. Stan hated lying, he had been brought up to tell the truth. However, he wasn't going to inform Sandie of the unbearable facts. He explained that he felt unwell and was going home. She agreed to pass on his message.

Later, he noticed a road sign, 'Victoria 2 miles'. That's the right direction, he followed the guiding arrow. Next, he reached Holborn, finally Tower Hill. It took him two hours to walk just over five miles.

By now, he was dry, but couldn't identify if he smelt. Boarding the tube, he travelled home before the rush hour.

When he arrived home, he repeated the same porky to his parents that he had told Sandie.

Irene and Pete comforted him, he had a bath then disappeared to bed. He was ill, but it wasn't a physical illness. It was the attachment of a fear to his low self-esteem. Something he could never share with friends or family.

The next day he visited his GP surgery. Stanley told the doctor that he frequently needed to use the toilet. It was true, perhaps he did have a urinary tract infection, or maybe it was a sensory precaution so that he didn't have another 'accident'. The antibiotics he was given may have cleared the infection, but they didn't make him better. He was eventually signed off sick from work for two weeks.

Life had given him another kick in the teeth. This time some of them had been knocked out. He would be hamstrung with a fear of pee need for the rest of his life.

03-11
RETURN

Stan felt ashamed when he returned from sick leave to work at Buttons. He was so angry with himself for telling lies, but he would never be able to tell the truth about the real cause of his absence. He wasn't one hundred percent because he still had to combat pee need.

Nerves had even gripped him on his way in today. He had to alight the Tube to find a toilet at West Ham. Then, when he found a toilet, he had nothing to pass. It had become a frequent necessity, anxiety. Stan had to leave the train because he was bursting again. But in reality, it was in his head. He had to leave fifteen minutes earlier for work to accommodate his problem or be late.

In the office, he was greeted by everyone as he saw them. It was a great place to work. He had to laugh even Harry had now started to call him 'Simon'. Even Terry Willis called him 'Simon' this morning with a smile.

About an hour after Stan had finished his briefing with Harry and Ken, Charlie's rear end dropped on the corner of Stan's desk. Cigarette in mouth, cup of coffee in his hand. He asked after Stan's health as a pretext, before continued with a smirk.

"From what I hear, Stan, you may well be getting the receptionist job full time, soon?"

"No way," protested Stan. "That's not going to happen."

Charlie played the game, he didn't respond. Instead he grinned, then paused for effect, as his head slightly nodding up and down.

"Okay Charlie," continued Stan, "what are you up to? Why do you say that?"

"Well, from what I understand," Charlie whispered, "that Sandie in reception is leaving soon, in a few months."

"Why in a few months?" questioned Stan.

"Well, you know she broke up with that Spanish millionaire bloke, don't you?" Charlie executed the *coup de grâce*.

"Nooo," replied Stanley.

"I thought it was common knowledge? Everyone had heard about it? You know, she didn't appear too upset, either." Charlie reflected shrewdly, "Well it's a while now."

He continued, "Anyway, you see she went to Spain to arrange her wedding. Did you know about that?"

Stan nodded.

"Well, it seems that when she got out there, she got cold feet. Whether it was because he expected her to live out in Spain. His bossy dad, I don't know. Perhaps she fell out of love with this Spanish bloke?

Could be something I haven't thought of yet. But she was supposed to be out there for four weeks and she was back, working in here in two. Something went seriously wrong."

'I don't think, it's anything to do with you', Stan thought. "So?" he pressed.

"Well, in no time at all. Once she's back here, she's got another fellow in tow. I don't know if she was seeing him before she went to Spain and that's what the breakup was about. This time, it's an English bloke, from Thatford or somewhere, south London. I heard that he's a plasterer or something like that. From millionaire to pauper, ay?" elaborated Charlie.

"And now, she's up the duff. So, she'll be leaving for good."

"Oh, how is she in herself?" asked Stan.

"Blooming, they say pregnant women look radiant, she definitely does. Never seen her so happy, she looks well," answered Charlie.

04

BARHAM

Chapter Marker

04-01
MAYOR

In 1975, Stan saw an advert in his regional weekly newspaper which interested him.

It was for a vacancy as a draughtsman at his Local Authority. Only four stops on the Tube to the Town Hall plus he would save two hours a day in travel. Stan and Bronwyn were now engaged any extra money may help them buy a house. Being very selfish, perhaps the shorter journey would ease his pee need problems.

He applied for the post and received a date for an interview. The more he thought about it, the more he liked the idea. Stanley was doing so well at Buttons, but family came first.

Worse, his nerves were shredded by his condition. The thought of travelling on the train to London distressed him every day.

Stanley attended the interview at Barham Town Hall at 2.00pm. He climbed the exterior stairs to the main doors then entered the large hall. It reminded him of the bank where he had previously had an interview, but it was considerably larger. There was shining polished wood, but the floor was marble as were the columns. It didn't smell of polish as the bank had done but of fresh air.

He was collected from reception and taken to the second floor. There, he joined four other candidates sitting in a row of chairs. On arrival, Stan nodded to the others, each one responded. The corridor they sat in was finished in polished walnut veneer panelling.

A middle-aged man exited the room opposite, thanked the person inside, closed the door then sat with the job seekers. Stan assumed he was another candidate. Shortly, that person was escorted away. One by one, the applicants were escorted into the room opposite for a short time them taken somewhere else.

Stanley was fifth, only a lady about his age remained after him. He made conversation with her and exchanged names, she was Sue.

When called, he walked into the room and met Mr Will Clark the

Head Mechanical and Electrical Engineer. Mr Clark introduced himself, he talked Stan through the interview. This was a 'knowledge and experience' interview. Later he would be taken to a 'suitability' interview. Mr Clark clarified that local government officers had access to public buildings and people's homes. 'They couldn't employ someone of bad character as this person would be allowed into tenant's homes'.

For more than half an hour, Stan sat with Will, they chatted about Stan's qualifications, the projects he had worked on and the duties he had undertaken. Stan talked Will through the drawings he had brought with him.

"Mr Paterson," Mr Clark began, "I like you. I like you a lot. I believe you would fit into my department. The only thing is that you may be over qualified for the position. If you come here, you won't be doing site meetings, calculations or tender submissions and alike. You will be just a drafter.

So, my concern is if we offered you the position would you accept? You see, if you worked here, you may become bored then leave after a short time?"

Stan nodded, "Thank you, I would really like to work for you and I would not leave." More money, pension, closer to home, he would love to work here.

Stan was enthusiastic because of the travel and other benefits. In his eyes, getting bored was a hidden benefit? He was used to working his socks off. Did Mr Clark have a valid point? Well, regardless of a promise, if Stan worked here and didn't like it, he would have to leave?

"Okay," answered Will, "thank you. I will take you to your next interview, please come with me."

The pair left his office. Mr Clark asked the remaining candidate to wait in his room, after Sue entered, he shut the door behind her.

Will and Stan followed the corridor to an area with an atrium in the centre. Looking over the balustrade it was above the main entrance into the building. Will moved his hand to guide Stan to a line of chairs outside another room. A few of the candidates previously outside Mr Clark's office were now seated here, waiting for their second interview. Stan joined them, Mr Clark returned to his room.

Slowly, Stan's turn for the second interview moved closer. His turn arrived, the door of the interview room opened, an old lady popped her head out. "Please come in," she waved him through. Stan obeyed.

The room was enormous, it was something out of a Stately Home.

Stan gasped; the space was about ten metres wide by twenty metres long. There were floor to ceiling leaded windows along the external wall, two enormous glass chandeliers above a huge central table. It took Stan aback. However, he found the number of aged people sitting around the table more distracting. There must have been fifteen or twenty, each dressed in their Sunday finery as if they were going to a wedding.

Stan was offered a seat at the end of the table. The lady about eight metres away at the other end, introduced herself. She then introduced every person seated around the table.

Stan didn't hear any names or titles. He was shell shocked, he felt very self-conscience.

Was she the Mayor?

They didn't want to look at his drawings, or how to design a heating system, they wanted to know if he liked dogs?

"Do you have any pets, young man," a creaky voice from somewhere to his right asked.

It took him a minute to collect himself before he focussed enough to hear their questions.

The door opened, in walked Will Clark. He apologised for interrupting, pulled up a chair and sat next to Stan.

Will was very professional; he could see the blank look in his protégé's eyes. He left Stan to answer the questions but every now and again prompted an answer. The elderly Councillors said such obscure things, Stan often couldn't recognise there was a question in what they said.

If there was a silence, Will picked up the pieces.

"Stan, tell the Committee about your interest in photography," or Stan, "tell Councillor James about your pets."

The interview was concluded, Stan was asked to wait outside. He held the door for Sue as she entered the room to replace him in the hot seat. After a short while, she returned to the atrium seating area. The lady looked uncomfortable.

"Everything alright?" Stan questioned.

"Not sure," she replied, "strange interview, I'm not sure if I would work here. Really curious questions? Not so sure about the boss either."

"Me neither," Stan lied, "they asked me about my..."

The opening of the Committee Room door interrupted him, Stan was invited in. 'Yippee!' He thought, 'Got it'.

He was asked to take a seat at the table.

Shyly, he looked towards the lady at the opposite end of the table, from the sides of the table a frieze of nodding, aged faces smiled at him. One craggy face winked, but it may have been a tick in his eye. The main lady at the head of the table spoke. The Committee would be offering the position to the young lady. Stan would be first reserve. If the lady turned it down, he would be offered the position. Would he accept the proposal? Deflated, he agreed, and was dismissed from the room.

"Well done," greeted Sue as he walked back to the atrium seats, "you got it?" She smiled. Before Stan could answer, the door opened again, this time Sue was called in.

Two minutes later, she was back. Slightly, unsettled, "They've offered me the job," she announced, "I don't know what to do?"

Stan offered his congratulations. "What way do you go home?" he enquired.

"To the Tube and change," she replied.

"Same as me, shall we walk together?" he offered. She nodded.

They chatted as they walked to Barking Station. 'Sue worked in London for the Post Office's telephone division. She was more an electrical tracer than a drafter, working on electrical wiring projects. She lived in Essex with her husband, they had a mortgage'.

Together they boarded the eastbound Tube. 'She had applied for the job because she thought it would be easier than travelling to London but in fact there wasn't much difference. Also, the Barham job paid less than her current one. She was now concerned about the effect that would have on paying the mortgage'.

The train arrived at Dagenham Heathway station. It pulled out. Cleverly, Stan was aware of all of Sue's concerns. He had three minutes until his station, but hours of listening to Harry at site meetings to cement his future.

"Well Sue, I understand your problem. But I think you need to talk it through with your husband. It's not that I am talking about just your situation, I would say the same thing to anyone."

Do they really want to take a cut in wages? Will they be happy if they have to change their lifestyle? Problems paying the mortgage?

The train pulled into Dagenham East station.

His leaving thoughts, "It's tough for anyone to make a judgement about something like this, especially when it means so many things in your life will change. I understand your uncertainty and hope you make the right decision."

Stan continued, "This is where I get off." The doors opened, Stan stepped off, "Take care, nice meeting you." He waved; she waved back. The train doors closed as Sue continued her journey home.

APPOINTMENT

Stan had handed his notice to Kathy at H.W. Button four weeks earlier. He had received a letter of appointment from L.B. Barham notifying him of his success in applying for the vacancy of draughtsman. 'Thank you, Sue!' He celebrated.

A short time since, he hadn't even been looking for a new job. It was emotionally hard for him to move on, to leave H.W. Button and his friends. He had been there over three years. The young engineer had begun his employment there unaware of his knowledge and capabilities, with limited confidence. He was still a shy person. However, in a working environment under Buttons trust and training he had developed to become confident in his own competence. Stan loved the variety of tasks, site work and comradery with the 'goons' who worked on the tools. They were just like Brian and Ollie.

Stan had taken so much from Buttons he felt a responsibility to stay put and give more back, but life is not a rehearsal. He had to play with the cards he was dealt.

Economically, it was easier for him to make the decision. The money side made sense. Now he was working closer to home, paying less on train fares and receiving an increased salary.

Seeing Bronwyn of a morning had ceased months before, due to her office moving from London to Croydon.

It was his first day at the new job. On arrival at the Town Hall, he was asked to take the stairs to the first floor. Waiting to greet him at the top of the stairs was Reg Doyle the Senior Mechanical Engineer. He was tall with black curly hair and a large belly. He looked a nice, gentle sort of chap with a happy face.

Stan noticed that the decoration of the building here was not as grandiose as when he had attended the interview. This was the employee, local government officers' part of the Town Hall. The floor where he had been before was the Council Members domain.

Reg showed him around. In this corridor, the lift was around the corner, then the toilets at the end. Across from the stairs was the typist's office. Opposite the windows was a lobby where Will's office was, the second office was shared by Reg and Albert.

Next, they walked past two doors into the main drawing office then to a few smaller offices. Stan would be in the first small office, but first Reg took him into the main office. It was quite large, the doors into the corridor were at each end.

"I won't introduce you to everyone now," noted Reg. He was a very quietly spoken man, "You won't remember anybody's name anyway." He smiled.

He called for attention, "Good morning, everybody." There was barely a hush.

Stan stood with Reg just inside the large room looking at about twenty or more animated people. "Ahem, you rabble, quiet please."

Veiled insults aimed at Reg zipped from different places in the room.

"Now I have your attention," Reg jested, "I have a new gentleman starting today. Not like you lot, this is Stan who is starting today. He is the new draughtsman working in the Energy room, next door."

Smiling faces turned to Reg and Stan in the doorway, a few waved. "Don't do it Stan, leave while you can," someone shouted. A few laughed.

"Good luck Stan, you'll need it," another shouted.

Reg took Stan to his place of work. There was no one else in the room, just a drawing board next to three empty desks. The Senior informed Stan of meal times, start and finish times etc. Two of the desks were for the Energy Team, two engineers who travelled around Council buildings to find ways of reducing energy usage. They were Joe and Chris, commonly known as the 'meter men'.

The engineer Stanley would firstly be working for would join him in half an hour.

"I'll leave you now to sort yourself out. If you need anything, I'm in the office in the small lobby," Reg left.

The drawing board was next to a large window. He could look out while working. There was a narrow 'one way' road below with a large supermarket opposite. Stan set up the equipment he had brought with him. His Retring drawing pens with an adapter for a compass took pride of place.

A delicate tap on the open door compelled Stan to turn. In the doorway stood a short balding man with a comb over hairstyle and Hitler moustache. Grinning, his back slightly bent forward the man raised an arm.

"Come in, please," signalled Stan, "are you bringing work for me?" he enquired.

"Oh, no," replied the short man, "I thought I'd break the ice, come and say 'welcome'. I'm Kelvin, Kelvin Foot. Are you okay? How are you settling in?"

"Yes, I'm fine, thank you," replied Stan, thinking, 'this could be Charlie at Button's brother, but a weaselly, shorter version'.

Kelvin was friendly, he chatted about everyday things and put Stan at ease. He made Stan aware of a RULGO newsletter underneath an application form on Stan's board. Kelvin explained that RULGO was the trades union for white collar people who worked at the London Borough of Barham.

Stan was direct, he told of his belief that Trades Unions had a role, but he was hesitant about joining. Kelvin advised that there was no choice. If you worked for L.B.B. or any local authority, you had to be a member, it was mandatory. Not to worry, Roger Harton, the union rep, would probably be in to see Stan soon. Roger would explain.

Shortly after Kelvin had left, Des Hooper came into the room. He had some work for Stan, the full draughting design, layout and detailing of a plant room. They chatted about the project, the design, exactly what Des would expect to see on the drawings.

Stan was left to get on with it. A few hours later, Will came into the room.

"Good afternoon, Stan, how are you settling in?"

"I'm very well thank you, Will," he replied.

Will smiled, "I just thought I'd come to say 'ello'. You were my number one choice at the interviews. I had to pull a few strings to obtain the best engineering option for the Department. And we got there in the end."

Will, grinned, "It would have been blasted embarrassing for me if you had declined. So, thanks again for joining us."

Will continued, "You see the Councillors are very nice people. They do have the Borough's interests at heart, but when it comes to technical issues, I think I know best. You shall find out later anyway. I have recently taken this position so I'm restructuring the Department. There will be a few changes, but don't worry as you are in my long-term plans. I hope you will be happy working here."

Stan thanked him.

Will turned and left the room.

04-03
TEA

Reg came to visit him four days after Stan had started. He explained that people made their own hot drinks in the main office using a kettle, however it had been decided that a tea urn would be better and safer. Stan was the lucky person to have been voted the 'tea smith'.

He would make the drinks for everyone in the morning at 10.00am and mid-afternoon.

Looking at Stanley's glum face, Reg tried to ease the instruction. "It will help you remember everyone's name," he grinned. "At any other time, they will make their own."

The young man could tell Reg had thought about the chore, "Perhaps it might be an idea to get in Will's good books, collect his cup, wash it up and take his tea to him?" He winked.

There was also a new signing in sheet. This was a form on a table next to the tea urn, similar to the one at Duckles.

Everybody had to sign in and out as they arrived or left the office. There was an information section. If you were late in, or were leaving the office, the reason had to be recorded in that box. A red line would be added to the form by Reg at 9.15 each morning. Any names under the line would be classed as late arrivals.

"Also," continued Reg, "Will has spotted that people disappear to get cakes and sweets. He has ordered a cash box and a lockable cupboard to keep sweet meats in."

"You are his choice of shop keeper. He wants you to look after the tuck shop. The plan is he funds the initial supplies. You buy cheap multipacks of chocolate bars and crisps then sell them at the normal price of an individual item. Say you buy a pack of four chocolate Banqict bars for 16p and sell them for 5p each. For a £1 purchase, we get back £1 25p, which goes into the tuck shop kitty. When the cupboard arrives, I shall give you £3 to start you off."

Reg retired to his room.

160

Stan continued with his work for Des. He started thinking about his conversation with Reg.

'Don't know about this? I came here as a technician engineer, within four days I'm a teaboy. Washing up the bosses' cup? S***, now I know why Will spoke to me about leaving soon after I started. What about, 'you are in my long-term plans'. Yeah, it seems I am, but as a teaboy and Tuck Shop Executive. Promotion already?'

Stanley wasn't happy, he was never going to wash Will's cup nor deliver his tea. Maybe Reg was over eager?

He put his mind to the task for Des. Around 4.00pm the young draughtman had finished the drawings, used to working where everything was urgent, he went into the main office to find the engineer. "Hi Des, how are you?"

"I'm fine, thank you," replied Des, "how can I help you?"

Stan explained, "I have finished the drawings for you. Is there anything else you need doing?"

"Thanks Stan, can you do the sections next then, please?" requested Des.

"I've done all of those as well," replied Stan.

"Really?" responded Des in disbelief, "Er! Can you add the notes then please?"

"Sorry, but I've done those as well," answered Stan, with an apologetic smile.

"Really?" Des was amazed, "I'll best come and have a look."

They walked together to Stan's room where he talked Des through his work.

Three A0 negative drawings rested on Stan's board. Des was very happy with what he saw.

"The problem is Stan, you have completed four weeks work in four days. I have nothing else to give you. Your work is good, I can't find a fault. For now, please keep your head down and keep 'working' on these drawings. Best to stay away from Reg and Will. I'll try and get something else for you."

Stan had three weeks to kill.

04-04

FRIDAY

As Will had previously informed Stan the offices were eventually rearranged. The main office now had an aisle along the internal wall connecting the two doors to the corridor. This became known as the tea aisle. At ninety degrees to the tea aisle were rows of furniture, like a comb. Up to eight people sat back to back in each row with a walkway between.

Stan's office was now the MEL office. It housed Iris on Maintenance and emergency with the two 'meter men' on Energy control and Lifts.

Stan's new position was at the end of a row next to the external window. He sat back to back at a drawing board with Bruce Jennings, a young Graduate Engineer. Neither had a cabinet nor desk. Bruce always laughed that they shared a windowsill together. Cups, ashtray, cigarettes, pens, pencils, catalogues, drawings - everything went on their shared windowsill.

Stan's tea urn was in the main aisle next to a door into the corridor. The new tuck cupboard was adjacent.

He had not been sure about having to provide 'domestic' duties for the office, but it seemed his engineering work wasn't going to stretch him so he went with the flow. He knew everybody's hot drink preferences, how many sugars etc. He was happy to chat while at the urn. Some people like Simon regularly drank their tea at the urn so they could natter. More importantly it meant Stanley knew everybody, plus they knew him.

As he breezed through his engineering work, he needed tasks to keep him occupied, away from boredom.

Also, when he was late arriving in the morning, he would walk into the office holding a supermarket carrier bag giving the impression he had been buying provisions for the tuck cupboard. If he was really late, he would actually nip into the supermarket and buy some tuck supplies before entering the office.

On Friday, the staff in the MEL office were elsewhere. There was no one to answer the emergency phone for the MEL groups. In Iris' absence, Bert asked Shirley, an elderly lady drafter to cover the MEL telephone.

Shirley was short and trim. She was the sweetest, kindest person in the world. However, this meant in order not to create offence she regularly over thought things. The result was often an upset confused lady.

On one occasion, while travelling to work she identified a skinny cat. The trauma affected her so badly she turned around to rush straight home where she prepared a saucer of milk.

Then, when she returned to the same area the cat had disappeared. Shirley spent thirty minutes walking around holding a saucer of milk, calling 'kitty'. Arriving at work two hours late, she immediately whisked into Bert's office to apologise, but proclaimed her lateness was due to a 'matter of life or death'. When Bert asked how she knew the cat was hungry, she explained that it had been 'meowing'.

Shirley was also very stubborn. At first, she declined Bert's request to work in the MEL office. But then, after he changed his request to a demand, she had no choice.

"Shirley," Bert spoke quietly, "it is really important that you answer any calls to MEL. Someone may be in trouble and they need to speak to us. All you need to do is ask the person's name, the problem and address, then write it down. If you have any troubles, ask them to hang on, then come to see me or one of the engineers."

Under duress, Shirley agreed. She dejectedly followed Bert to the MEL office and sat down.

Thirty minutes later Alex picked up his phone, he dialled a number then started talking in a disguised manner.

"Ello, is that the Police?"

"Sorry, I need the Police."

"No, no, don't go, who are you? No please don't hang up."

"Did you say Shirley, allo Shirley, you say you're not the Police, who are you?"

"A draughting lady, ok, thank you. You do drawings at the Council? Wow, good, I need help, can you help me?"

"You can't? I see, nooo, please don't hang up. I'm phoning the help-line, can you give me their number?"

"You are the helpline. Can you help me then please? You are helping because no one else is available. Okay, thank you."

"I'm stuck in a lift in Barham, yes Barham."

"Yeah, Barham, is that where you are? Good, that helps. Would you like to know where I am?"

"No! Oh, I would like to get out of this lift please. Can you help me?"

Barry started to make the sound of a barking dog.

The main office door flew open. In ran a distressed Shirley. "Can someone help please, I have answered a call and there's a man and his dog trapped in a lift. It's a Cocker Spaniel."

"How you do know what type of dog it is?" asked Barry.

"I recognised the bark," replied Shirley. The people in the office were desperately holding back laughter.

Bruce volunteered to go with her. He picked the phone up and spoke to the 'caller'. "Hello sir, you have managed to get the lift started again? Oh, that's good."

Alex retorted, "Bruce, I'm still stuck in the lift, what are you doing?"

Bruce responded, "I see sir, that's good news we are glad. And your little dog is safe? Good, no problem, sir, thank you." He replaced the handset. Shirley now had a new favourite, Bruce, he had 'saved the dog's life'. She was so grateful. He would find two chocolate biscuits from the tin at her home wrapped in tissue paper on his desk the next morning.

Alex wasn't amused that Bruce had aborted his jape. But he couldn't argue with him. Once the dog appeared in the lift, Shirley would have walked to the lift herself to save it. They were lucky she ran into the main office and not to Bert.

Shirley answered three other calls that day, each time she ran to Bruce and fetched him to talk to the caller. None of them were emergency calls.

Friday afternoon was fun afternoon.

They always played Animal, Vegetable, Mineral on a Friday afternoon as it could be played from their seats. Shouting questions, they took the Michael and insulted each other. If Will appeared, they only needed to look down, if Bert or Reg walked in the men would usually join in.

Peter Nelson started.

"What is it," asked Roger.

"Animal," answered Pete N.

"Is it a fish?" asked John.

"Nope," answered Pete N.

"Is it very heavy?" posed Roger.

"No," replied Pete N.

They had used eighteen questions, there were only two left. So far, they knew it was a mammal, four legs, not heavy, no particular colour, had a tail.

"Come on, two questions left," warned Pete N.

"I think I know what it is," claimed Barry, "shall I go for it?"

"Are you sure?" queried Alex, "we know what you're like." A few mumbled noises agreed.

"Okay," Barry continued, "if it stood on its hind legs, would its head come up to my belt?"

Uproar! "You plum Barry, what you doing?" yelled Alex,. "What a stupid question."

"Well, let him answer and we'll find out," argued Barry. "Come on, Pete?"

Pete answered, "No."

"I thought it was a dog," Barry continued with a whisper.

"You dipstick!" The others chimed in, "it could still be a dog."

"Bet it's a Cocker Spaniel," shouted Bruce.

FABLE

Stan placed the kettle onto the 30l stainless steel tea urn, picked them both up and walked to the toilets at the end of the corridor. He emptied the stale water from both into the hand basin to rinse them out. The 'tea smith' filled the kettle a number of times then poured the water into the urn. When half full, he took the urn back to the main office then made a second trip to collect the filled kettle.

He looked at the signing in sheet to check how many were present. A note under the red line took Stan's attention. 'Got off train at Barking. Young lady looked unwell. Loosened her clothing so she didn't faint. Called ambulance and waited with her until it arrived'.

Stanley was reading one of Barry's infamous excuses for being late.

Alex had told Stan that he was going to keep these fables and make a book of them. 'Barry's Fables - the Art of Kidology'.

The truth was Barry liked a flutter on the gee-gees. Most days at 9.00am he could be seen hanging around the bookies opposite the station waiting for them to open. He frequently arrived in the office approaching 9.30am. Directly, to show that he didn't care a jot about being late, or even less about the signing in form, he wrote these wild fantasy excuses.

Another fable, favourite, 'walking across main road in Barham, saw dog get hit by car. Cared for dog and called RSPCA. Waited for them to come. Dog died'.

Stan was shuffling the cups and sundries around the beverage making area when Aiden came in. As Aiden bent his head over the signing in form Stanley noticed the new arrivals face was cut and bruised. Aiden was also shuffling along with a bad leg.

"Are you okay?" asked Stan.

"Thanks," replied Aiden. The recently married young engineer was in his mid to late twenties. Just under six feet tall, he was built like a brick shithouse. With blond wavy hair, he was very good looking.

"How did you do the, er," Stan nodded to Aiden's face.

"Don't ask," he replied, "got done at football, Chelsea on Saturday."

"I thought you were a Chelsea supporter," queried Stan.

"Yeah, I am, and I'm black and blue to prove it." Aiden rolled up his shirt sleeves to expose bruised and cut limbs, "Fifteen stitches in these, and my back is bruised," he grimaced.

"Chelsea were at home to Liverpool on Saturday afternoon. I asked my mate from Merseyside if he fancied coming down for the match. We planned to later hit some clubs in London. He thought it was a great idea, so I got two tickets in the Shed."

"We won, so that was all good. Cautiously, we hung about to let the fans thin out a bit, then started moving slowly towards the exit. That's when my mate started talking, raw scouse as if he was at home. I trod on his toes for goodness' sake. Gave him a dig with me elbow. I had told him before, 'Don't open your mouth when you're in there, you will get us both done'. You could see eyes darting about, brains clicking. Suspicion. People around us were looking."

"It was decent. We were outside in the crowd walking to Fulham Broadway station. There was no 'ag'. A voice behind called out, 'Have you got a light mate?' The bloke tapped me on the shoulder. I dug my mate in the ribs with me elbow, and answered, 'No sorry mate'."

"Then another voice behind shouted, 'Ah mate what's the time?' My crazy mate looked at his watch, in a deep scouse accent shouts, 'abar feve fivfeen laah'. Next thing, I've been drop kicked in the back. I'm on the floor, taking a shoeing. Luckily the old Bill were close. I'm laying with me arms over my head, the Bill beat them off with truncheons. So they saved me from taking a real good hiding."

"How was your mate?" questioned Stan.

"Don't ask. The dickhead, he was gone like a F*** rocket. They didn't get him. He hid in the station, then went to my house and waited for me. Not happy, I've ruined a new pair of strides I was wearing for the clubs that night. My missus wasn't pleased, I can tell ya."

After Stan made him a cup of coffee, he went about his work. Aiden took a fluffy cushion from his bag and placed it on his chair.

04-05

EMPTY

Stan arrived in work early. He had not slept that night, he had not slept the night before.

He had left home early to meet Bronwyn at the bus stop she used to catch a bus to the Tube station.

It was now only 8.30am, he sat on his chair by the large window, watching the customers going in and out of the supermarket opposite the Town Hall. His eyes didn't focus. He didn't see any of these people. He just saw dull shapes moving around, like a sped-up traffic film. His mind was whirling, doing somersaults, just one unanswerable question kept returning. Why?

He would never knowingly hurt anyone. His intolerable pain was that he had hurt the person he loved most, and he didn't know how. There was no way back.

He had a joint mortgage with Bronwyn. It had been hard to get one, but his increased salary in moving jobs had just made it possible. They had purchased a house, it was only small but it had a garden. The location wasn't great, but the best they could afford. There was no argument, living in the house would be better than living with their parents or in a flat. He thought it would be the path towards marriage and a family.

The couple had not been out, out very much because of the lack of spare cash. But they had still spent a lot of time together at her mum and dad's house. True he thought, they had never had much time alone. But her parents were lovely, he felt one of the family. He had thought he was one of the family.

He tried to make sense of his life.

Five days ago, everything was rosy, now he was confused and felt useless.

What do you do? Your future life set out to be with the person you love, have loved for the last four years? Then, one day, when you knock at the door of her family home, her mother answers to tell you that her daughter is not going out. She says that your loved one has been locked in her bedroom, crying all day. She won't speak to you, she won't look at you. She won't come out of her room. Her mother, 'thinks it will be alright tomorrow'.

Nothing unusual, Bronwyn and Stan had spent the evening together at her mum and dad's house. They had, had an argument about the new house.

Because of his shyness, sometimes he may appear sharp or abrupt. If things were not as she liked, they could have talked. Why didn't they talk? Everything, anything, could have been changed for her. He had become angry, was that why?

What changed? He trawled his subconscious for the reason.

Stan had made today's early journey to try and see Bronwyn, to talk. He wished for them to get back together. But Bronwyn's choice was important, if she wanted them to breakup, he would have to accept it. He could bare that their relationship was finished, but he couldn't fathom why. It was like grieving for a family member who passes on before you have the opportunity to tell them that you love them.

He had waited at her bus stop. She turned into the main road and saw him. The young lady looked at him with pure hatred in her eyes. Again, he couldn't understand. She actually hated him? They boarded the bus together, then the Tube. She never looked at nor spoke to him, after four years? Stan alighted the Tube at his normal station and made his way to work. He couldn't tell his parents; they loved her like their own. He couldn't go home.

The office slowly filled, his colleagues let him be, they could see how distraught he was.

Every morning at around 9.20am Will would have a 'walkabout'. He entered the main office via the right-hand door, moseyed along the tea aisle and left by the left-hand door. He very rarely spoke when on this tour.

This morning someone must have informed Will about Stan's demeanour. This time, Will entered the main office as usual, but he slowly walked to Stan. Putting his hand on Stanley's shoulder Will invited him to his office. There, he sat with Stan for over half an hour, talking and listening regarding the young man's reason for his distress. It was a chat Stan would never have had with his parents. It wasn't because they weren't supportive, they were always available for a chat, ready to listen, talk problems through. Stan understood, they always let their children come to them. They wouldn't interfere, never ask questions that were best left unanswered. It was his problem, deep inside he felt ashamed. He had lots of questions but no answers.

After their conversation, Will told Stan to go home immediately. He was to have as much time off work as necessary. "Book it all as sick leave," he instructed.

Stan left the office and travelled home by Tube and bus. He now had a second thing he could never share. But unlike the 'pee need' occasion, this time, he had no inner strength to hide his feelings from the public. If people looked or stared at his tear stained, red eyed and puffy face, let them. He was past caring, he was empty.

04-07

SPANIEL

Ten months since the collapse of Stan and Bronwyn's relationship. He was trying to create a new life. His first day back in the main office at L.B.B. after returning from a summer holiday with four of his friends in Benitorm.

The eternal teenager had bought a plastic poo in the Spanish resort. It had followed him to the office and was hiding in his work bag. He knew if he listened hard enough, he could hear it trying to escape. It was a realistic colour and shaped in the pyramid style. The mound looked authentic, even better than putty and piping compound.

When everyone was settling down with their morning hot drinks, Stan slipped the richard behind his back. He left the main office by the right-hand door, made his way along the corridor and placed it just inside the left-hand door. He retraced his footsteps making it back to his seat without detection.

Alex had just collected his mug of tea. Walking back to his desk, he saw it smiled and walked on.

Shirley walking in, she saw it. The lady went ballistic, "Oh my goodness, what is that, oh dear, how did that get there? There must be a poor dog loose in the building, poor thing." Shirley was the type of person who would never imagine that someone could take time to make a fake poo. Why would they? Poo wasn't funny.

"Sorry everyone," she addressed the office, "has anybody seen a stray dog in the office? Could be a medium sized one, a Spaniel? Perhaps?"

At that time, only two other people in the office knew what the S*** she was talking about.

"Shirley?" called Barry, "I saw a big pink one when I came in, not sure if it was a dog?"

"Nope," shouted John, "that was an upadumper."

"Yeah, I saw that John, it had a man wearing a turban on its back," added Alex.

"Bet he had to lean forward to ride it along the corridor," joined Des.

"I think he must have hit his head on the ceiling," laughed Barry.

"Ooh, you lot, you're mucking about, always pulling my leg," Shirley acknowledged. "I'm not looking for an elephant. I'm looking for a dog. Elephants are not a type of dog, you sillies. I'll have a walk around the building to see if I can find it, cheerio."

She mumbled to herself, "Must get a bowl of water for it." As bold as brass she swiped a saucer from the beverage area, added a few drops of water and off she went. Dog patrol or safari?

Everybody looked in disbelief, but 'that' was Shirley. "What was all that about?" questioned Des, "She's F*** mad."

Alex explained, just a little not to spoil the joke, "Screw loose Shirley has seen some dog waste, she's looking for the owner."

Minutes later. "Seen it," cried Bruce standing over the sordid object. About half of the office took a turn to view it.

When the poo was no longer an object of interest, Stan repeated his route to retrieve it. Slithered back towards his seat, he had a moment of inspiration. As he crept past Shirley's drawing board he reached down, surreptitiously placing the poo in a compartment of Shirley's unzipped holdall.

"11.30am," called out Aiden. "It's my birthday today."

A few 'happy birthdays', responded.

"Is there anyone here who doesn't want a cake?" Aiden continued. Silence.

"Make mine a big one," Kelvin proposed, laughing.

For some reason, Aiden acted offended. There was a bit of history between these two? The young athletic man didn't seem able to tolerate the weedy, waffling, older one. They very rarely spoke.

"Okay," granted Aiden, "if I get you a big one, you have to eat it all in one mouthful."

The pair squabbled about how much of the cake Kelvin would have to eat, including the technique. Both sported a smile as they spoke, but there was no pleasure in the exchanges. It was sad that a throw away, lighthearted gag had become a contest of words.

Kelvin told Aiden to forget it. He would go without; he was fed up with arguing. Regardless of Kelvin's withdrawal Aiden was rabid. He wanted his pound of flesh.

The young man was remorseless, finger pointing and thrashing around he left on his campaign to purchase the treats.

Aiden returned with cakes for all, eclairs, doughnuts, twirls, Danish, muffins. Everyone wanted to know what he had bought for Kelvin. The biggest, 'most unappetising, sickly cake ever available', just to annoy the little man and put him in his place.

The great reveal, from a carrier bag Aiden produced a jam and cream Swiss Roll! All the drama, the aggression, the disappointment!

The crowd were not happy, 'all the B*** arguing, and he bought Kelvin a Swiss Roll? Bet Kelvin is upset he has to eat a whole F*** Swiss Roll?'

Aiden passed the Swiss Roll to Kelvin, who, to be truthful was very relieved. They actually smiled at each other? Then, Aiden left Kelvin to eat it at his own pace.

Everyone sat and enjoyed their cakes washed down with a nice hot drink. Simon made his way to Stan; they chatted about football. Both were crazy about football, Stan was now playing on a Saturday afternoon and a Sunday morning. Si was medium build, not athletic, very stiff but he still enjoyed kicking a ball around. He checked with Stan where the match was being played on Sunday, he planned to make the journey to support the team.

"The other reason I'm here Stan," Si shared, "is I know you are not going out with Bronwyn anymore. My sister has recently split with her long-term boyfriend. I was thinking, I'm having a housewarming party in two weeks, sort of wondered if you would come? I've told my Bronwyn about you, she can't wait to meet you. I think you'll get on very well together."

Stan was taken aback. He didn't want to disappoint Si, anyway she may be a nice person, he agreed to pop in and meet her.

A little later, still holding the saucer of water 'screw loose' came back into the main office.

She had been missing for ages, apparently been 'all over the Town Hall' looking for a stray dog. Shirley explained that she had looked in every office, adding that she also had a 'catch up' chat with each of her buddies.

'Really?' Thought Stan. 'Is she daft, or actually very clever? Are we to accept that she's been out of the office for nearly two hours, looking for a dog? Conveniently, she had got back just at lunch time'.

A loud scream interrupted the trail of engineers leaving the room. It was Shirley, she had put her hand in her holdall, and touched 'it'.

"What's up?" Roger and Pete W ran over to her.

"I thought it had been cleared away, but it's in my bag, I touched it," she shrieked. "How did it get into my bag? I'll have to throw everything away now."

Everyone tried to placate her, she was having none of it. They tried to show her that it was plastic, she wouldn't listen. Eventually, her friend Iris attended to calm the cat lady.

Together, they went to the toilet where Iris pretended to clean everything. Shirley sat on the pan with the cubicle door open to look or help. The sandwiches that were in her bag were placed in a bin; the poo vanished.

Stan thought it best not to own up, nor claim ownership of the richard.

Poor Shirley was so distressed she had to leave for home at 2.00pm.

SHTUM

Stan got into the office a bit early. Before setting up the drinks equipment, he searched for a clean attendance sheet under the pile of used ones sitting next to the tea urn.

He went to place the new form on top of yesterday's and noticed there was a Barry fable below the red line. Barry's reasons for being late were always convoluted, a tale rather than a simple excuse.

'Got to Barham, felt hungry went for burger. Grille caught light, helped extinguish fire using wet tea towel and spoon. Waited for Fire Brigade'.

Looking high on the wall above the urn at the large white faced, black clock Stan had a cheeky thought. What if he turned the office clock back thirty minutes? Barry would arrive with another fable he had developed on the walk from the Betting Shop only as he looked at the office clock he would be on time. Barry wouldn't understand how he got in on time. It would be worth seeing the look on his face. Stan moved a wooden stool adjacent to the urn's position climbed up and reset the clock.

Around 9.15am the office phone rang. Peter Nelson picked it up, "Okay, just a mo."

He turned to Stan, "You are the secretary of a football team, Stan?"

Stanley nodded, "Yeah," he replied.

"It's for you," Pete N passed him the phone.

The call was from a reporter on a national Sunday newspaper, The News of the Globe. The caller was interested in the Cup Final between Derrie Sports, Stan's team and Ben United on the Sunday just gone. The reporter understood that because of the fighting on the pitch during the game and the fighting outside the changing rooms after the game, the league had refused to hand the Trophy to the winners.

Stan smiled, most of the fighting after the game was between the girlfriends and wives of the two teams. The men had to leave the changing rooms, half dressed, to break them up. He had to think quickly.

"Mr Paterson, could you talk me through the incidents on that Sunday morning, please?" requested the reporter. "Particularly, the sending-off of one of your players for 'extreme violent conduct'."

"Well, I wasn't playing in that game," answered Stan. I was on the touchline. Afraid I must have missed that incident, I can't remember - he lied - perhaps I was bent over cleaning the magic sponge when that happened. Sorry, about that. Sorry, I can't help." He hung up. 'Whoo, national press, onto me. What to do?'

Aiden arrived, they chatted, made their tea then retired to their drawing boards.

"What a mess I made at home last night," offered Aiden. "You know me and the missus moved into an old house after we got married?"

Stan nodded, dipping a biscuit into his tea.

"Well, we are knocking the two living rooms into one." Aiden stopped. "Did I tell you about when I tiled the kitchen?"

"No," answered Stan.

"Okay, I'll tell you about that first." Aiden continued.

"See, we ripped out the old kitchen and put in a new one, yeah? Okay. We bought these really nice units and tiles, fancy sockets, everything. I did it all myself, her brother helped sometimes. Well, it looked really kosher. I had just finished the last tile, stood back it was amazing. Then me wife says, 'Where should they go?' She points at the box of sockets."

"I'd forgot to shape the tiles to fit around the recessed boxes and tiled over them. There were no holes for the sockets. 'F*** that', I thought."

"What did you do?" asked Stan.

"We couldn't rip all the tiles off, so I bought some surface boxes with trunking, then mounted everything on top of the tiles. Looks good, but not what we wanted," confessed Aiden.

"I'm F*** useless sometimes," Aiden continued with another story. "I beaver away an forget the details. Last night, like I was saying. Nothing on the tele, I thought I'd have a crack at getting the middle wall between the two living rooms down. So, after tea, I got a ladder and chiselled away all the cement joins where the walls attached to others at each end and the ceiling along the top. Didn't take long. I tried to push it over, but it was too strong, so I ran up and drop kicked it. That done the trick, it hit the floor and broke up."

"Only thing though, some of it broke the floorboards and went into the void underneath. I haven't shown the wife. When she's not about, I'm going to lift up the floorboards and hide the other bricks underneath."

Their attention was drawn to Barry, standing at the signing in form. Barry was confused, he was on time? How could he be at the office for 9.00am when he didn't leave the bookies until 9.20am? Assuming he was right, he could hardly use that argument. To allow him to add a fable, did he argue the clock was wrong? Maybe, he should sign in at 9.00am for the first time?

Iris came in from the MEL office, she was anxious. The emergency helpline was going into melt down. People were getting angry, irate. They were shouting at her down the phone. She was being blamed for them being late for work. Others moaned their children were late for school. The Town Hall tower clock which people living in Barham used as their everyday clock, was thirty minutes slow. Iris had been outside and checked.

She had dialled 'TIM' the telephone speaking clock to check, the complainers were right. How could that happen?

Shirley arrived carrying two loaded carrier bags. She was very happy. When she arrived at the Town Hall the first time, the clock read 8.35am, so she left and went wedding shopping.

Joe, one of the meter men joined them. "Iris, oh, here you are," he declared. "Your phone won't stop ringing, what's going on?"

Iris explained about the angry callers, that the tower clock was slow.

"No problem, okay Iris, you dial 'TIM' now, please." Joe moved a nearby stool below the clock that Stan had altered. He pointed to the white face.

"This is the master clock for the entire Town Hall, including the tower clock. Every clock in this building reads the same as this one. It looks to be running slow, I don't understand how? Shout out the time please Iris, I'll reset it against 'TIM'."

Stanley twisted on his seat to face his drawing board. Another episode he should stay shtum about.

The phone rang again. Pete N answered again. "It's for you again Stan. It's a reporter from The Sunday Populous. Another national newspaper?"

04-08

This time Stan was prewarned, he asked Pete N to tell them he wasn't available. Then he telephoned the League Secretary and Fixtures Secretary to advise them that the national press were chasing the Cup Final story. He suggested they warn the Club Secretary of Ben United.

04-09

DEREK

It was good to get out of the office. At Buttons, Stan frequently worked away from the office engaged in surveys, meetings and new installations.

Today, Alex had asked him to visit a school which was undergoing refurbishment works. There was minimal available space for some new equipment in the basement plantroom. Stan was asked to survey, measure and sketch the area, then plot the locations of the new equipment. He would then determine the necessary piping layout to achieve the installation.

He arrived at the school, making his way down the concrete steps he avoided the lengths of pipe and fittings laying on them before turning right into the plantroom.

He could hear chatter, occasionally metal clanging on metal. A face turned towards him.

"Hi, I'm Stan, Alex sent me." Stanley introduced himself.

"Come in Stan, I'm Colin, this is Basil," he pointed towards a large vertical pipe.

Half a head appeared to the side of the pipe. "Nice to meet you Stan, I'm Baz," the half a head informed him.

Stan nodded. This was the part of his job he preferred. The nitty gritty down to earth workmen.

Colin continued, "Stan, Alex said you would be coming, follow me and I'll show you the problematic zone."

Stan listened and observed. Colin explained the issue, "If you want to get started, we are here, just a gnat's away, give us a shout if you need anything."

Thanking him, Stanley commenced his work. Colin returned to his.

"Oi, Baz, got anything planned for this F*** weekend?" enquired Colin.

"Cheeky F*** monkey. I hope we do it tonight, well every F***

night really, if I had the chance. Not, oh wait, you mean for The F***
weekend," replied Baz laughing.

"Sorry, actually, we've got tickets for the F*** ballet on Saturday.
F*** Romeo and Juliet, wonderful."

"Never F*** fancied that. It's for F*** fairies, ain't it?" claimed Colin.

"No. No it F*** ain't," retorted Baz. "You would be surprised; it
helps if you know a bit about the F*** plot. It's not all F*** airy fairy,
it's like proper F*** acting to music. They don't all ponce around in
F*** dresses and tights, you know. This one's at the Royal F*** Ballet in
London. We go quiet F*** often.

We have been to the F*** London Coliseum an all. F***, I tell you,
live F*** voices, singing opera. Knocks your F*** socks off. You should
give that a F*** try sometime, as well."

"Naaa, wouldn't F*** get me watching that F*** shit," confessed
Colin.

"Unfortunate, some F*** people F*** judge something before they
have seen or F*** experienced it, and some F*** people judge it after
they have F*** seen or experienced it.

You see, you are in the first F*** group, and I'm in the F*** second
group." Proclaimed Baz.

Stan called Colin. "Can you help me move these pumps and valves,
please? They are in the way."

"No problem, mate, me and Baz can do it, you stand back, over
there," Colin pointed in the direction Stan should move. "Come on
Basil, give us a hand here please, help me move this stuff for Stanley."

"Okay, anything for one of our engineers," grinned Baz. He winked
at Stan. "How long have you been working for the Council, then
mate?" he enquired.

"Just over a year," answered Stan.

Colin and Baz took hold of a large pump, they lifted it off the floor
to move it a metre, "Like working here?" asked Colin.

"Yeah," confessed Stan. He told the fitters his work history, about
when he worked at Buttons.

The area was now clear. "Hope that's okay for you, anything else
just shout," called Colin.

They got back to their jobs.

"Coll?" Baz called.

"Yeah?" Colin replied.

Baz continued, "Have you heard that F*** record with all the F*** swearing? There's two geezers talking to each other, an all they F*** do, is swear all the F*** time."

"Yeah," replied Colin. "It's rubbish, I don't get it. It's not F*** funny. As if normal F*** people swear all the F*** time. It's them two F*** comedians, Del and F*** Cliff, I think. The story is they got pissed up one night and made a F*** swearing record."

"What a load of codswallop, waste of money," concluded Colin.

04-10
POWER

A cold, wet, foggy November morning, but Roger was excited. RULGO and L.B.B. had been in long negotiations to refurbish an old storeroom in the basement of the Town Hall.

Finally, it had been agreed. The Council would refurbish the room as a bar at its expense and RULGO would manage and fund it through their bar sales. As well as access from the offices, the Council had accepted the external door and stair to the car park could be used outside office hours. This meant, it could be open during weekends and at night.

Will entered the main office as tea and coffee were being served. He wasn't best pleased.

He called for attention so he could explain the situation. "As you may all understand, we as a nation shall again have problems with our electricity supply. After problems in recent years, we get to 1977, still the CEGB and our Government can't guarantee our supply.

The Central Electricity Generating Board is to introduce a rationing system. Areas around the Country shall alternate having a supply. We will have no supply for parts of every day. Information regarding this arrived in today's post.

The Borough has also been zoned, the times of cuts vary to where you live. I am going to sit with Stan to produce mark-ups of architects' maps, so that we can apply colour to identify the timings for each area.

The Town Hall zone shall have a supply from 9.00am until 1.00pm each day. So, as it's now early November with the night's drawing in, we shall only be able to work until around 3am each afternoon. After that, it will be too dark to even see each other. Thank you.

Stan, please see me in an hour?

Any questions?" There were no questions, Will returned to his room and set about gathering information ready for Stan.

The general opinion in the office was that they would be finishing work early. There were a few smiling faces. Stan considered his situation. At least, he was working for clients who were also the Council. This helped if work and programmes were to be delayed. It was all the same organisation.

These power cuts with loss of electricity would be viewed very differently at Duckles, and Buttons. They had to produce information for other design professionals and the builders. During a normal period, there were always panics and heated exchanges regarding programme timings and finish dates. He was glad he wasn't there now. It would be far worse than during a normal design or construction period.

Later, as requested, Stan joined Will in his office. They sat together to review the information. The Architects had provided a street map of Barham, printed on a large A0 paper sheet.

Will talked Stan through his plan. Each zone would have a different coloured fill which related to a legend in the corner. Different colours would denote the times of the power cuts in that zone.

The maps would be needed for each Councillor, Department, School and Council building.

Will always nurtured the Councillors. Stan wondered why he went to so much bother. He would personalise a set of maps for each Councillor, identifying the zone they lived in. Will estimated they would need around a total of two hundred maps.

Stan set about his assignment. After two days, Will recruited Shirley and Iris to help him. Not only was it a massive task, they were working reduced hours as it was nigh impossible to follow colouring boundary lines in semi darkness.

At home, to spread light into a room Stanley's mum placed a mirror behind a lighted candle. Unfortunately, after a short time, candle buying panic made it difficult to find any in the shops.

For staff use, a large completed map was fixed to the inside of the left-hand office door.

One afternoon in the dim available candle light, Alex and Barry stood at the door and fiddled. They were secretive, although the whispering disclosed the pair were up to no good. In the gloom, it was hard to distinguish what they had done.

One of them had found a spare brass door handle which matched the present one. They had screwed the spare to the door, positioned below the genuine one. The hanging map on the door was then taped lower to cover the genuine handle. Onlookers soon realised this was a trap for Will when on a walkabout.

Every time someone entered through the right office door it was possible to feel the suspense. People giggled in expectation. Unusually, Will didn't take his walk that evening, the audience would have to wait for the morning walkabout.

Next morning, all was prepared. Even Barry had forgone his visit to the Bookmaker's and sat expectantly. Alex made a last-minute check on the taped map covering. Everybody quickly got their drinks and sat waiting, as if a Blockbuster movie was about to begin. There would be no starter's flag, but at 9.20am the handle on the right-hand door moved.

As clockwork, Will entered. He walked along the tea aisle, looking into the room. Taking stock of who was present, he walked to the left-hand door to leave the room. Still looking into the office, he felt for the door handle. His hand wavered then it made contact. He twisted, pulled, nothing happened. From the expression on his face, he was confused. Will looked at the handle.

A muffled giggle roused him to look up, all he could witness was a sea of heads bent over desks and drawing boards.

Will turned back, slowly he walked to the door on the right. His outstretched hand took hold of that handle and it turned.

No one dared laugh for fear of reprisal. The next couple of sniggers brought looks of distain.

Here was the most senior man in the Department, having a problem opening a door. His face was flushed. Will gathered himself then returned to the left door. He grasped the handle, it didn't twist.

He wasn't an engineer for nothing, a moment later he lifted the map, exposing the real handle. The boss rapidly vacated the room after finally opening the door.

The antagonists realised this episode had become more of an embarrassment than a joke.

The group sat quietly. Was Will waiting outside to hear a clue? Perhaps just one snigger would convict someone. On occasion, they did laugh and replay the day that Will couldn't open an office door, but only providing Will was well out of ear shot.

BATTLE

A few weeks after marking up the 'power cut maps' Des and Pete W paid Stan a visit. Did he have any blank power cut maps spare? They needed two. The Architects had challenged the Engineers to a game of Battleships.

Stan found some for them. He was to draw a matching grid of 27 x 20 squares on each.

With supplementary staff from other groups, each Department had fifty personnel to position on their map. As with the rules of Battleships, personnel were rated at different scores, relating to their importance. The Borough Engineer and Borough Architect were worth fifty points each. Stan and Shirley were both worth five. With the exception of Will and the hierarchy, each person chose the square where their icon and label would reside. Stan was in a swimming pool, Shirley wanted to be in a 'dog's home'.

Their maps were completed, the game began.

Everybody got involved. Twice a day for a month a different person would attempt to 'sink' individuals on the opposing Department's map.

Each Office would telephone three sets of co-ordinates to the other. This gave a 'one in three' chance of wiping out the 'enemy'. If there was a hit, the information and score value would be relayed back to the attacker. For safe keeping, the Engineers map was kept in the second drawer of a large planning chest next to Des.

The game had been running for over two weeks when Will was in the main office collecting his coffee and a chocolate bar. The telephone next to Des' seat rang.

He walked over and lifted the handset, "'Ello, drawing office," he answered.

"24 : 10, 15 : 7 and 5 : 12," said a voice.

"Pardon," exclaimed Will.

"Okay, I'll say them again. Are you writing them down?" questioned the voice. The numbers were repeated, "24 : 10, 15 : 7 and 5 : 12."

"What are these co-ordinates for, please?" asked Will.

"For the Battleships game, of course," came the reply.

"Battleships game?" queried Will, none the wiser.

"Yes," replied the voice, "are you new to this? There's a Battleships grid in the planning chest in your office. You need to check the co-ords I just gave you against the personnel on the grid. You then tell me if we have any hits and how many points."

Will, bemused, put the phone on the desk. He opened the planning chest drawers. In the second drawer, he found the A0 Battleship gridded map. It was marked with red and blue crosses and circles. There was a legend. Crosses = hits, circles = misses. Red = our used cords, Blue = theirs. He was amazed at the detail. When did they have time to draw this map? How long had the **** been playing the game? He pushed the drawer shut.

Raising the phone to his ear, he explained to the caller that the game had just been terminated. He asked, to whom he was speaking. Brrrrr, the line went dead.

Will replaced the phone on the receiver, he took the map to his office for examination.

On a schoolboy impulse, Will checked his own value, thirty-five points. He then checked the value of the other targets. He was second only to the Borough Engineer. Umm, he smiled, someone valued him. Also as a bonus, he hadn't yet been sunk by the Architects.

Disregarding his delight, something had to be done.

A couple of his team were in their fifties, some over forty. They were hard working individuals, but together they bounced off each other and acted like high spirited kids.

After lunch he phoned through to Alex, 'could he collect Barry and Des then come to his office'.

Will revealed that he had found the map. He dressed them down, telling them of his surprise that they had allowed the game to commence. They were all Senior Engineers, acting like children.

They had been informed by the architects that he had the map so they had come prepared. Des argued that the game only took place outside office hours, which Will didn't believe.

Will thought he was one man against the office. For bonding purposes, he liked the concept of inter department competition. But this was occurring in office hours and wasn't respectful of the employers. He decided to reiterate his disapproval of what had happened. He gave back the map, while asking them to reconsider their behaviour.

The three 'unclean' left and went to the MEL room for a meeting. They discussed Will's opinion; he could have caused a scene. It was agreed that they had been very lucky.

Later, Des had a brief chat with his counterpart in the Architects Department. They spoke about the seizure of the map, agreeing to keep Will on their side, the Battleship game was 'sunk'.

Des subsequently informed Will of their decision, the Senior man regained trust in his boys.

WEDDING

Christmas had been and gone, the 1977 power cuts were a thing of the past.

The office was busy, mid-morning, Bert walked round looking to set up a Squash Ladder. He was chatting to John Parker and Bruce. Stan had one ear cocked.

Bert explained. With a Ladder, a player can only challenge the player above and the one below to a match. The winner of each match then moves up one position. So, after a series of matches, the people with similar abilities are grouped closer, this means the matches are more equal.

The response was disappointing.

"Sorry, not with these knees," chirped Bruce, "I'll play Pool or Darts?"

"Sorry Bert, more equal? Yeah, me neither," declined John, "I've got his knees as well." They laughed.

Bert moved to Stanley.

The office door swung open. The back of a tiny lady with blue grey permed hair pushed the door again, as she reversed into the room. A flustered Shirley staggered under the burden of a crammed, heavy carrier bag in each hand. She was beside herself with anxiety. Bert went to comfort her.

Shirley explained. Her daughter was getting married, which the whole of Barham already knew, because she had been banging on about it for months.

As mother of the bride, she needed time at home to help with the preparations, but there was a problem. Because she hadn't controlled her holidays, she didn't have enough leave days left. Shirley had applied to the Borough Engineer for five days unpaid leave, which would be ten days leave in total. But she hadn't received an answer.

Today, was her last day at work. She had to be at home tomorrow, 'there were so many things to do'.

Bert calmed her. He advised her to take the time off and enjoy the wedding. There would not be any problems. He would support her if things got difficult.

"Thank you, Albert," she expressed her joy through a tear, her cheeks red and blotchy.

"I am so grateful." Never a person to miss a chance, she pleaded, "Do you think it would be okay if I went home, now?"

"What now? No problem," replied Bert, "why don't you collect your things and off you go." In no more than two minutes, Shirley carrying a host of carrier bags was seen disappearing through the door.

Stan sat hatching a plan.

John called Bert over, "Bert, that Squash thing may be alright for young uns, like Sonny Jim here, but not for us oldens. What about a Darts Ladder?" Bert agreed to check the consensus.

Stan had it. He collected two L.B.B. envelopes with four L.B.B. headed sheets from the typist's office. Over the next two weeks he managed to sneak into the MEL office and type two letters with related envelopes.

The day Shirley was due back at work, Stan placed the two letters in their envelopes at an angle against the tee square on her drawing board. She arrived late as normal but full of love and laughter. Her tiny face beamed happiness, as she retold wedding stories to anyone not moving fast enough to evade capture. After taking wedding cake to her friends in other departments, she reappeared to start work. Within two minutes, she disappeared again, probably to tell more work friend's wedding stories.

After another hour, she returned.

Shirley saw the two letters; she opened the top one first. It was from the 'Borough Engineer' and read, 'Dear Mrs S. Basset, we are very sorry, but due to the current workload, we are not able to grant you unpaid leave. Please accept our apologies and we hope this does not affect your wedding plans'.

Shirley's face was grim, she folded the letter slotted it back in the envelope and placed it on her board. Next, the old lady looked around nervously. She gulped, shut her eyes then opened the second letter.

Watching from a distance, Stanley suddenly thought perhaps he had been 'too harsh'.

Shirley read the second letter, 'Dear Mrs S. Basset, we are sorry to hear that although you were not granted unpaid leave, you took it upon yourself to take the leave regardless.

Therefore, we have no option but to terminate your employment'.

Stan heard her whimper. He looked at her dear little old face, he had definitely been 'too harsh'.

Shirley was stoic. With no fuss or outcry, she placed the letters on her board, dressed in her coat and was gone.

Stan ran after her, "What's up, he called?"

"Nothing, don't worry," she called back. Stan persisted.

"I've been sacked," she answered. "I shouldn't have had those extra days off."

"Shirley, please, it's a joke, please come back, I'll show you," begged Stan.

It took all his cogent powers to get her back into the office. Stan took the letters, he showed her who they were from, "Look please, read this out," he pointed to the sender's name, "what does that say?"

"Where's my glasses?" Placing a hand in the bag she fought against pieces of wedding cake, belated cards and a present for her daughter, finally she retrieved her glasses and read, "Richard Nixon, Chief Corruption Officer, Watergate, USA. I don't know him?" she confessed. "He must work with the Borough Engineer."

"Nooo, but, please Shirley," he pleaded, "who has signed it?" He pointed again at the letter.

"Looks like 'Richie N'," suggested Shirley, "I don't know him either."

The people in the office were not quite sure what was going on. They could see Shirley was agitated. Stan was 'helping', but he appeared more agitated. However, when they heard Shirley read out the correspondent's name, they laughed, aloud.

Stan turned to them for help. When he turned back, she had gone. Where was she? Pete W told him she was in the MEL office saying goodbye to Iris.

Stan grabbed the letters and ran into the corridor. Shirley was now at the end of the corridor, nearly at the lifts. What to do? He ran in to Reg and Bert's office. Reg looked up and gave him a curious look. Stan warned him that Shirley was leaving the building, she was going home.

"Please Reg, can you go and get her she won't listen to me?" exclaimed Stan.

"What, where is she?" asked Reg.

"By the lifts," replied Stan.

"Well, why is she going home?" quizzed Reg, rising from his chair.

"Because I gave her the sack?" announced Stan sheepishly. He stepped sideways as the large man flew out of the door.

04-13

FLIGHT

Bert had good news. He had talked to Will about having a couple of dart boards in the office. As Will was partial to a game of 'arrows' he had agreed. Bert later met Roger to ask if RULGO could apply for Council funding.

Stan arrived late, the previous day he had been on Election duty at the Polling Station in Hayesbrook School. Thought he'd have a look at democracy from the inside.

It was the Local Elections. His rewards were paid £2.50, plus a day's holiday in lieu of a day off work. Which was debateable as the hours working in the Polling Station were much longer.

It sounded great when he signed for it, but he wasn't so sure he would do it again. Working at the Polling Station from 6.30am until 10.30pm. Bored silly during the mid-morning and mid-afternoon when no one came in for hours. Then, madness after tea when there were queues around the playground.

Des called a meeting of the 'unclean', with Alex and Barry in the MEL office. His friend in the architect's office had asked if they fancied a flying competition. After the Battleships fiasco, he thought it best to check on their viewpoint before making a decision.

It would be on the Friday afternoon before the Town Show, in about four weeks' time. All the Senior Officers and Councillors would be at the Show Ground on that day to resolve last minute problems and meet the local press. The 'unclean' agreed that the date of the plan had been well thought out. The competition should be safe from inquisitive eyes and snoops.

Des tabled 'The Competition Rules'.

1. Planes, or flying devices, will be launched by hand from a standing position at floor level.

2. The 'arena' will be the first-floor corridor.

3. Each aviator could have three attempts.

4. The device which travels in the air the furthest in one movement shall win.

The 'unclean' gave their approval, they decided to accept the challenge. However, each understood if any of this information got back to Will, or the Borough Architect at least one of them would be looking for a new job. They had to ensure that everyone in the office kept mum.

To reduce the chances of Will finding out, Alex proposed that they tell no one until six days before the competition. They agreed.

Two weeks later, a paper form circulated around the office. It was from Will, asking for volunteers to work on the Engineers kiosk at the Town Show. Stan was interested.

Since about 1960, he and all his family and mates had attended the Show every year. He had played in the adult section of the Five-A-Side Football competitions for the last six years. It got better, his home was a fifteen-minute walk from the Show Ground.

Stan asked Bruce for his perspective.

Bruce advised, "It will definitely be better than your Polling Station, experience," he grinned. "The marquee construction starts about three weeks before the Show. They allow the exhibitors access to the marquees on the Thursday before the Show. So, you will be working in the sun in a park for four days. Also, you get a meal allowance plus a free pass and access to the Funfair."

'Tell me more', thought Stan.

Bruce continued, "On the Saturday and Sunday you will be a general dog's body, getting coffee and sandwiches for the Engineers working the kiosk, you may get bored? But you'll have most of the time to yourself. What do you think?" requested Bruce.

"Too late," replied Stan, with a smile, "I've already filled in the form."

On the Thursday, a week before the grand event, the 'unclean' released secret information regarding the upcoming Flight Competition. There was so much excitement and banter amongst the people in the main office, they worried they had liberated too many details. It became the common subject of conversation which was very nerve racking for them.

On the Friday, Stan was working at his hot drinks production.

Chris walked up with his newly washed mug and handed it to Stan. "How, you doing, young man?" he greeted Stan.

"Okay, thanks," replied Stan, "how you?"

Chris nodded. "This secret flight thing, do you know anything about it? I have an interest in aviation and man powered flight," he revealed.

"It's coincidence I know, but I'm building an aero craft, at home. Well not actually at home, I've leased a warehouse. Myself and a couple of enthusiasts, spend weekends and some evenings designing and building the craft."

Stan looked at Chris, 'quietly spoken, he used a deliberate vocabulary. Nearly bald with an ear moustache each side, a few uncontrollable long strands of hair on top hung where they wished. The engineer wore a short sleeved blue check shirt under a beige sleeveless vee neck jumper. Both were tucked into his trousers with a leather belt for support. On his face were a pair of National Health glasses, leather sandals with socks covered his feet'.

This was definitely boffin material.

Chris continued, "It will be about 100 ft long with a similar length mono wingspan."

"Whoo," cried Stan, "incredible."

"We have to build it in small sections to move it about. When we have a trial, we will join all the bits together. Better go. I'm going to build a miniature for the competition," he winked, picking up his hot drink he left the room.

04-14
COMPETITION

Stan entered the main office on Monday morning carrying a few shopping bags of provisions for the tuck cupboard. He felt happy, and sad. He made a cup of tea before sitting at his board.

The note from Will on Friday was still under his tee square. He was pleased that Will had chosen him to work at the Town Show. Also Bruce the swine, hadn't let on that he had applied so they would be together.

The irritation was Stanley would miss the Flight Competition. After the Battleships calamity, he would have loved to join in the contest. That's life!

After Stan had made the mid-morning hot drinks, Chris called him into the MEL office. He showed Stan his aero plane for the competition. Merely three pieces of balsa wood glued as a triangle with a void in the middle, Chris had made it over the weekend. Each corner joint was shaped to a point. Each 'wing' was about 20mm wide x 150mm long. Stan was considerably underwhelmed. It couldn't have taken long to build, probably about fifteen minutes' tops.

Chris explained, "It's the lift that makes it fly, not the force." He took a piece of sandpaper from his drawer and rubbed it against the underside edge of a wing, "We shape the edges so that air pressure under the wing is greater than that above. That way the pressure pushes the wing up. All the work is in the sandpapering."

Stan thanked him, disappointed he returned back to the main office. Still, he would have liked to see it fly, but that wouldn't be possible.

Friday, the day of the aeronauts had arrived. Will was out all day at the show ground as expected.

Eight contestants from the Engineers brought their flying machines to the office. Some were in 'kit form' like Barry's. Some half build, others complete.

Barry's kit contained a long piece of 3" x 2" (80mm x 50) timber, a bag of 4" (100mm) nails, a ball of string, a saw and a hammer. He explained to the assembled, laughing work mates, that as he hadn't had time to work on his plane he had brought the components with him.

Barry took the 'kit' with his chair into the corridor outside the main office and set to work. Using his chair as a horse, no measuring, all by eye he cut the timber into pieces. "I don't need a tape, used to be a draughtsman, you know."

The doors from a number of other offices off the corridor twitched. Although he was wearing a jacket and tie, most observers thought he was a maintenance man going about his work repairing a Barham piece of furniture.

The Borough Engineers Secretary did pay him a visit when he was nailing the thing together. There are scant ways to quietly hammer a 4" nail into two pieces of wood. The noise in an empty enclosed corridor reverberated throughout the building. Barry was politely requested to complete his work outside. Off he trundled carrying his chair upside down with pieces of wood, tools, etc balancing between the upright legs.

About sixty minutes later, there was an enormous crash from the corridor. Alex and the others ran to help. Doors along the corridor opened as heads emerged to check the ceiling was still in place. Standing in the corridor, the centre of attention stood Barry in disappointment, his plane at his feet. The noise had been the crash of his crafts maiden flight as it landed on the wooden parquet flooring of the corridor.

The plane's front wing had come adrift. He cheered up.

"Not a problem," he announced, "I need longer nails." Off he went to the hardware shop.

The moment was approaching. There were ten architect contestants gathered in the corridor. The most notable difference of the craft was their appearance. Generally, the engineers' craft were plain wood. There were a few roundels and crosses on the wings. The architect's craft were a myriad of bright colours with patterns, some were strange architectural shapes. All had ridiculous names.

On reflection, it was accepted that there was limited space, possibly too many windows in the corridor for Barry's craft to evade. They decided to move to the Assembly Rooms at the far end of the building.

Once in the Assembly Rooms the architects took control of the competition. In turn, each competitor propelled their craft from the oche towards the end wall about thirty metres distant. The furthest of each competitor's three attempts was marked on the floor with sticky drafting tape.

Barry took to the oche, his 'plane' was 600mm long with a 500mm fore wing, and a 300mm aft wing. Under the direction and scorn of the judge he placed his lead foot as far forward as possible. The volume of noise towards the 'villain' increased. To the accompaniment of jeers and barracking that his plane wouldn't make the distance, he motioned everyone up to the end wall away with his free hand.

Then, leaning back from the waist, he took a javelin throwers stance and heaved the plane with all his might. It tumbled, like a Catherine wheel through the air for about two metres, crashed then skidded along the parquet floor for another three metres. There was now a disagreement over the travel of his plane. The judge recorded the 'landing' location, Barry argued it should be the final position that was measured.

Everyone knew Barry was a windup merchant. He protested about the recorded distance, arms open he pleaded for the extra three metres to be included while the crowd booed him down, mostly in good humour. The judge checked with the rules. The wording was 'travelling in the air'. The case was closed, he lost the argument and sulked off.

The competition continued, very few planes actually travelled forward. Fewer achieved a distance longer than the length of the designer's arm. The craft twisted, veered to one side or another, or flew straight up and back down. Barry was leading, with one of the architects a close second. It came to Chris' moment, was the best saved till last?

Standing on the oche, Chris took a small 'S' shaped piece of wire from his pocket. He placed it inside the hollow centre of the craft and held the craft on the back of his fist. With limited body motion, he drew his hand back then slowly pushed it forward, like an aboriginal spear thrower.

The craft slipped off the wire and moved towards the end wall. It moved slowly, never loosing height. The people watching were bewitched, the craft maintained the same height, no deviation. It hit the back wall just below the level of its launch.

Instant celebrity, everyone was stunned. Everyone crowded around Chris, "Could they have a go with his plane," they asked.

"Of course you can, I'll make another one tomorrow," was his reply.

04-15

SHOW

On the Thursday morning before the last weekend in July, Stan and Bruce met at the Show Ground in Central Park. They had to unload and build the Engineers Kiosk. The kiosk skeleton was four large tables formed as a 'U' shape with a large wooden frame fixed around the outside edges. Information and decorative panels would be both hung off the wooden frame and laid on the tables. A magic tap and bucket would be positioned to one side.

There were so many different varieties of food and drink at the Show Ground that they could spend their daily allowance on.

Pete N in a supervisory position arrived at 10.30am. His first words were, "Hurry up lads, the beer tent opens at eleven. I don't want to be drinking on my own."

Stan was screwing the decorated information boards to a frame. The screwdriver was the wrong size and wrong shape. He couldn't believe that no one had brought any tools. Reg had given them the office toolbox which comprised, a hammer with half a handle, a blunt chisel and a small screwdriver. Pete N had brought a tape. Stan made a mental note to bring some of his dad's tools in the morning.

The young engineer spied a young lady working a few kiosks to the right on the Education Department Kiosk. He had noticed that she kept looking over when she thought it was discreet. 'No time like the present' thought Stan. He actually had a good reason to engage in conversation with her. Stan could ask if she had a proper screwdriver. He started to blush thinking about it, even before his legs started moving.

The young lady saw him coming, she blushed. When they met, they looked like two tomatoes.

She was very friendly, a bit shy, but they managed to have a congenial conversation. She was as tall, or short as Stan, with a cute button nose and dark hair in a bobbed style. The lady told him her name was Neev, spelt Niamh.

Niamh did have a screwdriver he could borrow. Stan thanked her and accepted it. He apologised that he couldn't talk longer as he shouldn't neglect Bruce and Pete N, who were working without his help. He'd best push on, joshing that Pete was an alcoholic waiting to get to the beer tent.

"Is it ok if I bring the screwdriver back tomorrow," Stan called back.

"Course," Niamh replied, "I'll be waiting here," she smiled.

They turned away from each other, but both had a matching smile on their face.

Stan knew then that they would spend a lot of time together.

After lunch, Stan built up his courage to call on Niamh. Together they had a stroll around the outside areas. Watching the Fair Ground rides being built and tested. The man on the Waltzer gave then a test run. Two men on stilts in stripy pyjamas wearing red curly wigs under black bowler hats raced the couple across the grass to the hot dog stand. They heard a lion roar, which was probably a sound effect. As they wandered between the rides, the music playing on a carousel changed to 'Whiter Shade of Pale'. The sun shone, they smiled.

They spent over three days with each other at the Show Ground. It was similar to meeting someone while on holiday. When they weren't outside walking around enjoying the arena area, they were in the marquee, still in their little bubble. Over that long weekend, Niamh and Stan got closer. They arranged their breaks at the same time, allowing them to meet for lunch or a drink together. He walked her to the bus stop each evening to start her journey home.

Sunday evening as the event closed Stan and Niamh were sombre as they walked to the bus stop for the last time, both nervous of the other's intentions. Stan asked the important question; each was over-joyed as they planned a proper date outside the Show Ground.

They laughed, 'back in the real world', they would still see each other.

Stan told Niamh of a party his friend Glyn was having, she agreed to go with him. As there wasn't a phone at her flat share, because she would be working at different teaching establishments each day they couldn't keep in touch.

The friends arranged to meet at Romford Station at 8.00pm two Saturdays hence.

Without contact for two weeks, Stan got ready hoping Niamh would be waiting for him. As there was no means of communication, trust played an essential part in the relationship.

He made his way to the station rendezvous, fingers crossed she would be there.

Alighting the bus he paced towards Romford station. She was there, he was so happy. Stan could see her waiting outside the station entrance. She saw him in the distance, a big smile grew across her face. Walking towards each other they met in the road to the bus garage, they hugged.

The party was okay but there was little atmosphere. Most of the time they sat together in the kitchen or on the stairs enjoying each other's warmth, catching up on where she had been. About 2.00am they left for Stan's parents' home where they spent the night in each other's arms on the settee.

Stan's elderly Aunt Bett was house watching while his parents and brothers were away.

Late morning, despite Stan's protests, Aunt Bett cooked them a large tasty fried breakfast. Then, they said their goodbyes and walked to the Beck. After a wet lunch, Stanley strolled with Niamh to the Tube station.

They thanked each other for a great day, they kissed goodbye. Niamh invited Stan to an open house party the following Saturday night at her flat share in Ilford. She wrote the address inside the lid of Stan's cigarette packet. He promised to be there.

The next Saturday, Stan, Roy and Glyn had a few beers in the Beck before making for the party. His two mates were buoyed by the knowledge that Niamh lived with three other girls. They had splashed on plenty of aftershave, just in case they got lucky.

"Buckets of it, the car smells like a tarts boudoir. If the Police stop us, we'll get arrested for illegal use of a dangerous substance," claimed Roy.

They arrived at the location. The flats were above a row of shops with access from a service road at the rear. Glyn drove along the dark unlit road. The sound of loud music suggested they were in the right place, the boys smiled to each other, bingo.

The flats were four levels high connected to the ground by dozens of iron staircases. One light inside a flat on the third level was shining through an open door onto the landing. It just illuminated the stairs below. The trio could just make out dark shapes in the shadows where people were congregating.

The scene was frightening, it was dark and aggressively noisy. There were the sounds of drunken shouting, swearing and glass smashing. For a minute perhaps the added pandemonium of a fracas. From where they sat in the car, the three boys couldn't see any door numbers, but it was odds on the party was at the flat with an open door. One of them would need to walk through that chaos to the front door to check the flat number.

"If it's this bad at half past nine," worried Stan, "what will it be like at midnight?"

"What do you think," asked Glyn, "I don't fancy leaving my car around here. If you want, why don't you phone her? We passed a phone box on the corner of the main road."

"She hasn't got a phone at the flat," mumbled Stan, "you have both met her, I can't think she's the type to mix with this lot?"

"Stan," stated Roy, "it's your date, your girl. If you go and check and she is there, we will come in with you. It might be the wrong flat? She could be somewhere else. What do you want to do?"

Stan was truly scared. He didn't have the confidence to walk through the manic people outside that flat. He didn't know if he was in love with Niamh. He did have feelings for her and didn't want to let her down. She could be in there dressed up, waiting for him.

He decided to have a look. Cautiously he left the car, passing people on the stairs heart in mouth he reached the third level landing. The rest of the stairs rising to the fourth level and the landing were crammed with party goers. He could see the open doorway was full of people trying to access or leave the party. Even if he got to the top landing it was impossible to know if he would be able to enter the building.

He decided against his inner feelings. A coward he decided to go back to The Beck. Who knew what the future would have held if he had gone to the flat?

Sunday, missing Niamh was one of those incidents that grate. The shy Stanley hated his lack of confidence. He was angry with himself for being a weed, for only getting to the third level landing. He made a plan.

He waited for Monday, back at the Town Hall he collected all his courage then went to see Niamh. Stanley made his way to the Education Department's main office in the basement. Disguised as a beetroot he knocked on the door with his knuckles, following a wait of five minutes he decided to enter the large room then stood inside looking for Niamh.

Seeing the nervous red-faced man standing alone by the door, a young lady smiled, rising from her seat she walked to meet Stan.

"Can I help you?" the smiling lady asked.

"Hello," replied Stan, "I'm looking for Niamh Sullivan?"

"I am so sorry," replied the lady, "she was away on secondment for a few weeks. Now she is back at Uni. You just missed her, todays her first day back. Is there anything I can help you with?"

Stan, thanked her, declined her offer of help then left the room. Deflated, he returned to his office.

04-15

04-16
LURE

Chris took his 1978 Flight Competition trophy into the main office. He had put it on his desk in the MEL office, but thought it best to share it. The 33cl tin of beer, wrapped in a coloured photo of Concorde against a pale blue sky was placed next to the tea making area.

Will, would often look at this object while on a 'walkabout' or collecting his tea. He would ponder where it came from and its significance. However, an inner feeling of potential trouble always stopped him enquiring, he was positive he wouldn't appreciate the answer.

There were now two dart boards on the office wall along the tea aisle, plus room for three or four Bridge schools between the desks and drawing boards. With lunch only ten minutes away, the office was half empty. In order to get a maximum one hour of play time, many staff members sneaked off early to buy their food.

They all got on so well. Bert and Reg would usually join in any social activity, Will made special efforts to join darts and sometimes Bridge sessions.

When the scoring of the darts was close, Bert had two sayings which always received a groan from everyone in the room.

Firstly, 'It's like my front room, there's nothing in it'. Secondly, 'It's like the Arabs, in tents'. Usually he said the first part, then the rest of the group said the punch line.

Most were competent darts players, whereas Alex and Barry were very experienced at Contract Bridge. Over months of lunchtime matches, they had patiently taught a majority of their office colleagues how to bid using the Conventions. Everyone was at a different level, but the teachers had insisted the pairings were permanent. It was better to understand one partners bidding and leads to develop each person's game.

The afternoon was slow. Bruce and Stan were looking out of the window at people coming and going from the supermarket opposite.

Aiden and Pete W were looking out of the adjacent window at the same scene. Patrons of the supermarket parked in the narrow road alongside the Town Hall.

As one customer laden with shopping bags removed her car keys from her purse a £1 note dropped to the pavement. Each time she bent to reclaim it the wind moved it a tiny distance away from her hand, a smidgen out of reach.

The boys were enthralled, it had the makings of a TV Game Show. Could she get it? Down on the street a chivalrous fellow moved to assist her. He had no luck either. Another passer-by appeared she stalked the note as prey, moving upwind.

Someone in the main office giggled.

More giggled, there were faces at every window, watching. Eventually, a passer-by stamped on the money. She bent to seize it from under her foot. The window watchers cheered and clapped. Surprised, the triumphant lady seeing she had an audience bowed then returned the note to its owner.

Aiden, 'had an idea', he left his spot at the window. "Please, all stay where you are," he requested.

Aiden came back with a pair of scissors, a 2p coin and his cigarette lighter. He slightly opened the scissors, placing the coin across the blades he held the lighter flame below the coin to heat it. When ready, he nodded. Pete W slide the lower part of the sash window up to form a gap allowing Aiden room to flip the coin from the scissors onto the pavement below.

It didn't take long before their first bite. The second person walking along the pavement saw the coin. He bent down to pick it up then yelped in pain and quickly dropped it. In the moment, the office observers bellowed then dived back into cover. Giggling out of sight, they waited for the 'all clear'. Bruce supplied another coin, Aiden worked the trick again.

Stan considered the lady's £1 note blowing away, he borrowed 'a nicker' from Kelvin.

Untrusting Kelvin followed Stan, he watched as the young man photocopied both sides then quickly reclaimed his money. Stanley trimmed the copies to size, coloured both a darkish green then glued them back to back. Subsequently, he 'borrowed' thread from Shirley's 'Vitality Girls' emergency sewing kit to stitch a long thread to the fake.

"Stand back," he ordered as Bruce opened the sash window.

04-16

Holding the thread in one hand he cast the lure out of the window. Contrary to his intention it didn't sink to the pavement below but took off like a kite, the velocity nearly pulled the thread through his fingers.

A number of times they tried but it was a failure. What to do next?

Bruce shared an idea. He disconnected the thread replacing the lure with a pencil. Next, Stan made his way below the window with the loose lure and a paper clip.

It worked, holding the free end of the thread Bruce tossed the pencil end across the basement footpath over the wrought iron railings to Stan on the pavement. Stan swapped the pencil with the lure.

Stanley returned to the office while Bruce learned to control the bait. It needed to be held motionless against the breezing wind on the floor, but able to fly when released.

A few potential victims walked along, only one saw the '£1 note', he disregarded it.

Later, Bruce had a nibble. As a young girl saw the lure, he released it to the wind. She moved to catch it; however, the unsuspecting girl's mother called her away. Bruce was close, but the mother had cancelled the girl's interest.

Si, was off to buy some fags, he offered to reset the trap and stay in attendance on the opposite side of the road.

Finally, they got lucky. An older man strolled towards the trap. Bruce freed the lure when the victim was two metres away. It rose in the wind, rolling in a spiral inches from the man's face. He stumbled back in shock, nearly falling over. Wafting slightly too high the man jumped and stretched to reach!

In Bruce's mind, he was playing a blue marlin, it mustn't slip the line. The man reached, missed, stretched out his fingertips, caught it. Bruce restrained the thread; in his fervour the dupe unknowingly pulled the paper clip and thread from the note. With the note held tightly against his chest, he evasively turned his head to glance in both directions. All clear, he furtively put the '£1' into his inside coat pocket.

The gallery watched quietly, they could see his hand moving, feeling the note. After some minutes, it reappeared. The victim examined it again then dropped it in the gutter.

04-17

BAR

It had taken over a year from the initial agreement in November 1977, but finally the new RULGO bar was open. RULGO had worked with the Council on the design and layout but the granting of a License to sell alcohol and food had taken the most time. As expected, the Council had granted one almost immediately, however the local Police had dragged their feet.

Nevertheless, 'Roger Harton' was now Licensee with his name above the door. The License was for Friday and Saturday evenings from 5.00pm to 11.00pm. Special Licenses could be applied as they were needed.

As the bar was in the basement next to a car park there were few passers-by. It became common for the keyholder to lock the exit door at 11.20pm to meet Licensing Laws, then close the full-length curtains for a 'lock in'. After a while, the curtains were always pulled when the bar was open. Generally, kicking out time was at about 2.00am or when they couldn't drink anymore.

Pete N would drive Bruce, Stan and Raj home. If Johnny was there, he too would jump in the motor. The first time Raj travelled with them he had them in stitches. In a 'blitzed' Indian accent, he directed Pete N to his home in Barham.

"Please, please, go left that will be alright." Pete N turned left followed by the next right.

"Oh, no, no, no, why did you go right?" Raj groaned.

"That's what you said," answered Pete N.

"No, no, you will right, if you turn left," Raj detailed.

Around in circles they drove.

"No, no, you will be right, right. If you turn left," Raj explained.

It took some time to understand, "Raj, you mean 'if you turn left', you will be correct?" asked Bruce.

"Of course, you will be right, if you go left," Raj confirmed. From

207

that day, every time they took Raj home, they played the 'right, left' game.

Roger organised and chose four pair of bar stewards who would work on a monthly roster.

Bruce and Stanley had volunteered to work behind the bar. The wages were enticing. They were 'drink as much as you like, no payment necessary'. The wage meant the pair were also very happy to cover for stewards unable to fulfil their duties.

It came to Stan and Bruce's first session behind the bar, Roger took them through the use of the till, changing barrels and pricing.

Simon and his wife Faye, came in about 9.30pm, they had been for a curry in a local restaurant and agreed to finish the night with a few drinks in the RULGO bar. Stan served them without mishap.

The couple retired to a table and chairs in the corner where Stan brought them their drinks.

The night was getting heavy, Bruce was feeling the pressure on his waistband. He moved from beer to white rum.

Stan left the bar to collect the empties.

Simon stopped him at his table for a gossip. Si told Stan of a new project he had been told about. The Council had obtained planning to build a new all-weather artificial surface training centre near Dagenham East station. In a few weeks, they would be releasing application forms to a limited number of local teams. Simon had acquired a form from his friend in the Education Department. Was Stanley interested and would he like the form?

Stan thanked him. However, with the commitment required he thought it best to first check with his mates to gauge the interest.

He turned towards the bar: Bruce had gone. Simon stood to look and pointed.

"He is still there, can you see a glass in a hand just above the bar," identified Si.

Stan looked again. A hand appeared holding a shorts glass, slowly it rose through the air. The glass fixed onto an optic, wobbled then dropped. Seconds later, it lifted to the optic again for a double shot.

Tentatively, Stanley made his way behind the bar, the hand and glass belonged to Bruce, now slumped against a chair. He was so pissed he couldn't stand up, but he could still drink.

Stan worked the bar alone allowing his friend to enjoy himself.

A little later, Bruce had descended onto the floor. Stanley served a customer and his wife seated at the bar.

As he pulled the man's beer the pipes gave a tell-tale gurgle as air spat into the glass. The bitter tap was empty, Stan apologised. He disconnected the empty barrel and rolled it to the outside store underneath the car park. Minutes later after swapping the barrel for a fresh one, he rolled it to the bar and made the new connection.

The new barman drew off three pints before giving the fourth to the customer. "Eww, this is crap," gasped the man. "It's off!"

Stan had a taste, 'ick, yuck, it was off. But it's a new barrel?'

He was confused, pulling off more beer made little difference. Again, he checked the barrels in the store. He couldn't determine where the problem was, so he changed the new barrel for another.

Stan drew beer from this and served the customer a new pint. It tasted as bad. He offered the man a choice of a different beer or a short. The customer decided that it didn't taste that bad, so carried on drinking it. 'Bless his stomach linings in the morning', thought Stan. 'I wouldn't stand behind him on the Tube'.

Monday morning when Stan was back at work, he had a visit from Roger. The Licensee was responsible for all products sold in the bar. There hadn't been a complaint but there was a rumour. Roger had heard about stale beer being served in the RULGO Bar; he wasn't very pleased.

Apparently, there were two barrel stores for the bar. One was for barrels of fresh beer, the second was for empty barrels, old barrels where the beer had 'gone off', called slops. Slops were kept because they had a resale price. The brewery bought it back for beer vinegar production.

On Friday, someone had connected a slop barrel to the beer tap. Stan accepted full responsibility. He had too, although Bruce was unable to remember anything he certainly hadn't been able to connect a barrel.

LADIES

The Dagenham Town Show of 1979, had for the first time included a Ladies category in the Five-A-Side football tournament.

Si's wife Faye was thinking of organising a Ladies team from the Barham Town Hall. Through Si she asked if Stanley would manage the team. He agreed, he was a bit shy but anything for a laugh, he loved football.

There was no real time to get together or train with the girls. The first time they met with Stan was at Central Park Pavilion on the Saturday morning of the matches. Aware that even some of the girls hadn't met each other Stan asked everyone to introduce themselves.

He was told that prior to match day there was a squad of ten ladies. However, some of the girls who had signed up to this adventure had become aware of the reality of the situation. From a squad of ten, only five arrived at the meeting place. In addition to the five absentees, the body language and self-conscious laughs of the group implied more of the current girls wished they were somewhere else. It was only because they didn't want to upset Faye that they stayed.

Stan had provided the kit, which was a bit big on some of the petit girls. He decided to be straight with them. He wasn't there to manage them, he was there to help them have fun.

He took a deep breath before his face was completely red. "To be honest, ladies, I don't think we will win the competition. So, there is no point in getting physically hurt or upset if we lose. Please treat today as if you were on holiday playing ball on the beach with you families. If you are thirsty afterwards, we can visit my local for a few cool drinks and something to eat.

The good news is, that one of the other teams in our group hasn't signed in so you will only have to be play two matches."

They smiled, relieved. The noise of a crowd watching an adjacent man's match roared, a whistle blew a short phwwwhht.

The sun was shining, the hubbub of visitors entering the park grew. In the distance, they could see queues of people in line waiting to pay their admission fees at the Town Show gates.

Simon shuffled around, getting in the way. He offered to administer the 'magic sponge' to any injuries, but Faye put a stop to that with one look.

As was expected, the ladies' matches drew large crowds of noisy men. The ladies tried, the men cheered. The other teams were also in it for the laugh. It was all good natured.

Barham Ladies FC began to relax and enjoy the moment.

Their first match ended 0-0, mainly because the players on both teams rarely connected with the ball. They lost the second match 0-1 when a mighty punt evaded everyone and whistled into the BLFC goal from halfway.

Stan was pleased to see five happy, smiling faces come to him at the end of the second match. High fives all round, then they all collapsed prone on the grass. Most of them had never run farther than to catch a bus. Si handed out water.

Faye looked up, "Where's that B*** cool drink you promised."

"I'll second and third that," added Jenny.

After the ladies changed out of their football kit, most of the gang went to the Beck for cool drinks and nourishment.

Roy, one of Stan's friends was in the pub when they arrived. He met everyone and bought the first drinks. They had a great time, laughing, chatting and drinking. Glyn, another good friend joined them. Simon and Faye knew him from the RULGO bar.

It got to 3.00pm when the Landlord called 'last orders'. The group decided they had all had enough, Si and Faye would go home. The lads had a Darger Paint Disco that night, they should also go home.

Stan was going to walk Vickie to the station, but Glyn and Roy insisted she shouldn't go home on her own. Glyn would drop her off, if the other two rode 'shotgun', the journey to Woodford would take about thirty minutes. The four left, Vickie with Stan chatted in the back, Glyn and Roy in the front.

After about twenty minutes, Roy realised it had gone silent behind him. Well not actually really quiet, there were some other types of strange wet slobbering noises. He looked back, then nodded to Glyn. "Look in your mirror," he whispered.

Vickie and Stan were chewing each other's faces off, unaware or not concerned where they were or who was watching.

Ten minutes later, Glyn coughed, "Err! Ahem! Vick. We are getting near your home, if you're not hungry any more where shall I drop you off?" he chuckled. He always chuckled.

Vickie looked into Stan's eyes while talking to Glyn, "If you drop me off in the High Street by the green, I'll walk from there."

"Okay," Glyn answered. A few minutes later, he pulled over, "How's this?"

"Great, thanks. Is Stan going back with you?" she asked, pursing her lips, gently placing her hand on the inside of Stan's right thigh.

He didn't need to hear another word. Stan proposed without further persuasion to walk her home from where they were parked.

Glyn offered to pick Stan up later if he rang Glyn at home. The driver now with one 'shotgun' turned around to commence the return journey.

The cuddling couple drifted onto the green opposite the shops. They glided between couples and families sitting and playing games on the grass, enjoying the afternoon sunshine. Vickie found a quite spot, she sat and compelled Stanley to unite with her.

They laid on the soft grass, their continued wooing becoming more and more passionate.

As their desire intensified, they wished to be alone, away from onlookers. Vickie rose, taking Stan's hand she whispered as her lips gently stroked his ear, "Come with me."

Now hidden behind a small glade of trees they concentrated so much on each other they weren't aware of anything two metres from them. She was just taller than Stan, twenty-five, full lips, slim and toned with curves in the right places. He loved laying there drawing circular lines around her belly button joining them to larger ones on her little rounded belly with his finger.

Vickie sat upright. In a soft whisper, she advised Stan that she had a long-term boyfriend who she loved. She wasn't going to cheat on him.

A little later, she whispered in Stan's ear, "Do you want to do it?"

He smiled and gazed into her beautiful blue grey eyes, softly he replied, "If you're sure?"

"Not here," she purred, "at my home, my mum and dad should be out shopping, as it's Saturday."

To a degree, they ordered their clothing before rising as one. As if fixed at the hip, with arms around each other's waists they traced their footsteps back to the High Street where Vickie led the way to an elegant building. Stan held her hand as they took the lift, just enough time for their lips to engage, the lift arrived at the third floor. She removed her keys from her bag before opening the front door, the vixen turned to Stan and placed her index finger to her plump lips, "Ssssh."

The door opened, she moved into the hall with a second door ahead. Stan followed stroking her fingers with his as they moved through the passageway.

Vickie opened the second door. "Hello love, how are you, good to be home?" An attractive, smartly dressed older lady welcomed her daughter?

"Come in pet, how was the footie?" called her dad.

For a few hours, the young couple's relationship had been synergetic. Now, Vickie's hand instantly dropped from Stan's. In an apologetic tone, she quickly introduced him, "This is Stan from the football tournament." Clearly embarrassed, she explained, "Stan from the football has seen me home safe, he just needs to use the toilet then he'll be leaving."

Stanley understood, the couple's daughter had a boyfriend. Vickie's awkwardness could have been far worse. He used the faculties, declined the offer of a cool drink then bid his farewell. Firstly, he set off in the general direction of the High Street, then after fifteen minutes found a telephone box and rang Glyn. Thankfully, Glyn was ready to party. He splashed on some aftershave and shortly after left home to collect Stan.

04-19

DISCO

When it came to food on a Friday evening, a regular pattern soon emerged. One of Stan's friends would often interrupt his journey home from work to join Stan and his work mates.

Before he left work in London, William Sheaf or Johnny as he was known, would take orders by telephone for fish and chip suppers from Stan. He would then purchase the order in Barham and walk it round, piping hot, to the Town Hall bar at around 6.00pm. Friday Discos started about 8.00pm so they had enough time to eat, play cards or darts before the music started.

One Friday evening a member of the Housing Department was having his leaving drinks in the RULGO bar. At about 6.00pm, the man was called to join his boss in the space in front of the exit door to the car park. Those attending were called to form a crescent facing the duo.

Stan noticed Vickie had entered the bar from the office stairs. She looked furtively at him before joining her work mates playing darts. After throwing her arrows, she collected them from the board, at the same time she looked at him again a sullen expression.

Since he had taken her home on that sunny afternoon, he had kept his distance from Vickie.

He remembered, she 'had a boyfriend she wasn't going to cheat on'. When they met her parents, she had released him pretty quickly. Stan understood Vickie was a one-man girl?

He didn't want to upset anyone, but he was puzzled. Was she looking at him in that way because she actually wanted him to contact her, and he hadn't, or as a warning to stay away?

Stan and his colleagues moved from their seats to mingle with the farewell group facing the exit door.

The presentation included a long rambling speech. Five minutes in, the exit door behind the curtains opened. It closed quietly. A bulge pressed into the curtains as a pair of black shoes appeared below them. Alex motioned to Bruce, "Johnny."

A smell filtered into the air, the assembled started to sniff. It confused the people from the farewell presentation, but those from Stan's office knew exactly what it was. Johnny remained hidden until the gathering dispersed. As he appeared the hungry engineers dived into what was making the smell - freshly cooked hot fish and chips.

The disco started, tables and chairs were stacked out of the way. The dart board cupboard closed. More people trickled in. Stan noticed Vickie seemed more relaxed, she was now with a tall smartly dressed young man, probably her boyfriend.

Kelvin arrived with his wife Angela. She was well named, a delicate young lady, years younger than Kelvin. Stan was gobsmacked, talk about 'Beauty and the Beast'? What was she doing with Kelvin? She had a natural beauty, long golden hair, trim figure a pretty face that didn't need makeup. It was Angela's first evening out since having their new baby, six months previous. Angela and Iris chatted baby talk.

Kelvin was talking to Simon. It turned into a disagreement. Kelvin was arguing that smoking was 'good for you' because it promoted breathing exercises.

"Look," asserted Kelvin, "if you need 20% oxygen in your lungs to breathe but when you smoke you only get 18%, it means your lungs have to work harder. That means they get stronger so their efficiency increases."

Simon didn't comment, he just walked away to find Faye.

Johnny and Stan stood together observing Angela. She was so sweet, so innocent. How could she share a bed with Kelvin? How could she have a child with Kelvin?

Johnny handed his beer to Stan and went for a 'gypsies'.

Stan stood holding the two beers, groups of people were still arriving, most who working there changed in the offices. His shoulders bounced listening to the music.

Alex was the only one dancing, he didn't care. 'Dancer' by Sino Goccio was playing, one from his collection. Alex was seriously into Imported American Funk and Soul, he would lend Stan his 'Blues and Soul' magazines to check out the new releases. On the way home, some evenings Alex took Stan to a specialist record shop in Dagenham where the pair would bop around the store. His setup at home was amazing, he even sent the stylus and turntable away once a year to have it realigned and speed checked. He had brought in a couple of his 12" singles for the DJ to play and was now enjoying himself.

An excited Chris came up to Stan, a smile across his face. I have wanted to tell you for a while, but not with people in the office listening. As well as my manpowered flight project, I have designed a luggage chest. A couple of days ago the Patent was approved. Rather than strap suitcases to a car roof rack they are placed in a box on top of the car. I have calculated the aerodynamic drag coefficients to develop the shape of the box. The only thing is UK manufacturing is so expensive, sadly I may have to go to Asia for construction.

Kelvin arrived; Chris retreated mid-sentence. Stan was fair game. They chatted about the new baby, work and things in general. Johnny came back, collected his beer, winked at Stan and quickly moved away towards the dance area.

Kelvin moved away from small talk. "What about the rumours concerning Alex and Sian, do you think it's true?"

Stan shrugged his shoulders.

Kelvin kept speaking, "I think it's 80% true, it seems they got together at your party and they've been at it ever since. I feel sorry for their spouses, especially Abigail. Did you see anything?"

Stan shook his head.

"Stan," he probed, "how often do you have sex?"

"Ah," replied Stan.

Kelvin continued, "Do you use gimp masks and rubber suits? Who wears them, you or your girlfriend?"

"Er," Stan responded. He didn't have a girlfriend, but that didn't seem to matter, "We haven't, I haven't, used jump suits?" He had never heard of them.

"Do you find one of you wants to be dominated, or submissive?" asked Kelvin.

Stan's face was very red by now. He took a glug of beer, shock his head. Perhaps, he had the wrong perception of 'sweet' Angela.

Kelvin continued, "It's the smell of the rubber, lack of air, the fear of suffocation that is so exciting. The pain of a whip, biting your flesh."

Stan nodded, he didn't know sex was supposed to be painful. Was Kelvin advertising?

Perhaps WITH Angela? Stan made his escape, "sorry, I must use the loo." He gave his apologies, still carrying his beer quickly left the room.

He later shared the conversation with Johnny, who immediately suggested Angela must be a right goer. He expressed his desire to see her in a nurse's outfit, with black stockings and a whip. Stan didn't mention it to any of his work mates for fear that Kelvin would be verbally crucified.

Stanley stayed away from Kelvin for the rest of the night, he later pondered on the personality of the real Angela. He would never know if Kelvin was just bluffing to scare the S*** out of him, or offering Stanley his wife for sex?

05

GENESIS

Chapter Marker

Page	Title	Finished?	Notes
262	05-14 Choir	☐	
266	05-15 Assembly	☐	
268	05-16 Saved	☐	

05-01

PETE

Irene and Pete had met when he finished his National Service in the summer of 1948.

Pete had been conscripted into the Royal Artillery regiment of the British Army in 1947. He served in Palestine for eighteen months, managing the arrival of the abandoned Jewish population of Europe. The Palestinian Arabs were not happy that their homeland was being overwhelmed and the Palestinian Jews classed the land as their historic home. Pete and his comrades were there to peacefully keep them apart, to stop them killing each other.

The youngest of eight surviving children he had lived with his family of ten in one room in a tenement block with a single shared external toilet. Pete was orphaned at a young age.

During the Blitz, his family were moved into different family homes three times. All in London's docklands district, each time they moved the new home had been bombed and destroyed. The third time all their meagre belongs as well as the building were destroyed or lost. In the confusion of the air raid, walking through unrecognisable flattened street layouts each of the remaining family lost contact with each other. Aged just thirteen, dazed, alone and hungry Pete walked the streets looking for a friendly face to provide shelter.

Eventually, he travelled the forty miles to Guildford in Surrey where his sister Bett was in service. There, she looked after him as best she could. To earn some much-needed money he worked helping the milkman. Pete would lead the horse drawn cart while the milkman ladled milk from the metal churn into the customers' individual vessels. For the remainder of his youth, until conscripted, Pete lived with Bett.

Thankfully, when released from National Service and the Army Pete was offered a temporary home in Dagenham with his brother Charlie. Charlie had previously been offered this home away from the debris of London. He had serviced in the Merchant Navy, working on the Arctic Convoys. Evading German patrols these ships took the very dangerous route below the icepack to deliver food and supplies to Russia's northern ports. His first shipwreck had been on a ship that hit an iceberg. On three different occasions, he had been torpedoed and rescued from the icy waters. He thought himself lucky to be alive and able to tell the story.

Blonde, wavy-haired, blue-eyed Pete made his way from the Dover Docks to his brother's home in Dagenham. He was relaxed and tanned. Pete, had just finished R&R in Famagusta on the island of Cyprus before being released and shipped home. On a hot, summers day, he was greeted by the family. They sat on the back doorstep with a cup of tea, smoking a roll your own cigarette to catch up. Pete hadn't seen Charlie for over five years. They had only kept in touch by using the address of Bett's employer's home as a central post box.

Sitting on the step, Pete recalled one incident while in Palestine.

"Do you remember the riots over here, after two British Sergeants were kidnapped, killed, and then hanged from eucalyptus trees? The 'terrorists' planted booby traps on the bodies so that as they were recovered, the bombs badly injured the rescuers." Charlie and his family nodded.

Pete continued, "I was involved with the revenge a few weeks later, but in a different location. Everyone was fed up with being a target. Nearly all the lads out there were conscripts, poor buggers. We had no experience of war, booby traps or bombs. Most of us hadn't fired a rifle. As peacekeepers the Government thought we would be safe."

Pete stopped for a minute, had a thought then continued, "A few Jocks come to see me on a Thursday afternoon. I had just left the mess. One called me over, he asked for a light. Big ginger B***, he was. Mentioned the murder of the 'two sergeants' and how sick everyone felt. The B***, they couldn't fight like men. Cowards, killed people when their arms were tied behind their backs.

Anyway, there was going to be a payback beating, not murder. No one was going to get killed, just 'hurt a lot'. Give the B***, something to remember." Pete looked up at the white clouds moving across the blue sky and paused, "Like we had to. This Jock asked when I was 'on'. I told him 11.00pm to 6.00am. He smiled, 'Just right'. His words made my blood chill. He told me, 'The punishment was going to be handed out on the Saturday morning'. Could they trust me to turn a blind eye? I agreed.

On the Saturday at 2.00am, I was on guard duty at the army camp entrance, when they left. About twenty Jocks in vest and shorts, without dog tags, no ID. They was carrying various clubs, truncheons and rifle butts. I didn't see them until a few hours later when they came back. By all accounts, they tiptoed into the main town to exact revenge."

The gathering heard a noise across where the garden fence used to be. Pete stopped talking, the neighbour's back door creaked as it opened. Out, into the sunshine popped a petite dark haired young woman carrying a bowl containing the washing. Beside her, a Dalmatian dog bounded around trying to grab a piece of washing from the bowl. The sun caught the dark hue of her hair against a bright red hairband. She heard the chit-chat next door, turned and smiling called 'hello'.

The Patersons, sitting on the doorstep next door, returned the greeting. Charlie introduced Pete. The youngsters smiled.

05-02

IRENE

Irene lived with her family at the southern end of Drapery Avenue in Dagenham.

She had been born at The Angel, Islington. However, as Joseph her father worked on the railways, each time he took a new job they moved around London to be close to his place of work. Joseph had taken advantage of this rehousing rule. Worried by the poor London air quality of the 1935 'peas soupers', then the advent of war he managed to change jobs from Paddington in west London to the safer, rural Dagenham.

Irene's dad was one of the first called to arms. Being in the Reserve, he was sent to Egypt at the commencement of WW2. Irene's three older brothers were also called up. Jack was in the Army, Dickie the RAF and Young Joey the Navy.

Jack and Dickie's work took them away, but Joey was nearer home, stationed at a secret base in Scotland. Working as a despatch rider Joey tore around on his BSA M20 delivering secret messages. Most of the time he worked in the Scottish Highlands or on the edge of Scottish Lochs where prototypes of top-secret military devices were constructed and tested.

He often arranged his time to allow a quick weekend visit home to Dagenham to be with his mum and sister. On one excursion, he was busting to tell them a story. Irene heard the unmistakable roar of his bike when he was just twenty yards away at the end of a six-hundred-mile journey. Mum and sister rushed excitedly to hug him and check he was safe.

Beat went to the scullery to retrieve the hidden tea and sugar. One small spoon of tea in the pot made four cups, two for her son. A pinch of sugar with a splash of condensed milk in each cup completed the treat.

"Okay boy, how has your week been," enquired Beat sitting on the sofa.

Joey sipped his tea then passed a paper wrapped parcel to Irene, "I got these off a G.I. for delivering a package" he smiled.

Being careful not to damage the wrapping, Irene gently untied the object to reveal a pair of nylon stockings. Elated, she gave her big soppy brother another hug.

Joey told his tale, "Well you know I move around, last Wednesday I was on a much bigger Loch where they were testing. Everything was extra careful; Marines had been there two days checking things over. There was a rumour Top Brass was coming to witness a special demonstration. My sergeant told me to go across the Loch with the Landing Craft pilot to get fish and chips for the Squad before the event took place.

We chugged over to get the food. When we came out of the shop, there were five large polished black limousines on the quay. Guess who was there?"

"Don't know, go on, tell us," responded Beat eagerly.

"Churchill and Ike, both of them. They were standing looking across the Loch," grinned Joey.

"Churchill called me over, with ten fish and chip suppers under me arm he asked who owned the Landing Craft." Joey continued to explain the thrill of transporting two of the most powerful men in the world, including their entourages across a Loch in Scotland by Landing Craft.

During the war, Irene and her mum were the only people living in the house. Irene had helped her mum Beat, when she could. They had a horse stabled in the back garden, a dalmatian called 'chutney', rabbits, chickens and geese. Every spare piece of land around the Anderson Shelter was planted with vegetables. Irene had also worked at a nearby clothing factory as a seamstress since she was sixteen. She would sew shaped pieces of heavy fabric together to make 'bib and brace' for industrial workwear.

Beat, with Irene's help would use the horse and cart as a removal service. It wasn't full time, but people 'bombed out' in London often needed a way to move heavy items to new homes in Dagenham. Every day refugees were leaving the flattened Capital to find shelter. It was a good earner. The mum and daughter team also sold spare chickens, rabbits, eggs and vegetables as food.

Pete was overjoyed that the coincidence of living with his brother had brought Irene into his life. He and Irene often 'accidently' met in the garden to sit on the doorstep and chat. The dog 'Chutney' was always there to help start the conversations.

It didn't take long before Irene and Pete started courting. Subsequently, at a wedding which cost £14 a few years later, Irene Ryan became Irene Paterson. The energetic seamstress created and produced her own wedding dress along with those of the bridesmaids from old parachute silk which Young Joey had acquired.

Both the Ryan and Paterson families enjoyed a typical cockney 'knees up' in the street outside their homes in Drapery Avenue. After the loss of so many loved ones, amidst the S*** and pain they had all gone through, the wedding was a way of reclaiming their lost lives. The beginning of new ones.

Once again, the Ryan's moved home, but this time only along the same avenue closer to Chadwell Heath station.

STANLEY

Pete tap danced down the stairs into the lobby which lead to the hospital exit. There was no one about. It was semi dark inside but the falling, settled snow outside made it seem brighter. At least, six inches of snow lay everywhere.

It was nearly 3.00am but he didn't care. At that moment, he had nothing in his life to worry about.

He felt good inside. The exhilaration that a man feels when he becomes a dad. More intent perhaps, when it's his first child. The new dad pulled his jacket tight, closing the Maternity Hospital door behind him as he walked into the storm. 'Snowing in March'?

The date of birth of his first child, '21 March 1952, a bonny boy 6 lb 5oz', kept going around in his head. He didn't want to forget it. Would he ever forget it? 'Born twelve minutes past two in the morning.' Cold, wet and flipping windy - what a lovely day.

It was too late to catch a bus. Then again, the severity of the storm had caused the cancellation of all types of public transport. There was only one way to get home, 'Shanks's Pony'.

It was a blooming long way, but with wings on his feet and happiness in his heart it would not be a problem. He looked up into the black sky, feeling the refreshing falling snow on his face. Then turned and counted the number of windows along the Ward to where Irene's bed was. He spoke aloud, "Thank you, Irene. Rest and sleep well tonight my love. Thank you so much for giving us a beautiful, healthy baby. I'll be back to see you both later today."

Pete blew a kiss to the window in the hospital building behind which his beautiful wife was recovering. A heavy blast of freezing wet weather into his face signalled it was time to set off on the journey home.

The nine mile walk from Stepney to Chadwell Heath took him close on three hours. He and Irene, had set up home in Irene's parents' front bedroom. It wasn't their preferred option. It was their only option. Things can get fraught when families have to share a living space, but at the moment he couldn't be more thankful of Beat and Joseph's warmth and kindness.

He couldn't wait to tell Joseph and Beat that their only daughter was a mum.

ABODE

Joseph walked down the garden path, through the gate onto the snow-covered pavement. He had an early start today due to the blinking weather. Firstly, he would need to move the coal braziers to positions next to the railway points, then after lighting them keep stoking for the rest of the day. Hopefully, the heat would stop them sticking or freezing. He placed his hand over the gate onto the latch and sensed someone close. Looking up, in the distance to his left the outline of a shape approached. He could just hear the soft crunch of footsteps against ice above the whistling whoosh of the wind.

Trudging through the blizzard a snow-clad figure came towards him. It came nearer, he had no idea what it was but guessed it was his son-in-law. No one else, without good reason, would be out in this storm. Joseph couldn't distinguish the face; he had snow blown by an icy wind biting into his eyes. The snow encased face with frozen red cheeks and nose, drew closer. Somehow an enormous, euphoric smile broke through the snowstorm, it was his son-in-law.

Pete raised his hand, in greeting to Joseph.

"How is Irene?" Joseph asked, "is she well?"

"Fine," answered Pete, "6lb 5oz."

"And mum?" asked Joseph.

"Mum, is a lovely mum, so proud of her," announced Pete, "she did really well, 6lb 5oz."

"Congratulations," beamed Grandad. He was so happy, this was not his first grandchild, but it was his loving, caring, only daughter's first child. "And baby?" he enquired.

Pete smiled, "He's fine, 6lb 5oz."

"Well done," praised Joseph. He wanted to shake Peter's hand, but it was frozen blue, it might snap off if any pressure was applied.

Pete was shivering from the cold.

This wasn't the time for Joseph to remove a glove either. He reached out to hug Pete, but man embarrassment resulted in him only grasping both Pete's arms above the elbows. A clumsy, awkward manly embrace followed.

"Well done," he repeated released Pete's arms. Joseph turned to continue his journey to work.

Grandad had served in the war wearing the three stripes of a sergeant. He knew how to command men. He had an imposing presence.

Stanley and the other grandchildren were not scared of him, but very respectful, as were his own children. It was just the way people lived in 1950's Britain. If your offspring did something wrong, you helped the Police, not hindered of argued with them.

Unfortunately, society only works when the people in it of all ages, understand and accept the standards required. Stopping or resisting thuggery and robbery means people can live free from fear. Joseph believed it didn't matter whether people were in a World War or in the High Street, their behaviour should be no different.

It wasn't until Stanley was a teenager that he suddenly realised Grandad was only about 5' 3" tall. Stan had a subconscious image of him being immensely powerful, at least six feet tall. The reality was, that the man's character was so much bigger than his physique.

Joseph did have a compassionate side. He loved Beat, he loved all of his children and grandchildren. Beat was born in 1895, six years before him. When he first met her, she had a young child. She had been working in service in a big house in London. Her employer had forced himself upon her, the consequence being she fell pregnant. Beat was thrown onto the street. Destitute, she moved in with her elder sister. Later she met Joseph. The young mum felt so happy to have met a man who loved her, a kind man who took her son as his own.

Joseph spent a lot of time with Stanley. He would give him a cuddle, tell him stories. When Stan was three years old, Joseph would sit him at the dinner table to oversee the infant draw and colour books with crayons. He would chastise the infant if the colouring strayed outside the shape or across a line. Grandad would also supervise Stan when drawing lines in dot-to-dot books. He would point to the next dot, telling him the number as he guided Stan on the route of the line.

Although Beat had a very special bond with Irene, life was up and down at the house in Drapery Avenue. The new family was given the main bedroom, Nan and Grandad slept in the second bedroom, poor

Young Joey was evicted to the box room. Luckily, for all concerned both Jack and Dick had already married and moved out.

Nan and Grandad enjoyed people's company, Grandad was not averse to a trip to the pub.

They had really enjoyed Irene's wedding and reception. But Joseph had been through the house share before with his own family. He was at the age when patience becomes limited. He and Beat loved their daughter and grandson, they knew things would eventually be less hectic, but for now it was a chore.

Joseph worked on a shift rota. He would become displeased if a small person decided he had stomach ache when the older man was trying to sleep. To reduce conflict, Irene got into the habit of going for a walk while her dad slept. The calming effect eased family tensions. In all weathers, Irene took baby out in the pram. Food, drink, nappies, bye!

She would regularly be out over four hours, sitting on a park bench, feeding the ducks or walking.

If the weather was good, she could sit and knit Stanley a new cardigan or pair of leggings. If it was raining, cold or she needed a comfort break the new mum would visit Beat's best friends. Maude and Sophie both lived close, they had treated Irene as their own since she was born.

Irene always tried to get home just before her mum left for Ilford where she worked as an evening cleaner in a Jewish tailor's shop. The tailor was a nice man who always gave Beat a discount if she sent family or friends shopping there for a new suit, overcoat or pair of trousers.

Sometimes, on a nice day Irene would take Stanley to the station to visit Grandad at work.

On one occasion, they were standing on the platform chatting when an Express train ran through towards Liverpool Street.

A Great Eastern steam loco with coaches, total weight in excess of three hundred tons, and travelling at fifty mph hammered through. Firstly, they became aware of the ever-increasing mechanical noise, then a faint rumble as it approached. Stan looked alarmed.

The train appeared in the distance. The shockwave of ambient air preceding the Loco pushed paper and leaves high into the roof void. A deafening thunder and smell followed as it charged into the station, running alongside the platform only two feet away from the family group. It was impossible to talk to each other, Stan clung around his mum's neck screaming with fear.

Finally, the smoke, thick black acrid smoke filled the station. Amber glowing sparks rose with the smoke into the canopy of the roof, replacing the paper and leaves, then dropped to the platform. The smoke and smell hung for a few minutes before dispersing.

Grandad took the shaken little boy from his anxious mum and comforted him with a cuddle.

Irene, Pete and Stan lived with Nanny and Grandad for over three years. It was not until Irene became pregnant with twins that the Council offered them a three-bedroom house in the eastern side of Dagenham.

05-05
HOME

The largest domestic building site in Europe had been started in and around Dagenham during 1921. The Patersons were lucky to be offered a three-bedroom home at Beckvale End on the border with Romford.

It wasn't a new build, but in 1955 Irene, Pete, Stanley and the 'bump' were very happy to move into their new home in Hawthorn Road. The previous tenant had been an old man who had passed away.

The house was semi-detached with side access which could be adapted for off road parking to accommodate Pete's Austin A30 car.

Peter and Irene had little money but bags of enthusiasm and love. All they needed was a bucket of soapy, disinfected water plus a couple of pairs of old holey knickers. Together, the pair cleaned every object and every surface. They removed all soft furnishings immediately, then when they had the funds or took out a 'Never, Never' loan cheque, slowly replaced them.

Outside, was a small turfed garden to the front. A larger garden at the back was turfed on one side. The other side had space to grow vegetables.

On the left at the back were three old wooden buildings connected as one structure. These were separated as a shed, coal bunker and wooden lean-to. To the boys these would become a castle, a fort, a ship, anything their imaginations could dream. They would spend whole days climbing on top, in and out of the structures. The boys would fight make believe battles, build camps or dungeons. A simple wooden stick taken from the cleft paling fence separating the gardens could become a rifle, a spear, a sword or even a ships mast. After the three youngsters played in the coal bunker for an evening then sat on the new settee, Irene forced Pete to build a fence around it.

The grassed area could be Wembley Stadium, Wimbledon, Badminton, Madison Square Garden.

As well as the main fireplace in the lounge there were others in two of the three bedrooms. To keep the upstairs warm in winter, Pete would place a paraffin heater on the top stair landing.

Hot water was produced by a back boiler positioned behind the lounge coal fire.

Consequently, as the fire was only alight in the winter Irene would have to boil a kettle or saucepan to produce hot water in the summer. Carrying hot kettles and large heavy saucepans of boiling water through the downstairs lounge to the upstairs bathroom was a hazardous task. It became even more dangerous when the family grew, with a young child and two tiny tots running around.

Irene had the twins later in the year. Two boys, John and Eddie arrived ten days early. They were delivered in the main bedroom late one night, where Irene was assisted by two friendly midwives.

There were no complications, the boys were beautiful and healthy. John arrived at the end of 20 May and Eddie at the start of 21 May, so John became the middle brother. John weighed nearly the same as Stanley did at birth, Eddie was smaller.

The family settled in, once a week Irene would walk with the three boys in the pram to see her mum. The two-and-a-half-mile walk took just under an hour. She always timed it for when Joseph was not in bed. On Saturdays, Pete would take them in the car.

Winters were just as much fun as summers, playing in the garden, building snowmen and rolling in the snow. Pete bought a puppy for the home but it chewed all the new furniture, so he returned it.

The best times in winter were after Saturday tea when they pulled the settee up close to a roaring coal fire. The five of them would squeeze together to watch the black and white TV. At least, one son would sit on the floor between their feet, perhaps one would sit on Mum's lap having a cuddle. If they were lucky, Dad would produce two Mars bars from his coat pocket. One would be cut in three for the kids to share, the other in half for him and Irene.

Dad's treats didn't always go down well. After working overtime one Saturday, Pete decided to investigate a new shop in Olive Lane. He had driven past it when travelling to work and home. Pete pulled onto the extended pavement outside the 'Golden Dragon'.

The menu card was in the window. One dish caught his eye, 'prawns', this dish was not expensive. The choice of other items was too dear, but he could just afford the shellfish.

He pondered, remembering when he was a young boy living in Chinatown, Limehouse.

There were lots of Chinese people living in the East End then. They wore long silk coats with pantaloons and tended to live in one area. The Jews were the same but dressed formally in black. He hadn't seen a Chinese person for years. Pete and his friends would run up behind them and tug their ponytail. When the boys were playing on the cargo barges moored in the Thames, the Chinese guards would chase them. That was when his mate Yosef fell between two barges and was squashed to death.

Pete's eyes lost focus on the menu. For a moment, he thought of his mum and dad.

He had decided, entering the first Chinese Takeaway shop he had ever seen he ordered five portions of prawns. The kids had never seen a prawn, nor heard of Chinese food, it would be a nice surprise.

Pete arrived home and revealed he had a surprise for tea, prawns. Irene was just as excited as the children. He took the five white paper bags from the bigger brown carrier bag, handing one to each of the expectant family.

The boys jumped around, "We having pawns for tea," they sang. John jumped off his seat at the table running in circles with the white bag looping up and down as a ship in a storm.

They looked inside their bags, excitedly putting a large white, crispy cloud into their mouths.

Irene smiled inside; she was married to a wonderful man.

The boys wondered what the fuss had been about. They decided that they weren't keen on pawns. Irene silently ate her portion, knowing how let down Peter felt. There was no reason to exacerbate his disappointment.

INFANTS

Stanley's first day at school, he wasn't amused. The child was shy, small and thin. He was so thin that at his pre-school medical the nurse prescribed Malt Extract. This was a sweet gunky, brown substance given as a tonic to build up underdeveloped kids.

Poor Irene worried about little 'tin ribs'. One neighbour suggested he needed worming. Beat calmed her daughter. The little boy never stopped eating, he never stopped running. She explained that Stan had been cut from the same tree as his mum and dad, none of them were large.

The allocated school, Gunter's Hall had no vacancies, so as a temporary measure he was instead sent to Hookery Farm. Being a number of children were affected the Council arranged a coach to collect the pupils from designated pick-up points.

If Stan was unhappy about going to school. He was traumatised having to leave his mum at the pick-up point. Abandoned, he climbed onto a massive coach to join a load of strangers. Irene was equally devastated. She thought of poor Stanley all day. A comforting distraction was having the twins to look after, once she was involved with the little ones her thoughts were solely on them.

So that Stan didn't have time to think, the first morning Irene had arrived at the pick-up point outside Kandy's chip shop on the dot. The second morning, Irene arrived at the pick-up point a bit earlier. She hoped to bond with the other mums to help Stan integrate.

Irene watched his behaviour. Although he held tightly onto her hand, he seemed to recognise and acknowledge a few of the other children. When the coach arrived, Stanley sobbed with red eyes, dejectedly he climbed aboard. Irene noticed that he sat next to a boy from the pick-up point. He had found a wee bit of courage, she hoped he would make some friends.

Strangely, although Stan was scared of his own shadow, he had the ability to make close friends and retain them. Over time, he had become good pals with Glyn, Roy and John from the pick-up point. This was a good thing, as after only twelve weeks the boys were moved to Gunter's Hall School.

Stanley remained pals with the people from Hookery Farm, he later made even more friends with the young people at Gunter's Hall. One new friend was Jon who was a close pal of Glyn. Another was Lisa Poppen, who Stanley liked a lot. He tried to kiss her in the school playground once and received a slap. A year later, Stan tried to kiss her at a birthday party in Hawthorn Road and she pushed him into a bramble bush.

One evening, Stanley was sitting at the table joining lines in a 'dot to dot' book. Irene could hear him singing to himself, "Hi, ho, eye, ho, it's off to work we go. With a pin, a shovel an' a walking stick."

Irene asked him about the song.

"It's for the school play Mummy," he answered. "I'm a dwarf."

"Oh, that's nice," his mum smiled. She thought, 'Well, it's a step up from the nativity play when he was a tree'.

"Mum," he added, "I need a walking stick. Miss Shirly told us to ask an old person, so I'm going to ask Daddy?"

The little blond haired, brown eyed mummy's boy got down from the chair and walked to Irene. Putting his arms around her legs, he looked up and declared, "I love you Mummy."

The mums from the pick-up point would still meet, chatting and gossiping together as they undertook the twenty-five-minute walk to the new school. They would demonstrate the amazing ability of pram pushing mums. Able to walk in a long line, or pairs talking to their children and other mums at the same time. These dual actions being performed while keeping an eye on their own, and other's offspring, as they careered around them in all directions. With a sixth sense, while recognising danger each mum could talk to their neighbour and shout commands to prevent the kids running into the road, a tree or another pram mum.

Irene chatted as she strolled back from the morning school trip. Roy's mum called to her, "Are you taking your brood to Martina's kids for the Measles, Mumps and Rubella Party tomorrow night?"

"Yeah," replied Irene. "Best to give the boys measles before their bits drop to save them problems later."

"Yeah, and no pregnant ladies are allowed?"

"I'm not planning to have any more," Irene giggled, "I'll walk with you and the kids after school, take care."

05-07

NOEL

Christmas Day, blurry eyed the five rose at 6.30am. The twins were now four, they shared a double room, Stan had the box room.

The boys were so excited, they had first entered their parent's bedroom at 4.00am. Frequently the children returned, excitedly jumping on the bed. It was so cold Pete went downstairs collected his and Irene's overcoats then laid them on the bed over the eiderdown.

Each time the boys raced in, Pete sent them to their rooms. The last time, ten minutes previous the three of them had gone into the twins' room and started playing bouncing on the bed.

Irene looked at Pete, "Time to get up? I think. Before they break the beds." Pete agreed.

The boys needed no encouragement to go downstairs. The moment they heard the wood creak as Irene stepped onto the landing, they were off.

Yelling and cheering they ran past her, bumping into her legs and each other.

"Whoa. Be careful," the young, beaming mum shouted.

Dangerously trying to stride two steps at a time while holding the handrail with both tiny hands they skated to the bottom. Irene walked into the living room to see them sitting in a line on the settee wearing their pyjamas. They were bursting with excitement, tiny arms crossed on their chests to control themselves. The boys waited patiently, grinning.

Irene and Pete joined them. The youngsters had four presents each, Irene and Pete one each.

Daddy went to the coal fire and started the tinder burning. He placed a few small pieces of coal on top then went to the bathroom to collect a flannel.

Irene was cute. She allowed the boys to open two presents each, then she announced, "You have to have a wash, before you can open anymore."

Grudgingly, they agreed, each knew what Mummy said was law. Before walking into the kitchen, Mum pulled out the flap from the gate leg dining table. In the kitchen, she half-filled the washing up bowl with warm water from the kettle, collected a towel and soap then carried the three items into the living room. Standing at the table she added these items alongside the flannel and readied herself for the cleansing contest.

"Who's first she asked?" Each child kept one arm crossed and shot the second into air. They stretched their arms and necks upwards to appear taller.

She laughed, "I have never seen this before, all of you want a wash?" With disbelief, Dad preparing breakfast in the kitchen poked his head round the door to witness the miracle.

Eddie was first. In turn, the boys stood next to Mum and stripped naked. She picked them up, sat them on the towel, then gave each an all over wash with a soapy flannel. As the flannel whooshed into their ears, up their nose, and other hidden crevices each one wiggled and complained, "Mummy, why do you rub the flannel so hard?"

Eddie was clean, he set off to claim another present, but Pete stopped him.

"I am afraid you will have to wait," he told Eddie, "only after you are all washed, can you open the other presents." Eddie didn't stop, disappointed he went straight upstairs to lay on his bed.

Finally, the clean, washed boys had all of their presents. Then after a fried breakfast, a wipe of their faces and hands prior to get dressed.

To save money, Irene made most of the children's clothes herself. She knitted their jumpers and cardigans. Patterns bought at the 'wool shop' were used to tailor the boys' shirts. The only element she couldn't complete to her desired finish were buttonholes. She would hand stitch these individually as she didn't have a buttonhole machine.

Irene had saved some money from the weekly shop. As today was a special day and to look smart at Nan and Grandad's, the boys were wearing new shop bought clothes. The four of them had gone with Nanny to Ilford to the shop were Nanny worked as a cleaner. A hefty discount applied by the shop owner had allowed her to buy all three boys a new outfit for Christmas.

Pete went outside to warm up the car while Irene wrapped the boys in warm coats, gloves and hats. The wind was biting, the family set off in their grey A30 to meet the family and for Christmas Dinner.

Despite being very happy at home, Irene and the family always visited Nan and Grandad's home on Christmas Day. They had been doing this since they moved out in 1955. It was the sharing, the company of friends and family that always made Christmas special for them.

All of Irene's family would be there. Unfortunately, Irene's brother Jack had died recently from bad health. Hopefully, his widow May and the two teenage children would make the effort to travel by public transport from north London to be with them.

GATHERING

Nan and Grandad had set up the tree and decorations, the turkey had been in the oven for an hour. All they needed now was the family. Nothing beat Christmas Day with the grandchildren, although the adults always found something to laugh about and entertain themselves. People arrived from around 11.30am. The front lounge was initially used as the dining room, then later a nursery. The larger back room was the socialising area with the tree, TV and Joseph's drinks cabinet.

The mums controlled their offspring and shared the kitchen tasks. Once all the men had arrived, Grandad invited them to visit the local pub 'for a few jars'. Liz and May were not required in the kitchen, nor on children watch so they accompanied the men to the pub.

Liz, was Young Joey's wife, she had been a bridesmaid to Irene. The lady had a smile and personality that would brighten any room. She and Joey adored children, but unfortunately they were not able to conceive. They always made a point of playing with and spoiling Stan, John and Eddie. The three boys knew they would get the most amazing presents from this uncle and auntie.

While the adults where in the pub, the eight grandchildren had their turkey dinners. Nan was ever thoughtful, dessert for them was ice cream with trifle rather than Christmas pud.

When the kids had finished, they were ushered into the back room to make space for the adults. The kids sat on the floor by the tree reading labels on the presents, trying to predict what the coloured wrapping paper was hiding, but were not allowed to open any until everyone had eaten. They played 'climbing over the furniture', 'running up and down the stairs' and 'hide and seek'. After just over an hour, the six adults returned from the pub to the dining room where the three cooks / child minders were waiting.

Later, once everyone had eaten, they returned to the back room.

Grandad stood by the decorated tree adjacent to the back window and called them to order. Each year, he would say a few words thanking God for the love of his family. This year, he also remembered the passing of Uncle Jack. Irene could see a tear in his eye, May left the room followed by Beat.

The children became significantly more excited as presents were handed out, later they were allowed the full run of the house to tire them for the journey home.

The TV was never turned on until 9.00pm. Only then, to watch the Billy Cotton Band Show. In later years to watch the Black and White Minstrel Show. Grandad allowed some time for chat or rest then declared the 'games open'.

Everyone laughed. The highlight of the day were the games. The one thing each of the children remembered years later were the games. Adults and kids would play games together. There would be leg pulling and banter with silly prizes. The children didn't understand most of the wordplay, but they joined in with the laughing.

Flap the Kipper, Bingo, Charades, Pin the tail on the Donkey. To produce the most fun Joseph ensured that when playing Pass the Apple, chin to chin, the people in the line were alternate child, adult.

He had setup a cardboard box covered in Christmas wrapping paper as a Prize Chest. This contained rewards for the winner of each game. The prizes inside the box were wrapped and tied with a piece of string which hung on the outside of the box. A prize winner was allowed only to pull a string without a visible clue to the shape or size of the prize.

Dick won a prize playing Charades, he guessed the film, *The Searchers*. Grasping a single string he pulled, a small oblong pack appeared and popped out of the chest. He fumbled, removing the tightly sealed pack.

"If that's a wedge of £1 notes, I need a new wardrobe," May shouted.

"You need a new dress," cried Ruth, "I'm married to the tight wad, I'm first."

"It must be money, he's always been as tight as a duck's," Young Joey, put in his two pennyworth, "he can smell it, that's why his all thumbs."

The kids laughed along. Dick whittled his way through the wrapping to uncover a white box.

"Well, what is it," chimed Ruth.

"Azil, toilet paper," laughed Dick. "It's second-hand, only been used once!" He threw the box at Young Joey, who stumbled out of the way. Everyone joined in, cheering and laughing.

The prizes were a mixture of good and bad. A toothbrush, baby's bib, toilet brush, pack of screwdrivers, diary, box of chocolates, box of cigars.

It got to 'home time' about 11.30pm. The younger members of the families were asleep, laying on the floor in the front room. Pete and Irene said their goodbyes. Pete collected the presents and the three boys. He carried them, one at a time wrapped in a blanket to the car and placed them on the back seat. The presents went into the passenger footwell of the A30.

While scrapping the ice from the front windscreen, Pete became aware of a dark spill on the snow. It covered the road, bordering the nearside wheel and seemed to be from the car.

He went back inside the house to explain to the gathering.

"I'm afraid, it could be brake or clutch fluid I can't see in the dark. I'd best get underneath to have a look, just to be safe. If it's brake, we will leave it here, if it's clutch, it should get us home."

"How long will you be," asked Irene.

"I'll give you a hand," offered Young Joey.

Pete thought he would be a few minutes, but he needed a torch. Irene was concerned that the children were getting very cold in the car.

Beat professed her daughter was right to worry about the children's health so Pete, Irene and May returned to the car and collected a child each. They brought them back into the warmth of the house and returned them to the front room.

Beat went in search of batteries for a torch, Pete pushed the front door ajar to keep the heat in. He stood with Joey behind the front door, waiting.

Five minutes passed, "Where is she?" queried Joey, "Mum?"

A tremendous noise shook them, a heavy thud, breaking glass and scraping metal.

Joey threw the front door open.

The A30 was twenty feet from where it had been parked, in its place was a crumpled wreck.

Joey could see the driver slumped over the steering wheel. He gave Pete a shout.

Neighbours appeared at their windows and front doors. Curtains were tugged back. Joey and Pete bolted along the garden path, onto the pavement and fought to get the car door open.

They could smell petrol. Pete poked his arm through the smashed windscreen, stretching at full length he unlocked the door. Joseph arrived to help. Grabbing the driver's overcoat, they pulled him out of the car. He was a large, bald man who stunk of booze. Just conscious, as he moaned a slight trickle of blood ran down his face.

Joseph and Joey supported the driver, dragging him into the house. Pete turned off the ignition and took the keys.

Minutes later Elsie from next door knocked. Her husband had run to the phone box near the train station to phone for an ambulance. It would arrive in ten minutes.

Supported by Joseph, the driver responded. He slumped on the second stair, head against the wall.

Joey stood, arms folded, in the front room doorway. His eyes surveying the driver's body for signs of injury. Blood from the driver's nose which was probably broken, ran down his face. A blue red swelling grew as his left eye closed, a gash on his forehead dried. The family couldn't decide if his demeanour was the result of too much booze or the crash.

Beat heard a soft crying from the back room, she quietly went to investigate. There she saw Irene sitting with her head on Pete's shoulder, gently weeping. It was the shock of realisation. The jumble of incidents in Irene's head was becoming ordered. She was mentally grasping that the family had been within a few minutes of losing her precious sons, perhaps also her loving husband, maybe her brother.

05-09
NEIGHBOURS

The Paterson's new home in Hawthorn Road was a turning off Dacca Road. This main road ran from the Beck pub on the right, past shops, the school and three more shops. Further to the left it carried on towards the Lodge pub, Beckvale End and Chase, the River Rom and Romford.

As Stan walked out of Hawthorn Road turning left into Dacca Road, there was more than a mile of greenery in front of him. There were fields, woods, lakes and sand, gravel pits on both sides of the road. It was an amazing place for a young boy with a creative imagination to live.

All the new neighbours were friendly.

Across the road on the left was a tall, thin old man who lived with his two sons. Mr Lucas wasn't a well man. He had been a Chindit, fighting the Japanese in Burma during WW2. Taken as a POW his life in a prison camp had critically damaged his mental and physical health.

On the right was Mrs Gardner, she was very large and not very mobile. She always wore a bright patterned wrap around pinny, tied at the waist over her underwear. Often, as she bent over to speak with him, Stanley got an eyeful of something he didn't really want to see. Her son Michael lived in the house with her. Most days she would call over the back garden fence for Stan to run an errand. If there was no answer, she would hobble around the front in excruciating pain to knock at the front door. Mostly, her pleasure was ten cigarettes a day, sometimes a pint of milk.

In winter, he would take her empty paraffin can and fill it for two shillings at the machine outside the three shops. The houses had only a coal fire in the main room, so the occupants used paraffin heaters on the top landing to heat upstairs. In the morning, the heat from it helped melt the ice from the inside of the bedroom and bathroom windows.

Each day, Mrs Gardner would give Stan six pennies for running the errand, enough for a chocolate bar. Sometimes, she would pass him empty bottles to return to the Off Licence at the Beck pub. She would let him keep the returned deposit of one penny a bottle.

Some years earlier, six-year-old Stanley had made an impression on his neighbour.

He was playing alone in his back garden while Michael was playing in the neighbouring garden with his friends. These boys playing cowboys and Indians were around eleven years old.

The young boy was drawn to their game. It was exciting, "Bang! Bang! You're dead, aaaah." They theatrically fell to the floor holding the injured body part, choking on their last words, crawling until their demise.

He was intrigued, anxiously he moved up against the fence to watch through the gap in the wooden pickets.

Wide eyed, he observed them hopping on one leg as they galloped around the garden on imaginary horses. Each holding fantasy reins in one hand and a Colt 45 or a bow and arrow in the other. Michael was a cowboy; his comrades had been killed. The only survivor was captured by the Indians. Stan couldn't look, he closed one eye and watched.

The Indians tied Michael to the washing line post. They began to collect wood and grass, the makings of a fire formed at Michael's feet. While doing a war dance, the chief Indian took a box of matches from a pocket, he removed one from the box. Michael pleaded.

Tearfully, Stan looked around, he couldn't let his 'friend' be burnt. He saw the yard broom resting against the shed.

Stanley only had seconds. With lightning speed, he quickly ran, grabbed the broom then shouting, "Don't hurt my Michael," with all his might slammed the brush head into the chief Indian's cranium.

The release of real blood brought real screaming. The boy's head was slashed by a protruding nail in the broom head.

After running away, Michael's friends returned, they were angry, looking towards the neighbour's garden for revenge. All they could see was the top of a small boy's blond head protruded just above the fence. Hearing the commotion, Mrs Gardner shuffled from the house to comfort the victim, the lady ended up protecting the assailant.

"He's only a baby," was her defence. One of the cowboys ran to a phone box and phoned an ambulance.

The Indian chief attended hospital to have four sutures sewn into the top of his head.

05-09

Stanley hid behind the lean-to until he thought the cowboys had gone. He crept indoors to meet Irene coming out. Extremely upset, he was too shy and self-conscious to hurt anyone. Somehow, he had saved Michael's life!

JUNIORS

September 1959 Stanley moved up to Junior School. He was now in the Boys School on the left side of the same Gunter's Hall School building, separated from the Girls School on the right-hand side. All the classes and playgrounds were segregated.

He was happy with his friends, but struggled with the noise and hurly-burly at school dinners. Because he became so distressed Irene needed to collect him of a lunchtime, then return him after he had eaten. However, as soon as she allowed him to take sandwiches for lunch, eating away from the Dining Hall in the school playground he settled.

Stanley, had two favourite playground games played with cigarette and tea cards: 'Topsies' and 'Knockdowns'. Two boys would sit or kneel about six feet from a school wall, each with a handful of their own cards. The cards were held between the index and middle fingers and propelled at the wall by a flick of the wrist. Each player took turns.

When playing 'Topsies', if any part of a flicked card landed on top of any part of other cards, the player who flicked it, won all the cards underneath. With 'Knockdowns', each player arranged three cards with the top against the wall and the bottom angled away. The aim was to flick a card and knock down the angled cards. Whoever knocked down the last angled card won every card in the game.

At break times, there were so many card matches in progress, that often there was no school wall space available. Intrepid players would sneak outside the school perimeter, to play against the walls of neighbouring houses. Some kids arrived early, just to play before school started. Others met up after school and played.

Stanley slowly grew in confidence. During the smallpox epidemic of 1962, school children were given a day off to be immunised. Nine-year-old Stanley walked alone to the clinic in Bullock Lane, before waiting three hours in the queue for the inoculation. He was terrified.

The fearful look on his face prompted the nurse to dab smelly antiseptic on his nose to distract him, while she scratched the vaccine into his left arm.

The rosette scar on his arm, forever a sign of his bravery.

When he was nearly ten years old, Stan started to travel the return trip to school without Irene. He would meet John Law, his mate from Hookery Farm at the Beck traffic lights and run all the way. After school, they would run all the way home. Irene was grateful, because she only now had John and Eddie to look after.

John Law set up a team for a local Five-A-Side football league. The team was called 'The Five Jacks'. Matches were played after school in a park only ten minutes' walk.

Stan was asked to join. Enthusiastically, he told his friends he would play, then agonised about it for the next week. His lack of self-confidence caused him issues. He was very happy to be asked, but afraid that he wasn't capable. Would he let his friends down? Would he make a fool of himself?

Finally, he realised he had to play. There was no choice, it was too late to drop out.

On Saturday morning, he told his loving mum that he needed a blue football shirt for a match on Monday evening.

Irene had no idea. Where was she going to buy a football shirt? She had only until 5.30pm to get it. She reflected on his request, having little spare money and no time, she could have refused. However, perhaps playing football would be a tool to help him overcome his shyness. As a benevolent mum, she would help him. She would 'borrow' the money from the food budget to buy the shirt.

Irene asked him to get ready, to go shopping for the shirt, but he refused. He was anxious, he wouldn't put on his coat. He was too nervous to go with her. Eventually, accepting his description of the shirt she set off alone.

When Irene returned a few hours later, she carried a bag from a sports shop in Romford. A neighbour's son had advised her to shop at Ded Titchburn. The shop was owned by the ex-Spurs and England goalkeeper. Stanley was so pleased to have a new blue shirt, but it was to be short lived. Eagerly, he ran and pulled the jersey from the bag. His face dropped, to his dismay it was the wrong shirt.

In his anxiety, Stan had described a blue shirt with white sleeves. The description was accurate because that was the pattern John Law had told him. What he actually meant was a blue shirt with white trim to the sleeves. Thinking back later, Irene guessed that she went to the only shop in the area which stocked both patterns. The one type she had bought her son being unknown to the kids.

By now, the shop would be closed. Distraught, he wouldn't return to the shop with his mum to change it. He went to his room and cried. Why did this happen? Why was he too shy to buy a football shirt? He didn't have the inner strength to go into the sports shop. He worried the salesperson would laugh at him, 'You can't play football, you are too short and skinny'. Stan just wanted to be normal.

Because of his fear, Stanley would now wear a football shirt that was different to his teammates. This meant he would appear different, which was exactly what he didn't want.

It couldn't get any worse, but he started to understand. It was his inability to perform an action which actually made things worse. In some way, he had to take control, because it was the running away that caused the problems.

Stan forced himself to attend the first 'Five Jacks' match. From then on, even wearing a strange shirt he loved it, a boy's dream. The exhilaration of running around a field with no barriers. Kicking a ball, shouting loud, shouting so loud his ears hurt, getting muddy and wet. He started to follow Wolverhampton Wanders, the previous League and FA Cup Double winners. He watched for their results on the BBC TV football roundup. Each time he played, he would be Billy Wright or Ron Flowers wearing 'old gold shirts with black shorts', running down the wing, dribbling with the ball.

05-11

PLAYMATES

Weekends and school holidays, the kids in Hawthorn Road would have breakfast then go outside around 9.00am. They would meet up and play on the coach, in the street, or over the field. Sometimes, they would go home because they were hungry. Mostly, they would go home because it was dark when they could no longer see each other.

Their parents were forever buying them watches, but these would either be left at home, stop at 2.00pm or mysteriously run slow and lose an hour or two.

Sometimes, Stan and his brothers would just sit on the front door-step watching the world of Hawthorn Road unfold. They could be invited to join a game of 'hide and seek', or just sit quietly, watching white clouds move across a blue sky. Their imagination made shapes of objects formed by the clouds. Pointing, "There's a camel, a car next, then a butterfly."

The cold nor rain could deter them. They would either just get wet, jump on the coach or find a communal rubbish bin store at the flats to sit in.

The man who lived at number 133 Hawthorn Road worked as a coach driver for the council. He would ferry kids to and from school, vulnerable people to hospital and 'problem' children to schools like Bentree for 'special education'.

The man and his wife Vera had three sons. Unfortunately, each suffered from the same debilitating illness which caused mobility problems and a short life expectancy.

A gradual reduction in their mobility meant they had problems walking. The boys were born about three years apart. The progression of the disability was illustrated when the three were together. It was sad to see the deterioration in their health. The eldest the most effected, the youngest the least. Each had a personal spirit and love of live which had to be admired. Accepting their limitations, without sorrow or anger they lived their lives as heathy children would.

Each of the three boys were boisterous and loud. Stan went to school with the middle child, Cliff. John with the youngest, David. The Paterson boys played with all three of Vera's sons.

Outside work hours, the forty-four-seater dark green coach with a red stripe was parked outside number 133. It was a playground in the street for about fifteen or more kids with a bonus. If it rained, they didn't get called in by their parents.

When Stanley was nine, the oldest boy Brian was in a wheelchair. His dad would carry him onto the coach and sit him with the other kids. Brian had a tremendous sense of fun, a wicked tongue, a raucous laugh. At that time, the two younger brothers could just manage to climb up the deep steps without aid. Every inch of those boys fought to be part of the crowd.

The coach was a focal point in the kids' lives. They climbed on top of it, hid in the luggage compartments, journeyed on make believe holidays. Some sailed with Jason and his Argonauts. They would be paratroopers in the war, jumping out of the coach door swinging on the wing mirrors then falling to earth. Prone on the pavement shooting at the enemy.

Everyone was very upset when Brian's mobility deteriorated so badly that he could no longer come out of the house to play with them. At first, he would sit in a wheelchair at the open front window watching the groups' antics from his lounge. Always laughing, shouting to his mates Brian was still part of the group. One day he wasn't there shouting at them, they couldn't hear his laughter. He was never at the window again.

Stanley became troubled, over the next week Stanley became very upset. He wanted to know why Brian didn't look out of the window anymore.

Irene sat her emotional son on her knee, she told him that Brian had gone to heaven. Brian was happier there, but as he now had new friends he wouldn't be coming back to play on the coach. Stanley found relief now he knew that Brian was in his new home still happy and laughing.

When playing outside, the kids chose the top end the road, near Stan's house to play street games. There were fewer parked cars and more space in the road. They would play football, skipping, 'High Jimmy Knacker', 'British Bulldog', 'Can(non)', and others.

Two rules applied to all games. Rule 1, if a car appeared the first person to see it shouted 'CAR'. Everyone grabbed the nearest ball, jumper goalpost, can, sticks etc, and ran onto the pavement.

Rule 2, if someone's mum appeared at their door the first person to see her shouted 'MUM', then everybody hid behind a parked car or in a front garden.

As well as Stanley's 'street mates' he also had his mates from school.

One evening, Stan was on his way home after playing with his mates John Law, Roy and Tone in Brushwood Road. At the corner of Glen Avenue, an older, bigger boy blocked his way demanding Stan's jumper. Stan knew him: it was Tony Springer, a 'Bentree Bomber'. Stan stood his ground; Tony knocked him to the floor. Stan lay on his back with his shoulders on the edge of the kerb, head in the road. Tony jumped on him. They traded punches. Persistently, Stan flayed his fists into Tony's chest and managed to thud his knees into Tony's back.

The bigger boy rose to his feet, grabbing Stan's wrist he pulled Stan upright.

He smiled, "I thought I would do you easy, but you're tough for a skinny little one. Shake?"

Stan was shaking alright, from his head to his toes.

'Keep him calm', Stan thought, offering his hand. The pair shook hands. Stanley tried not to cry until he got home. He managed to walk away, but not too quickly.

After that incident, Stanley had an unwanted friend, but a useful bodyguard. Tony would 'knock for' Stan to play, plus he always made a point of greeting him if they met in the street.

05-12

FUN

Holidays were fun for the Paterson family. Even with limited finances Pete and Irene would try and get away for at least one week. The location wasn't important, it was the opportunity to be somewhere else. If they couldn't afford holiday accommodation, the time would be spent on day trips to the seaside, zoo or museum.

Minutes after arriving home from work on the Friday evening, Pete had the car boot and bonnet up. He removed tools and cans of fluid from the first and worked under the second. To service the old pale blue Standard Vanguard he checked the brakes, tyres and clutch. John and Stan were employed to help pump the brake and clutch pedals as Pete topped up the reservoirs.

Once those tasks were completed the three eager, bouncing-up-and-down boys offered to help with other jobs.

Pete found them a bucket of warm water plus a large tin of wax car polish and three old rags. He left them to clean the vehicle then polish it while he went indoors for his evening meal.

An hour later when he returned the boys were still beavering away. He smiled to himself at the amount of effort they were applying. The enthusiasm of the holiday transferring to the cleaning of the car. With beaming faces, the three boys would be ready for bed soon.

Disastrously, they were still working on the same side and the bonnet. He walked around the vehicle to investigate. The nearside resembled a dalmatian dog. The tin of polish was half empty, the missing half had been daubed onto the car in large dollops. Pete tried in vain to even the colour, to spread the wax across the surface but it remained pale blue with darker blue spots.

The next morning they travelled to a holiday site near St. Osyth, Clacton in Essex. The location was a patchwork of coloured, wooden single storey chalets along small interconnecting roads. It resembled something that their neighbour Mr Lucas may have recognised from his past.

The beach and sea where at the bottom of a set of stairs at one end of the main thoroughfare. The clever design of the swimming pool allowed a large concrete bowl built in the sand to retain sea water as the tide withdrew.

Holidays for Irene were not very different from being at home. The day before the family left, she had bought the normal food which they took with them. She would cook most meals as normal. They may enjoy a treat of a fish and chip meal on one day, perhaps an ice cream once or twice during the week.

It was all about being together, without having to look at the clock. For Mum and Dad, it was the simple things. Like sitting in a deckchair in the sun, with gulls screaming, waves softly moving the gravel at the water's edge. Having time to read a newspaper from cover to cover.

There was only enough money to hire two deckchairs, but it didn't matter, the boys never sat down long enough to rest. For them, it was having races, being buried in the sand, building a sandcastle or splashing in the sea. Irene had knitted her offspring new woollen swimming trunks from remnants left over when she knitted jumpers in the winter. Not really suitable, the trunks itched the boy's lower regions, were heavy when wet and collected the sand, but it was sunny. It was a step up from when they were younger, when Irene would let them play on the beach or in the sea in their underpants or even less.

Pete fell asleep in his deckchair. The mischievous giggling boys buried his feet in a huge pile of sand, woefully the sun baked them for hours. Pete's painful burnt feet and swollen ankles awoke him. He couldn't get his shoes on, was hardly able to stand or walk. He couldn't catch the little *** to smack their 'Khyber Passes'.

Irene instructed the boys to bucket cold seawater to their dad so he could bathe his glowing feet. Eventually, he hobbled back to the chalet, but wasn't able to drive for a couple of days.

There was no television in the Chalet, so under a single yellow wall lamp they played traditional card games like Newmarket, Rummy and Trumps. Mum helped them construct a jigsaw puzzle that she had brought with them.

The radio reception was terrible. Pete would move the aerial with the attached large wooden radio cabinet about the chalet until they could hear an audible noise. Success, with the radio aerial hanging through the curtain wire of the front window he achieved the best reception. They listened to Radio Luxembourg, the only music radio station broadcasting after 9.00pm.

In 1963, holding the radio aerial above his head Pete stood in the open doorway of the chalet listening to the fluctuating signal of the Henry Cooper v Cassius Clay fight.

One of Pete's greatest interests was 'anything' with an engine. If possible, he always repaired and serviced his vehicles himself. John and Eddie followed suite as they grew older.

While Irene was out shopping, parts of engines or vehicles would lay around the back garden or on the kitchen floor. One time a whole motorbike was stripped down in the kitchen.

An old cupboard under the stairs contained hundreds of copies of Speedway Star, a magazine for Speedway Racing enthusiasts. Before Stan came along, Pete and Irene followed West Ham at Custom House. They spent time cheering on the Hammers at each home event. Sometimes they would travel to New Cross Rangers or Harringay Racers to watch a race.

A couple of times they took the boys to Custom House as a treat, the route followed the same direction as when they visited Pete's brother Elfie. From Dagenham east past the Bombardier Pub on the left to Beckton, then left towards the docks.

The road through the Royal Docks was narrow. Amazingly, on their left they could see the funnels of ships in the docks. Forming a continuous mosaic behind the tenements, massive brightly coloured smokestacks towered above the four-floor high red brick buildings.

The smokestacks were so large and close that company's badges painted on them were clearly visible to the vehicles travelling along the road.

"Daddy, what's a red and white one with a blue star?" asked Eddie.

"That's the Blue Star Line."

"My turn, Daddy, what's a blue sign with BH in a blue diamond?" requested John.

"That's the Blue Harp Line."

"My turn, Daddy, what's a red one with a white star?" queried Stan.

"That's the White Star Line."

The family arrived at the speedway stadium; it was busy. The married couple reminisced. They talked of the days when there were

twice as many supporters. The atmosphere had been electric, they
recalled the names of riders who had superstar status.

Pete left them for a minute to locate his nephew Chas. Elfie had
phoned Pete some weeks before to inform him that Chas was working
at the stadium. The lucky young man had landed the tractor drivers
job, he would be driving around the track between races to smooth out
the ruts made by the bike's wheels.

The ten-minute bell sounded: the first race was soon to start. They
found a great place to watch the drama, up against the safety wall on a
corner.

From this position, they could watch the bikes come towards them,
lay down on the bend then accelerate away. The buzz from the crowd
grew louder. The noise grew as the four riders revved their engines.
Three riders rolled the front wheels of their speedway bikes over the
starting tape.

The air filled with a sharp, burnt sickly smell as the crowd held its
breath.

Nearly there, the marshal left the track as the four competitors
turned their heads to the left, hands simultaneously twisting throttles
towards maximum. The tape sprang high into the evening summer
sky, they're off.

The family watched in awe, the roar of the engines, the boys on tip
toe gripped the wall as the four bikes raced straight at them. Then a few
feet away, the riders dropped their bikes nearly horizontal, just eight
inches above the shingle they swept pass them. A second later they
were back upright, bombing towards the next corner. It was exciting
stuff, the boys were mesmerised, from nowhere a broadside of shale
from the track blasted into the family. They covered their faces bent
forward, trying to protect their eyes.

"Just remembered why no one stands on a corner," declared Irene.

The five excited people stepped back away from the corner for the
remaining three laps.

"Daddy, look what I've got?" Eddie showed Pete two hands full of
shingle.

"Throw them back over the fence," suggested Pete, "Cousin Chas
may need them later."

They stayed for the whole meeting. An evening of such exhilaration
with a promise they would return soon.

05-13

CYCLE

On Christmas Day, Stanley received a most wonderful present from his mum and dad. It wasn't wrapped, it was leaning against the wall in the passage.

Stanley walked down the stairs and couldn't believe his eyes, a bike. A grown up's bike. He didn't walk into the front room but used the base of the frame to climb onto it.

Stretching, he managed to get his bottom onto the seat. He grinned, he smiled with happiness. He pretended to be a Speedway rider, vroom.

Delighted, Pete entered the passage from the front room.

"What have you got?" he asked Stan.

"Dad, thank you and Mum for this present, it is the best present in the whole world," Stan beamed, he really had wanted a bike.

"Can you reach the peddles?" queried Pete.

"Not yet, but I will when I get a bit older, I'm only ten," assured Stan.

Pete made a suggestion, "If it is too big, we will have to take it back. If you like, I can screw some wooden blocks onto the pedals so you can reach them?"

Stan agreed, he wanted to get out to show his friends.

A few days later, once the weather had calmed, the wooden blocks were in place, Stan was set free on his bike. The blocks were necessary because his feet couldn't touch the pedals when he sat on the seat. He was unable to sit on the saddle and place a foot on the floor. When stationary, he needed to sit with one buttock on the crossbar with one leg stretched to the ground.

Stanley managed to cycle around the local area with his friends, but he was forbidden to ride in the road.

One day he was out with Glyn and some friends, riding around the semi-circular green near Glyn's home in Forest Avenue. While turning a corner, Stan slipped off the saddle, lost control then crashed into a wooden fence. He laid on the ground with the bike on top of him, shaken but unharmed.

His friends agreed to tell him the truth. His 'super present' was too big for him, it was dangerous. Reluctantly, he had to agree.

Immensely disappointed Stanley returned home to pass the message to his parents.

The bike with 27" wheels was too big for him. Pete wasn't happy, but agreed the bike should be returned to the seller. He was angry because Stan had been given the option to return the bike on Christmas Day, but declined. If Stanley wanted to return it now, he would have to do it himself.

Pete gave Stan the address of the vendor and instructed him to return the bike. He warned that the bike was now dirty Stan was ordered to clean it to an immaculate appearance. With a bucket of soapy water and a rag, Stanley began. As always with Stan's life there was a hitch. When he had crashed into the fence, the bottom edge of the plastic rear mudguard had split. The crack was about three inches long, unfortunately at the tear the red mudguard looked pink.

Disbelieving his luck, Stanley came up with a plan. On the plus side, the fact the mudguard was plastic was good. He had lots of solvent glue that he used for his Aerofix models.

He held the mudguard in place with three elastic bands then applied the glue at the back of the tear. Once Pete had removed the wooden blocks Stan was set.

Not wanting to tempt another disaster he walked the bike to the seller's home, a ground floor flat in a block about two miles away. Not daring to bump the wheel or ride the bike, at each kerb he gently lifted the rear wheel and then lowered it.

Stan found the address, leaned the bike against a hedge and surveyed the area. He looked around, he was alone. Nervously, he opened the gate then wheeled the bike through. Once it was stable, inclined against the wall, he removed the elastic bands from the mudguard. To his delight and amazement, the tear wasn't visible, it hadn't opened either. His heart was beating so much he bet the people inside the flat could hear it.

He placed the problem revealing bands in his pocket, took a deep breath and gently knocked on the door. He didn't want to annoy the man with a loud 'rat-a-tat-tat'.

A few minutes later, a grumpy looking man opened the door. His long unkempt thinning hair blowing in the wind, an unlit rolled cigarette in mouth. He frowned at the tiny boy standing at his door. The man wearing a white vest with the braces from his trousers hanging down on each side, looked down at Stan with contempt.

"Excuse me mister," Stan started his well-practiced speech, "me mum and dad bought me this bike for Christmas, and it's too big."

The man's face contorted as he sucked on the cigarette, "Well, what do ya wont me to do about it?" he scowled.

Stan blushed, he lifted his chest, "I want to bring it back, please," he answered.

"Umm," the man examined Stan with his eyes, standing closer than customary. He then stepped outside in his bare socks. He bent and inspected the bike, "Have you used it much? Been a while since Christmas?"

"No," lied Stan, "it's too dangerous for me."

"It cost £8, I'll give ya £7 15s back, 5s for wear and tear," the man proposed.

Stan nodded, was it going to be this easy? He was past talking, holding back a sigh of relief.

The grumpy man went inside his flat, the door shut behind him.

Stan stood in silence. He fidgeted, glanced around, fingers crossed. It seemed a long time, should he knock on the door again? Better to wait, the bike was still outside which comforted him.

The door opened, the man appeared. This time he was smiling, Stanley was confused.

"Here we are," the man extended his hand and offered Stan some money. "Take care," he said, and shut the door. The bike was still against the wall?

Stan was really content. He checked the money: it was all there. He was super happy, well chuffed. He had made the effort and achieved a result. He ran all the way home.

05-14

CHOIR

One tradition in the Borough was the school choir competition. This year it was being held at County High School. The contest was only for the top form of each school.

Everyone in that class would be in the choir, even if they were tone deaf.

The singing practices were arranged with Miss Jones in charge. The boys laughed, 'it was because she was the only person in the school who could play a piano'. Practice would be held on the seven Thursday afternoons before the competition.

The first practice session arrived. Miss Jones sat in all black at the piano, her Beatnik cat eye, tortoise shell glasses balancing on the end of her nose. Long dark hair held scrunched on top of her head by a band. The 'top' pupils shuffled into the music room. The 'music room' being a normal classroom where the seats and desks had been removed and a piano added in front of the windows.

There was the usual arm pushing, squabbling in the doorway as the boys resisted the urge to run away. Finally as the teacher shouted, the pupils succumbed to the inevitable torture of singing aloud. En masse, they moved to form three rows at the furthest point from the piano.

"Right boys," Miss Jones, greeted them.

"Hope she has earplugs," whispered John Law. No one spoke in case the noise influenced Miss Jones to pick the speaker to sing first. These boys knew they were rubbish.

Music lessons in the school had been compulsory for seven- and eight-year-olds. Three years earlier, Mr Salmon the class's music teacher had given up on them.

He could no longer tolerate spending the lesson with a throbbing headache.

To escape their rasping, unmelodic squealing, accompanied by raucous recorder recitals he fabricated a plan. It was really his wife's

262

idea to help keep him sane. 'Allow them to bring in records and play them in class. If you take time to explain the musical nuances, they will still be learning about music'.

Mr Salmon adopted the idea. Later, he used it on other classes. He could even listen to his own records in school time. One week, Elvis and Bobby Darin, the next Russ Conway and Lonnie Donegan. He enjoyed teaching music once more.

Miss Jones was unaware of the class's musical history. She explained the competition rules along with her strategy to win the competition.

"We shall be singing two songs. I thought the first shall be 'Hearts of Oak'. A seafarer's classic, rumbustious, animated. We can punch our fists in the air, throw our heads back and really sing our hearts out," she tossed her head in the air as she spoke.

Glyn suppressed a giggle, screwing up his nose. The boys looked at each other, they didn't understand half of the words she had used.

The lady continued, she bent forward at the waist extending her arm, shaking a pinched thumb and finger to convey the songs attributes, "The second song, I thought, a little bit more melodic, show our range. This time lots of joyous smiles and happiness."

Glyn, had to fight the giggle.

"Have you all seen Pinocchio?" Half of them nodded, the other half weren't listening, "We are going to sing, 'When you wish upon a star'. Shall we start?" she asked, her smile beaming.

The teacher looked at a sea of glum faces, this wasn't going to easy. Roy was asked to pass around the song sheets. The words for each song were on a different side. Miss Jones played the tune for 'Hearts of Oak', then counted the boys 'in'. It was abysmal. Some were even on the wrong side of the sheet, singing 'Wish upon a star'.

"Okay, not to worry," she relaxed, "we will try the second song, turn your sheets over." She played the second tune, then counted them 'in' again. It was as bad; some had turned the sheet over and were now singing 'Hearts of Oak'.

She excused herself and left. The boys watched her leave the room, then with blank faces at each other. Nobody spoke.

She fell against the corridor wall for support. This was horrendous. It was a lose-lose, situation, she knew she would fail. She would fail the school. She would fail the pupils.

Miss Jones made a judgement. She would sift out anyone who was awful, they would sing. Everyone who was really awful would be removed, they would mime. She returned to the class to reap the corn.

To the boys more embarrassing than singing was what came next. Each boy was called to stand adjacent to the piano facing the class. They would repeat the primary scales after Miss Jones had sung them,

John was first.

Miss Jones sang, "Ah, Eh, Ee, Oh, Oo."

John sang, "Aaah, errh, eaa, hoo, oooa."

He was sent to form a group to the left. The boys smiled, Glyn gave him a thumbs up, John sounded good to them, they thought he was in the musical group.

Later, after Stanley's audition, as he was sent to join John the boys realised John was in the discharge group. As Miss Jones nicknamed them, they were the 'growlers'.

At the end of the first practice, Miss Jones found that twenty of the twenty-eight boys in the class would form the choir. It was far better than she had initially thought.

The singing lessons carried on for weeks. At least, the songsters now recognised the difference between the words of the two songs, although perhaps not the tunes. Miss Jones made another tactical decision: she chose to concentrate on one song, discarding the other.

The Friday of the competition, the school coach took Miss Jones with the twenty-eight boys to the venue. They entered the huge hall, taking instructions from the usher on where to sit. The boys watched in horror as rows of the audience in front of them were called to mount the stage and perform to everyone in the hall. There were hundreds of people?

The fear of singing in front of so many people frazzled their nerves, however even they could tell that they were on a par with some of the other choirs. 'Dagenham must be a breeding ground for growlers'.

At last, they were called to the stage where they took up the choir formation. Growlers at the back and sides, three vocalists middle front, the rest filled in the gaps.

The music started, 'Hearts of Oak', they sang. Glyn got the giggles, he found it so amusing, moving his mouth up and down with no words coming out. He started to mouth random words, 'Hooorrsses' and 'saandwichees'. Then he became more adventurous and whispered them. The growlers could hear him, they bit their lips.

The choir sang on, they finished verse one. Verse two, they sang verse one again. A few realised and stuttered, then everyone sang verse one again. Miss Jones went with the flow. None of the boys on stage knew why she was holding a stick and waving her hands about.

The competition finished. All the choirs were back in their seats waiting for the results to be broadcast. Gunter's Hall Boys was placed equal last with eight other schools.

05-15
ASSEMBLY

Months away from starting at Senior School, Stanley was in the top form at Junior School.

A school institution, was the 'religious reading' at the Friday morning assembly. Mr Hatton the class form teacher, known as 'Sunny' by the pupils, invited Jim, William and Stanley to his desk. It was traditional for the Upper Forms to take Friday Prayer. These were the chosen ones for tomorrow.

The teacher held out a dark green baize bag, "In this bag are three folded pieces of paper. One has the 'prayer', one the 'hymns' and the last the 'reading'. Please take a piece of paper each to see what you shall be doing at tomorrow's Assembly. No peeking."

Stanley was offered first pick. He moved his hand towards the bag and couldn't believe his luck. A piece of paper had unfolded, it had only a few letters on it was it divine providence? Pleased as punch, he took it. His ideal. He didn't fancy standing on the stage in front of the whole school talking or reading loads. The least the better, he was very happy.

After each boy had taken a piece of paper, they checked their assignments. Stan read his aloud, 'Luke 2:41-51'. He looked at his form master quizzically.

"That's the 'reading' Stanley. You need to open the Holy Book at Luke and read Chapter 2, from 2:41 to 51." It was a lot more to read than Stan had hoped. Not the best, actually the worse option from the green bag. His cunning had tripped him up.

The next day at 9.10am Jim, William and Stan were nervously sitting on a long bench in the school corridor. They were dressed smartly, as the event demanded. Each wearing their dad's tie tucked into their underwear, beneath their mum's knitted jumper.

William felt especially proud, his mum had allowed him to wear his 'special occasion' long trousers for the whole day. The others wore short trousers as normal. This morning, Irene had even used extra 'elbow grease' to polish Stan's best black shoes.

Pupils from the Boy's Junior School filed passed the three speakers, the rest of the school walked along the corridor into the Main Hall. The Reading Team listened to the chatter from the pupils, the commands and controls shouted by various teachers. The pupils entered through two sets of double doors positioned at either end of the hall, forming rows from the front towards the back. The youngest at the front, the oldest at the back.

Mr Hatton walked along behind the last group of pupils. He understood this was a terrifying experience for the trio.

He sat with them, "Some advice for you lads," he volunteered. "Do not look at the crowd, talk to the back wall. If you see a friend, talk to him. Keep your eyes on what you are reading. If you look away, you will lose your place. Good luck."

On the signal, the red-faced trio stoically took the stairs to the stage. The smiling Headmaster watched them take a seat behind him. Stanley looked around the hall for a friendly face. The smile and smirk of Glyn draw him. Stanley was going to read his passage to Glyn, seconds later he decided perhaps the back wall was the best gallery.

The boys performed remarkably well. A few stammers, dry voices, and coughs, but Mr Hatton was very pleased with everyone. Well, at least it was a 'damn sight' better than the production at the choir competition.

05-16

SAVED

A few days before Christmas Stanley was cycling around the woods with school mates Glyn, Roy plus a few others. He loved the present of a bike he received from Mum and Dad on his last birthday. It had drop handlebars with five gears.

Roy spotted a rope swing tied to an overhanging branch above the river. They raced to the river bank and dismounted, it started to snow. At this location, the river was only about a foot deep but twelve feet wide. The bank was ten feet higher than the water level. The boys took turns to snake sideways down the bank, one foot leading while supporting their weight the other dragging behind. Grasping the rope, they would return to the bank's summit.

Because of the rope's extra length and to prevent their legs dipping into the river they needed to hold as high as possible. An additional danger for each plunge involved the sabotaging hands and kicks from friends.

The time came for Stan's launch. The barracking started as he grabbed the rope then gradually ascended the bank. Once at the top he quickly turned and dived into space. An outstretched foot from a baying friend collided with Stan's leg, he began to spin as he lost altitude.

"Let go," commanded his mates, "you are not going fas..." Their warnings changed to laughter. Stanley descended, he hit the bottom edge of the bank with his feet, bounced and was pulled horizontally through the river. Dripping wet from neck to toe he joined in the laughter.

Stanley knew he would get murdered if he went home drenched.

A few weeks earlier, the boys had been playing on a frozen lake. It was a game of dare, who could run the furthest on the ice away from the bank. When Stan ran, the ice opened and he fell through into the water. As his legs slid under the ice he fell backwards, his arms sprung behind him into the air. Amazingly, one hand grabbed an overhanging tree branch which prevented his head from submerging under the ice.

His friends had quickly seized his free arm to pull him to safety. If his whole body had gone under, it would have been curtains. At that time, he knew he couldn't return home and confess to his parents that he had nearly died. They would have killed him. Instead, he fabricated a tale about a water fight with his friends. Stanley's dad warned him to never return home in such a condition again.

This time, his only choice was to dry off. The snow had stopped but the wind was building up. He borrowed Jon's coat and sat at the top of the bank. Stan dearly wanted to have another swing, always in his mind he wanted to achieve a perfect swing, one when he stayed dry.

The freezing, waterlogged boy sat for three hours being entertained as his mates swung through the air.

They tried two at a time, also three at a time. There were always cackling bodies spilling down the slope just stopping before the water. Stanley refused his friends coaxing to have one more attempt. It was getting dark, the time approaching 3.00pm. The snow fell again. Everyone was cold, they decided to return home.

In spite of Stan's stubborn resistance, he really craved another go. He made a decision. He had to have one more swing, this time he definitely was not going to get wet. As the others collected their bikes, Stan took hold of the rope. He looked around, at least he was safe from mates tugging at him. He jumped.

The first his friends knew of his action was the sound of boy hitting water. Again, he was soaked, this time his freezing cold hands failed to hold the rope. They laughed again; the second time was funnier.

"All we heard was an 'aaaaahh!', then a 'splash' and a 'thud', snorted Roy, as he offered his arm for Stan to climb the steep bank. There was no time to dry off, Stan would have to go home dripping."

The gang cycled in single file along the original 'desire line' which now formed a bumpy footpath towards home. Ducking under outstretched branches and avoiding rabbit holes they climbed a ridge. Roy who was leading, stopped and pointed. In the murky distance, he could make out the dark shapes of two people against the white ground.

There was the muffled noise of hammering, skating across a lake.

"Is that Gary?" Joe, questioned himself. "From the shape yeah, think he's with Brad." A voice agreed.

05-16

"Let's go and see them," Joe suggested, off they cycled.

Following the leader the boys stopped on a rise to the right of Tom Toe Wood, above a small 'S' shaped lake. Below them Gary and Brad were hammering some old doors and wooden struts.

"Oi, oi," Joe called out. The two figures straightened up and waved. The boys continued cycling to them.

"Wat you doing?" shouted Roy.

The taller one, Brad answered, "Building a raft. Where have you lot been?"

Roy explained, "We found a rope swing by the old sewer pipe, near Vickers Corner. Good fun, we have been there for hours." He then recounted the story of Stan's stunt dives. Everyone had a good laugh.

"We saw that," noted Gary, "but didn't think the tree would take my weight."

"Oi, Brad," called Glyn, "you can't swim, like me, what happens if it sinks?"

"No chance, finest British Ship building tradition, nails and wood," declared Brad, "sail to America on this."

"When's the maiden voyage?" enquired Roy, "will we get tickets?"

Gary told them to hang around, "We sail in two bells."

Gary and Brad each took hold of a long stick, they clambered onto the raft. "Here we go," they shouted.

The mariners pushed from the craft with the sticks, in a rotating motion it spun away from the soil and floated away. Cheers all round. The watching boys dropped their bikes and ran whooping to the water's edge. The spinning movement of the raft made it hard to steer, the mariners found it hard to balance. The vessel started to wobble, one side below the water, the opposite side seemed to be moving skyward.

"You've been torpedoed," cried Glyn, with his normal chuckle.

Up to their ankles in water, the two jack tars stood firm. The boys ran away from the water's edge to avoid a killer wave.

"Finest British Ship sinking," hollered Glyn.

The merry mariners were sinking. In this scenario, the pair understood the need to step off the raft together. 'One, two, three, jump'. This momentum pushed the raft into deeper water as it sank. The boys ended up standing in water up to their waists, Gary stumbled on a hidden object and grabbed Brad's shoulder to steady himself. They waded ashore.

Time to go home, it was now dark. They said their goodbyes mounted their bikes and cycled off.

Stan reached Hawthorn Road, ready to endure a 'telling off'. There was a motorcycle combination outside his house. Could it be? The front window curtains were drawn allowing him to sneak down the front path, discreetly open the back gate and wheel his bike into the back garden. He had made no sound, no one had seen him.

To the sound of laughter, the dripping wet boy opened the back door. Thankfully the laughter hid his movements. The gaiety from the front room was definitely Uncle Joey and Auntie Liz telling a story. The 'combination' parked out the front belonged to them. Quietly, Stan moved into the kitchen, stepping out of his wet shoes and socks, he hid them under the sink.

He waited at the closed kitchen door for the right moment. Joey continued his story, Stan rushed from the kitchen said 'ello', then left the room by the other door. He flew upstairs. Undetected, he was able to change into dry clothes and have a quick wash.

Ten minutes later he returned, Joey was still describing the holiday in Spain with Nanny and Grandad. Dead fish floating in a pond, ghosts in their rooms and cobwebs.

This coming Christmas, Joey and Liz would be at Liz's brother's home. As they would not be able to hand presents to the boys on the day, they had brought them round.

Mischievously, Joey started to question and windup Stan about his earlier whereabouts. Also, why he was late coming home. Stan took a gamble that with family visiting he was safe from a slap. He told of the whole wet saga, which proved entertaining rather than criminalising.

06
JUVENILE

Chapter Marker

06-01
AFRAID

At the Gunter's Hall Junior School Parents Evening, Stanley's Form teacher had guaranteed Stanley would pass the 11+ Exams. He told Irene and Pete, that Stanley was a top six pupil in every test. Without doubt, Stanley had the intellect to be educated at grammar school.

It was therefore a surprise when he failed the exam. Perhaps, the reason was a lack of self-confidence, nerves, or fear.

For Stanley's parents, this wasn't all bad. It had taken their son three years to tolerate school. They worried that some of the anxiety may return if he had to make new friends at a grammar school. It could affect not only his studies, but also him emotionally.

When Stan attended secondary modern school, he would remain with most of his current friends. Moneywise, they wouldn't have to pay for school uniforms, compulsory sports or educational items.

Stanley would study at the Beck Secondary School. To him, this was also scary, perhaps more scary than being at grammar school without his mates.

There were terrifying stories about the school. The worse was 'The Wall'. Rumours, told how all new kids were ambushed by the fourth-year bullies and beaten up then thrown over the wall. There was a second horrifying anecdote. Anyone who got captured by the bullies a second time would be dragged into the toilet block and their head held down the pan while the flush was pulled.

Stan wasn't looking forward to big boys' school. He knew it was true also, that 'first years' were randomly beaten up by fourth years every day, just for fun! He was petrified.

He managed to move these daunting tales to the back of his mind. For most of the six-week school holiday, he played outside, on the coach or with his 'street mates'.

The week before school resumed, Stan met Glyn in the local sweet shop. They chatted, and together went to Glyn's home in Forest

Avenue. The pair talked of the chilling initiations at the school. Glyn was so scared he had planned to meet at Jon's house at 8.45am on the first day and walk into school with him. Stan agreed to join them.

Monday, 9 September 1963, the first day at a new school. The walk from Stan's front door to the school gates was not much more than one hundred yards. Dad had left for work at the Post Office, Mum had left with the eight-year-old twins for school. Stan was alone.

The clock ticked, Stan picked up his coat, it was 8.30am. He looked out of the front window to see a stream of school kids walking past.

8.35am, he paced around the room. Stan looked out again, more students walked past. Confusingly, he observed, 'that they didn't look worried or unhappy'.

8.40am, time to leave. He used the convenience, put on his coat and went to the front door. How, he wished his mum was there. He walked back into the front room then looked out of the window again. Still streams of kids passing, there seemed more and more. Surprisingly, everyone at school lived near him?

8.45am, he should be outside Jon's house in Beck Avenue. 'Aah! Come on, strength'! He cried. He wondered if Glyn had left yet. It would be better to go with someone rather than alone.

8.48am, 'Go, go, now or never'. He opened the front door, closed it, visited the toilet again. Opened the front door and ran. Dodging between the hordes of children he ran across Dacca Road to Jon's house and knocked.

Out of breath he stood shaking. Jon's mum opened the door, "I'm sorry dear, he left five minutes ago, with Glyn. See if you can catch them up?"

Stan ran. He dodged around everyone, zig zagging groups of students. He kept an eye open for an ambush, giving groups of boys a wide berth. At the school gates, he turned left along the internal service road. This was the most likely place to get beaten up. He kept an arm's length from everyone.

There were young, bigger people all around him. They were so engrossed talking to each other, they didn't see him. No one else seemed scared, it was strangely peaceful.

A man standing on concrete steps to Stanley's right, waved. He was wearing a suit and tie with a clipboard in his other hand. He called Stan over, "First day?" he asked.

Stan nodded. The man opened the door behind him, "Follow the

06-01

corridor to the 'quad'. Go through the door at the end." Stan did as instructed. At the end of the corridor, was another door, he could hear children's voices. The frightened little person opened the door, ahead was a large enclosed playground. There were school buildings around the whole perimeter. Happily, young children raced around or stood in groups chatting.

His first day at Senior school.

06-02

SENIOR

The school building was shaped as a figure eight. The girls' half was adjacent to the main road at the front, the boys at the rear bordered the fields. Each had an enclosed quadrangle which were used as the first-year playgrounds.

The main playground at the rear, was separated from the boys' sports field and facilities by 'The Wall'.

Learning 'The Wall' actually did exist made Stan and his friends quake. They would stare at it during sports lessons as if it were animate. The object of dread was not tall as expected, the height on the playground side was only two feet, however on the sports field side it was six feet.

After a few weeks of assessment tests, the pupils were allocated to their Forms and timetables. They were also informed of school punishments. Standing outside the class was a warning. Being sent to Mr Davies for the cane was a minor discipline, sent to Mr Kerrigan for the 'book and cane' a major punishment.

The second in command, who was actually very much 'in command' was Mr 'Dickie' Davies. The scariest thing the first-year boys had ever seen. If he were a movie, it would be an 'X' rated horror film. More feared than 'The Wall', Dickie Davis was the Headmaster's henchman. Rumoured to be 'well over a hundred years old' he was tall and scrawny. Built like a skeleton, his skin was not pink but like a blotchy grey colour. He had long gnarled fingers with nails like claws and a bald pate with three long wandering wispy hairs.

When Dickie spoke, he would lean forward with his arms behind his back. His tortoise shaped head and face, stretched forward away from his shoulders and rolled from side to side. White moisture would appear in the corners of his lips as his eyes rolled out of sight, up behind his forehead. Discipline was his master.

He enjoyed giving the boys a 'good' trashing. Word spread through families from siblings, 'Don't get the stick from Dickie'. The old master owned the voice that caused terror in many a boy's heart. One phrase he shouted in his gravel voice was, "Cooome heeere, boooy."

But worse were the words, that promised pain. "Gooo tooo my rooom, boooy," and "putt urr haand oout, boooy," as he flexed the cane in his hands.

If you were sent to Dickie Davies or Mr Kerrigan as a discipline matter, there were two ways to fake the distinct marks left on the hands after receiving the stick. Either hold your hand under scolding hot water in the cloakroom or place the underside of your fingers onto a very hot radiator for fifteen minutes.

Only once was Stan sent to Kerrigan for the cane. He was lucky that Dickie was away from school on that day. Stan tossed up the idea of the scolding water, but felt that the cane would probably be less painful.

Some teachers didn't have any peculiar ways, some did.

Stanley and the other members of the 1963 intake gradually became more confident around the teachers, becoming more aware of those with idiosyncrasies.

To see how far they could misbehave, or confide in each master, a few confident boys played tiny mind games. They challenged the master's tolerance of impudence, they also tested which ones had a rapport with the class. They learned which ones to avoid, respect, interact or have fun with. Basically, to learn each teachers limits, where to draw the line before becoming disrespectful.

One Maths teacher was Mr Desai, a big solid man from India. He would shout at the pupils, "I do not understand you English, you are so dirty. In my Country, I shower three times a day." In Dagenham, most showered once a week.

He used his amazing throwing arm to attain a pupil's awareness. If someone wasn't paying attention or talking while he was teaching, he would dispatch the board rubber at him. The target would only be conscious of the missile as it whistled past his face, smashing into the back wall.

There was no verbal warning. No matter in which row of seats the target sat, the board rubber would always fly the full length of the classroom and hit the back wall. Mr Desai ignored collateral damage. He was so accurate he could miss a pupil's head by inches, and usually did.

Mr Head taught German. He had greased down dark hair and a

small moustache. His favourite punishment was to tell the culprit to hold his hand out, palm down. Then with great personal pleasure, Mr Head would slam the edge of a twelve-inch rule across the boy's knuckles. He was dismissed on the grounds of violent conduct.

Mr Thomas, Sport and R.E., would use a size thirteen plimsoll on a pupil's buttocks. He also enjoyed 'short arm' and 'dead leg' assaults on the boys. He particularly enjoyed refereeing a 'games lesson' match of football or rugby and obstructing or holding a skilled player to give a lesser player an advantage. Annual Staff v Pupil games were a treat and watched by the whole school. Before the match, pupils would share their plan to seek physical revenge on a specific teacher. But invariably, if they were tackled by Thomas, they would end up the injured party to be substituted.

Mr Williams, another Welsh man taught English. He was a lovely gentle older man, easily distracted. A question similar to, 'Were you in the war, sir', could lead to a very relaxing talk on his experiences for the whole lesson. A proper lesson could be a lecture on the structure of English Grammar. Such as, the difference between 'please use the hand wash provided regularly' and 'please regularly use the hand wash provided'.

Sometimes, if the tutorial was important, he would answer with, 'If we get this work finished first, we can have a chat in the final ten minutes of the lesson'.

Mr Shaw, was the History teacher. Stanley was taught 'British Political and Economic History' in his final year. Each week the class would study one topic. Then, after Friday lunch they would have twenty minutes to sit a previous GCE 'O' Level question on a particular aspect. One day, while returning a book to Mr Shaw's desk, a pupil discovered that the exact test question was written in Mr Shaw's diary. From then on, each Friday after lunch the students would keep watch outside Mr Shaw's office while one went inside to copy the question.

Mr Roberts, with a shock of red hair taught Metalwork. He would make punishment a game by chasing the offender around the workshop with a yard broom. Often, he would climb onto and jump between the work benches to catch the offender.

Dickie Davis, R.E. and T.D. would use the cane. His pronunciation of 'King Nebuchadnezzar' from a wobbling, eyes rolling head was hilarious. When pupils formed lines to enter the school after break, he

06-02

would shout from a rolling head, "Boooy, aar urr tongues tied to urr booot laces?" In lessons he was fair, but authoritarian.

Art was taught by a laid-back Mr Wilson. He wasn't much older than the pupils. The sort of person who enjoyed life. Art was about communication, not regulation and control. He realised most people didn't understand art, even fewer had the ability to express themselves using it. He smoked in class. Always open to join a conversation on someone's artistic ideas which regularly developed into 'freedom' or Hippy culture. He taught 'Art Theory', but only to those taking national examinations. As long as the other pupils didn't disrupt his lesson, they had free time.

Mr Butler taught Woodwork. He was so old that he worked on Noah's Ark. He told the boys two principles. Firstly, 'you can always cut a bit more off, but you can't add any back'. Next, 'you measure with a rule, because a Ruler uses rules to govern a country'. He would get angry if someone called a measuring stick, a 'ruler'.

Polish Mr Lubanski taught Pottery. His catch phrase was, "Wats goink ong?" A favoured pastime for students in his classroom was to roll clay into small balls then throw them at the ceiling. The balls would stick, but when they dried a few days later would drop onto the oblivious pupils working below.

The French Language teacher was Monsieur Lemaire, he was very enthusiastic. He brought France to the classroom. Part of his teaching process was to create projects alongside the traditional methods. One activity was to follow the Tour de France.

During each lesson, the pupils would spend time discussing the previous day's event in French, 'Discuter de son itinéraire, de ses villes et de ses incidents'.

Monsieur, would be very animated when leading the class in pronunciation. He would stand at the front of the class in his crisp white shirt, dark blue suit and tie. Bent at the knees, arms extended, bobbing up and down he would shout, 'mare see, mare see, mare see'.

When it was the pupils turn, they would reply 'mercy, mercy, mercy'. "Nooo," he'd cry, in anguish, "it's not mercy! Maaare Seeee." But that's one of the pitfalls of teaching French to people from Dagenham.

SWIM

Class 1-1 stood with Mr Phillips outside the school gates in Dacca Road. They waited for the coach to take them to their first swimming lesson. A slight snow flurry drizzled from the freezing winter sky as a white dust, not melting but blowing in clusters along the road. The boys huddled together, to shelter against the brick wall which formed the boundary of the girls' school playground.

A large coach drew up, the boys raced, grappling with each other to climb aboard. After a short fifteen-minute drive, they disembarked at Hookery Swimming Pool. There was a high perimeter wall on three sides backing onto fields and wasteland. It was a short walk from the infants' school Stanley had previously attended as an overflow school seven years before.

They were ushered through the large wooden gates into a massive open space. In front of them at the far end behind a large learners pool was an Olympic size swimming pool. Other amenities were dotted around. There was a children's playground with toddlers' pool, raised grassed lawns, a canteen and sunbathing areas.

Mr Phillips pointed them towards the male changing area. There was no door, just a framed opening in the wall behind a screen. The entrance turned at ninety degrees to provide additional privacy. Inside, positioned on a concrete floor was a series of double back-to-back benches with a high-level rail and coat hooks at intervals. The roof was made from stained dirty corrugated iron or asbestos. Mr Phillips stood outside listening to the groans and shrieks as the freezing cold air abused the boys' bodies.

The boys got undressed and changed into their swimwear. The floor was so cold while queueing outside for the external cold-water shower, they hopped on one foot and then the other. The air temperature inside and outside was the same, about four degrees.

Following the shower, arms crossed on their chest, shivering, they walked together in a huddle towards the small pool. Ice cold water from the shower ran down their legs, water dripping from their hair dropped onto the chilled pathing slabs.

Waiting for them was a lady instructor, warmly wrapped in a track-suit, gloves and a large woollen bobble hat.

The boys could tell from her fake 'cheerful' greeting that she would have rather been somewhere else. She talked them through her lesson finally inviting them to enter the pool. Unbelievably she objected to them jumping in. Apparently, it was against the Bye Laws?

To the group's dismay, each boy had to gingerly descend into the pool by using the ladder. By now, their skin was purple Mr Phillips could hear their teeth chatter.

The instructor worked them through a programme of exercises, each designed to give them confidence in the water. One was to wear an inflatable ring around their waist, lean forward and practice breast-stroke arm movements as they walked in a circle.

Alarmingly, Stan slipped. The ring moved to his ankles pushing his head under the water. Splashing around in panic, he struggled and fought but there was no method he could use to get his head above water. Finally, two classmates grabbed his arms and pulled him through the ring.

He thought he was going to die.

The lady instructor laughed and shouted, "Could you do that again for us please? I missed it the first time."

After the lesson, the boys returned to the changing area where they were forced to endure another cold shower to wash off the chlorine. Next, they followed Mr Phillips to the canteen. Sitting shaking from the cold the novice swimmers drank mugs of hot Dovril and ate Orrowroot biscuits to revive themselves.

Previously, Stanley's claim to fame had been the bright red welt mark on his bottom after getting the slipper from Thomas. It had made Stan a minor celebrity with his classmates.

Now that he had nearly died, his profile increased. The boys fooled around on the coach back. They laughed about his near murder. That would be lady murderer, sent there by a secret spy organisation. She must be an assassin because the water was okay to swim in, but too cold for a life saver to jump into. Was Mr Phillips there just to watch and witness someone drown?

Over time, Stanley and a lot of his mates became proficient

swimmers. Years later, on a Saturday and Sunday they would cycle to Barrow Lodge indoor pool, spending up to six hours each day in the water.

06-04
BANGER

The first week in November four of the gang met at 'Dog Shit Island', a small grassed roundabout between Glyn's turning and Central Grove Avenue. Roy was excited, he had been given two bangers by his older brother Billy. The boys were apprehensive, so they agreed to set one off outside Glyn's house. In the dark, they crept to the target, giggling in anticipation.

The group stood at the front garden fence, Roy had the matches, he would light the firework. They discussed if he would have enough time to escape? Glyn suggested they use a fuse. He nipped into his back garden to search through the old car parts, jars, tins and boxes in the shed. Then, using old pieces of rag dowsed in petrol from a can he fashioned a fuse.

Roy joined him at the doorstep. The pair placed the firework on the edge of the step with the fuse perpendicular on the ground below. Roy lit the fuse, they ran. Their friends ran along the pavement.

There was no explosion? Four heads turned back in unison to see six feet high orange flames roaring into the night sky. The flames were inches from the front door, illuminating Glyn's brother's car a few feet away. Glyn ran back to the fire, the other three ran the other way. In the excitement, Glyn had ignored the two-tone white and pale blue Triumph Vitesse parked on the drive. Quickly, he stamped on the cloth fuse to extinguish it.

He retrieved the banger then ran to join his mates who were hiding behind a lamp post twenty yards away. The eleven-year-old mates agreed to go to Roy's turning to light the bangers.

Brushwood Road was a small housing estate ten minutes' walk from Stan's home, about the same distance to Glyn's home.

The road within the estate formed a 'U' shape. Generally, along the inner edge of the road were houses, the back gardens bordered each other. Against the outer edge of the road were blocks of three storey flats. One side backed onto Central Park with a single gate in the boundary railings for pedestrian access.

The Council should have named it, 'Hide and Seek' road.

Behind each block of flats were large tarmac areas for peoples washing lines. There were bin stores everywhere. Some single storey buildings with ornamental concrete screens had flat roofs.

Five of Stan's school mates lived on the Estate. Stan, Glyn and Jon would regularly join them to play. One game they often played was a type of Tag. A person who was 'IT' had to touch other players to make them 'IT' and join him. This was a chasing game, but players would hide anywhere, in dustbins, up trees, on roofs. When other kids from the Estate took part, there were often twenty or more participants in a single game.

During the journey, the boys decided the easiest location they could escape from would be inside a block of flat. They knew the concrete staircase and hall echoed when the security door slammed shut. The boom from a banger placed in the same place would be ear popping. Watching and waiting the mates settled down in a bin store.

As the access door to each block had an entry code, they needed to sneak entry.

Excited they sat, eyes peeled. 'It was like being on the Western Front, waiting for the command to go over the top'. Two buildings away a person appeared from a doorway, leaving the building.

Before the security door could click shut, Jon was standing inside holding the door open.

He waved to Roy. Roy sneaked in, he softly climbed the stairs, treading on each step with just a toe. At the second-floor landing, he placed a banger on the edge of the top step. As he fumbled in his pocket for the match box, he heard a slight noise. Looking up, he saw two very large mucky, steel toe capped boots on the landing just above his head.

Jon, was waiting on the ground floor, holding the door ajar waiting for Roy's running exit. Unannounced, Roy suddenly appeared leaping down the stairs, he barged into the door, shouting, "Ruuun." Jon followed him at speed escaping to the safety of the bin store.

A few days later, the boys were in school when Roy informed them that he had developed the ultimate weapon. Operation 'BBA' would be that night. They were to meet at his home at twenty hundred hours.

Jon, Glyn and Stan met at 'Dog Shit Island' before walking the ten minutes to Roy's home.

When they arrived, he squirrelled them into the back garden.

"Roy, what's 'BBA' then?" asked Glyn.

"Big Bang Armageddon," replied Roy. "I have taken the gunpowder from three bangers and made a Triple Banger. Plus, I have bought some proper firework fuse from a pyrotechnic shop in Romford." He was so eager to show them the cardboard tube with a string sticking out of one end that he nearly dropped it.

Looking like a miniature stick of dynamite, the tube had 'BBA' crayoned in red on one side, with a yellow and orange flame emblem on the reverse.

Roy resumed, "Because it's so huge we can place in on the bottom step. As Firework Night was a few days ago no one will suspect."

He smirked, then added with a smile, "Remember I've used a thirty second fuse, so no need to run."

The quartet sneaked from Roy's garden; they assembled close to the same flat they had targeted before.

Innocently, Jon wandered around the external paved area. A young woman left the flats, he grabbed the security door.

Stan and Glyn stood nonchalantly on the kerb opposite keeping dog eye. Roy, looked around at his three 'comrades', each gave him the 'thumbs up'.

He walked through the open door, looked around to be safe then laid the firework on the bottom step. Pleased there wasn't a boot this time he lit the fuse then walked slowly out of the building. Jon shut the door quietly behind him.

Together, the four walked slowly, then faster and faster until it was a run. As they hurried towards a corner behind them came the explosive noise, 'baarwoooom'. The security door and staircase windows rattled. The confined noise trying to break out, echoed. Elated, the boys ran down the street, 'BBA, revenge on the dirty boots'.

06-05

CONVEYOR

In the evening after most school days, the boys would 'knock for' each other to play. If they were going to play football, the last to be collected would be Scott and his neighbour Glen who lived at the end of the same road as Jon. Sometimes Glen's older brother Harry who played semi-pro would join them. They would climb over the large iron, pale blue double gates at the end of the street into the vast grassed area to the left of Beck Schools playing fields. Most evenings they would only return home after the darkness prevented them seeing the ball.

This day the earlier rain had created massive puddles across the field making it too wet to play football. Scott invited them into his rear garden and led them through a hole in the metal chain link fence into the fields at the back. They trudged along through the damp grass parallel to Dacca Road towards Beck Quarry. Scott's name was called by his mum, so dejectedly he returned home.

Up ahead a figure to their left in the same field caught the boys' attention, it looked like Bradley Evans. The person was swinging something around his head, a golf club perhaps?

After watching him for a while, they decided to make a detour to have a closer look.

They greeted each other towards the centre of the field, Brad informed them that he had borrowed his older brother's golf clubs and balls. A big, tall lad and very strong he was having a swing to see how far he could whack a golf ball.

The group stood about the length of a football pitch from Dacca Road. Facing the road Brad dropped a ball to the ground, taking a minute to remember his brother's instructions he steadied himself then swish, ping. The ball took off, it badly swerved to the right. Glyn ran to retrieve it but was called back.

Brad cautioned, "Please stay behind me, one of these could kill

288

you." Gingerly, together the group shuffled back a bit further, just to be safe.

His second attempt, the ball swung left.

"Here we go, third time lucky," expressed Roy.

Brad caught the third ball bang on. Contact with the club head made a sweeter sound, the ball went fizzing through the air.

As the ball flew towards the fence along Dacca Road, the initial 'whooooo' from the boys turned to silence, amazement. They cheered, "F*** me, look at that," admired Glyn, followed by a chuckle.

There was a loud 'bhoom', as the golf ball passed over the chain link boundary fence and smashed into the side of a tall van.

The boys watched as the van driver executed an emergency stop. The van door swung open then a man jumped from the van into the road. They were staggered. "Get down," Brad commanded, waving his hand near the ground, "Get lower."

They watched as the puzzled van driver walked around the vehicle, looking for the 'poor thing' he had run over. He knelt on the pavement and looked underneath the van.

Glyn's shoulders were jerking up and down, as he giggled. Tone, crept up behind and wrapped a dirty hanky around Glyn's mouth, holding it from behind. This application failed to shut him up, only resulting in more giggling.

The van driver took one more trip around the van, again he knelt in the road to search under the vehicle. Finally, he climbed into the cab and drove off.

Brad had had enough excitement with the golf clubs. He accepted an invitation to join the boys. The golfing equipment was left where they were standing as they continued on the route to Beck Quarry.

"Where are we going?" he enquired.

"Just to the lakes," answered Stan.

"Have you ridden on the conveyor belt yet?" Brad asked.

They shook their heads.

Brad suggested, "If it's running, fancy a go?"

They agreed, the six twelve-year-olds walked further from the road towards the series of steel buildings nearer to the lakes. Further away the animal testing labs, were the other side of the London Underground railway tracks. The boys could hear a dog in the distance howling, a second distressed dog returned its call.

Brad invited the boys to a camp he was building with Gary, Matt and Ollie. The estate where the boys lived was similar to Brushwood Road. A mile away by road but only a few hundred yards across the park Bluebell Farm Avenue was also built on the edge of the park. The Council had knocked down the twenty-year-old temporary bungalows built after the war and pinched a small corner of the park to extend the estate. They were building four rows of new houses plus two tall tower blocks of flats. Brad with the others had a camp in the roof of one of the houses. He described where to find a hidden ladder to climb into the roof space. They had made two rope ladders, one positioned at the escape routes each end of the block in case the caretaker did an inspection. Generally it was safe to go there after six o'clock, but Ollie nearly got caught the week before when some tradesmen were working overtime.

Before they got to the buildings, Brad took them to a large green steel platform about six feet above the ground. It was the extreme point of a conveyor belt, the closes point to the road. The three feet wide, dark grey rubber belt moved slowly on sets of rollers.

They were standing at the return corner. The belt arrived hanging below the platform, rose in an arc to above the platform then returned to the buildings. Any gravel loaded on the top was transported to a discharge position where it was automatically loaded into massive gravel lorries. They smiled; it was running.

The boys followed Brad. He scaled the metal ladder at the side then cautiously stepped onto the moving belt. It was like skiing, whizzing along they ran with it, the boys turned to run against it. They wrestled to push each other off, they bounced, belly flopped.

After about fifty yards, they jumped off, ran back to the beginning and rode it again. It was great fun.

Thirty minutes passed. The group were knackered. They abandoned the conveyor belt to wander around the lakes. Sarcastically, Roy asked Brad if he could sail on his and Gary's raft and received a slap.

They came to an area of quicksand. A hard dark orange coloured crust sat above the lighter coloured viscous custard that would grip, then suck objects to oblivion.

Impetuously, in denial of the dangers the boys raced onto the crust to jig and dance around.

Roy suggested a game. Ripping discarded corrugated cardboard boxes, he had found into squares he outlined the game. Simply, it was to skid a piece of cardboard onto the quicksand then run to retrieve it.

That was considered too dangerous because of the change in direction needed to return. The contest would be to skid the cardboard out on to the quicksand, then run in an arc to step on it. The return would be a continuation of the arc, forming an ellipse.

The person who reached the greatest distance won.

It was exciting, more so, because the more steps taken on the crust the softer the surface became.

Safety depended on speed, the least time in contact with the crust the better. Soon, each runner was sinking deeper than the soles on their shoes. Bright yellowish green footprints appeared in the dark orange crust. There were now ten pieces of cardboard stretched out in front of them.

Tony skidded his second attempt along the crust. It travelled the furthest, about fifteen feet from the start point. He strode out, leaping towards the marker, avoiding the yellow green footprints. Just three feet from his objective his right foot sank to above his ankle. Tony fell forward aiming to grasp the cardboard marker, he dragged his body forward until he was flat. Another manoeuvre and the cardboard was positioned beneath his stomach. He breathed heavily. His shoe and sock were lost below the quicksand.

The advice from his jittery friends standing on a firmer crust reminded Tone he wasn't alone, "Stay there, don't move, relax, forget about your shoe."

The boys tore the remainder of the cardboard into four large pieces and flicked them onto the crust to form a path. Tony repositioned the pieces he could reach into stepping stones. He arranged them so he could stand with a different piece of card under each foot, equally balancing his weight.

Nervously, he stood calling to his friends, "Quick, or slow?"

"Go, quickly," answered Glyn.

"Slow," shouted Roy.

"Thanks!" Yelled Tony.

"Start slowly, support one foot at a time," suggested Stan, "you need to even out your weight. When you can reach us or if you sink, run and dive at us and we'll pull you in."

They agreed, in turn Tony tested each steppingstone with a foot before adding his whole weight. Slowly, the gap to the boys decreased as they shouted encouragement.

He was only six feet away, 'Dive', they shouted.

Tony dived, he hit the floor arms outstretched hands near his mate's feet. They bent, grabbed his arms and hauled him to them, safe. They were all greatly relieved, but none as much as Tony.

"It's 'cos you're a fat B***," laughed Roy, no one else laughed.

06-06
SNOW

It was snowing again Stanley made himself ready for a big day. Today, would decide his future education, probably the rest of his life. Two years ago, he had failed the Eleven Plus Exams, a pass would have meant that he studied at a grammar school. Today, was chance number two, the Thirteen Plus Exams. He was not really concerned. Stanley had settled at the Beck Secondary School. He had close mates, plus he enjoyed the lessons. Previously, when taking the Eleven Plus Exams he had been worried about losing friends. He was too young to know or decide the type of learning that suited him. A grammar school education guaranteed better job prospects, but only if he could do the work. If he failed, he would still have nothing.

Two years later, did he really want to abandon what he now had? He wasn't sure, he didn't cope well with fuss or stress. Would he disappoint his parents if he failed again?

One of his pleasures was rugby. Mr Thomas had started teaching Rugby Union in games lessons. Stanley's year was the first to play. Initially, the boys couldn't understand how the ball could be moved forward if it could only be passed back. Stan played as scrum half for the school team on a Saturday morning, it was something he would miss.

The first competitive match they played was against Droxhill School. The 10-0 lose disheartened them, trudging off the muddy pitch on a freezing Saturday morning, cold and wet. Afterwards, the opposition sports teacher appeared in their changing room and shook everyone's hand. He pointed out that Droxhill were last year's County Champions, the 10-0 result was actually only two scores to none. The boys were elated.

Thomas chose the school rugby colours to be all black with white collars. The ignorant pupils didn't appreciate the significance until The All Blacks played at Twickenham in 1964. From then, all the school teams worked hard to play and emulate such illustrious masters of the game. The team Stanley played for were so superior that Thomas would allow opposition teams to field eighteen or even twenty players in order to give his boys a contest. They even toured Wales, winning one, losing one and drawing one. There was a tangible bond between Thomas and every boy who played for him. This bond wasn't just playing rugby at school but also other lessons the man took. Later, some seniors joined Thomas's own rugby club in Romford.

Stanley's attention was now on the exams. Collecting his bag, he met Glyn at 'Dog Shit Island'. In the distance, they could see Roy running from his brother Billy and friends. A bombardment of snowballs chased Roy towards them. The pair scarpered and met Jon at the school gates.

They walked along the service road, sliding on the slippery surface, watching behind for Billy and his friends. There was a commotion as they turned into the main playground.

Dickie Davis was in control, he directed students away from the main playground through the school into the Quad. The boys could hear the distant sound of an ambulance siren above the whimper of a few boys sitting on the wall sobbing.

Mr Wilson was on the steps by the door to the corridor, "Come on fellas, keep moving, don't look, keep moving into the Quad, please."

The boys followed instructions. Searching for some friends they saw Joe Law, John's younger brother, 'Wot happened?'

Joe informed them of what had occurred. "Do you know Mike Jones's older brother Richard in 4-2?" They nodded.

"It's him, he's hurt himself bad." Joe continued, "Their ball went over the high pale blue fence into the field, and he climbed over to get it."

"Is that the iron railings with the sort of semi-circular tops, near the hall?" asked Jon.

Joe nodded, "Well, he got up there, standing with a foot in the hooped bits. Somehow, he lost his balance or someone pushed him, not sure. He fell forward, but his feet were stuck in the hoops, they didn't move."

The boys were shocked, "No! F*** Hell."

"What's happening now?" asked Glyn.

Joe replied, "They can't get him down. John Thomas and Reg Alison are on the other side of the fence taking the weight by supporting his shoulders. Because his head and body are upside down, they have to lift his body up and back to free his feet. I guess Firemen will have to do it."

Mr Wilson arrived in the Quad and ordered everyone to their Form Rooms.

A little later, Stan with the other Thirteen Plus Examination candidates were escorted to the hall.

They followed the 'wall' along the main playground, passed the steps down to the sports field then waited to be called. Stan noticed a fire engine had been parked across the playground to screen the accident. An ambulance stood by, ready. He had no exam nerves. The horror of the tragedy had prevented him from even thinking about the exams.

The school authority was mindful of the effect the accident may have on some candidates. In turn, each candidate was called, monitored then shepherded to their seat. They sat English first, after a break it would be Problem Solving. The boys ate their lunch and were released. They were to be in their seats before 2.00pm ready to commence the Maths exam.

Keeping the rowdy pupils off the sports playing fields during breaks had proved impossible. Finally Mr Kerrigan had given up.

It was snowing again. Stanley left the hall in search of his friends. He weaved through snowball fights, slides and snowman construction zones. Eventually, he heard Roy screaming with laughter. Stan ran through ankle deep snow towards the noise. Roy and mates were having a snowball fight with his brother Billy and his mates.

Billy watched Stan arriving, he directed a barrage of snowballs at him. It was boundless fun. They played and forgot the earlier upset, time flew.

Belatedly, Stan checked his watch, it was 1.55pm. The exam candidate needed to get back to the hall. He would be just in time for the Maths Paper if he hurried. Jogging towards the hall he shouted his byes.

Seeing the exam candidate escaping, Billy shouted loudly, "Scraaagg him, get Paaat," he chased after Stan.

Stanley's retreat was blocked, he was thrown to the floor. The muggers buried him in snow, removed his coat and filled it with snow, wiped it around his face. Between giggles and laughter, Stan pleaded to be freed. He shouted that he was taking an exam, no one heard him. Snow was pushed up his trouser legs, Billy rubbed his knuckles into the top of Stan's head. Roy shouted at the assailants, finally they released him.

Stanley pulled on his wet, snow laden coat, straightened his clothing then continued to the hall.

Dave Wilson was on door duty. He watched a white mass coming from the field towards the hall and chuckled. The mass got to him, a boy stood brushing himself down, it was Paterson. Stanley took his seat, he read the exam paper, the time was 2.35pm.

Stanley failed the grammar school entry exam for the second time. He was delighted to remain at Beck, Mr Wilson had a tale to share.

NEWS

Mrs Williams watched through the window as Pete drove his Austin A60 Farina from the road into the space next to the house. He was now working at Darger Paints, near his in-laws. More convenient it was only a twenty-minute drive away from home.

The housewife waited for the car's driver door to open then stepped outside. On seeing him raise an arm in acknowledgement, she walked to the garden fence adjacent to the driveway.

"How are you, Peter?" the lady made polite conversation.

"Fine thanks Liz," he replied, "and you?"

"Fine, thank you, I wanted a word. Do you have a minute please?" She moved closer and spoke quietly. "Do you think your boys would like to work a paper round?"

Pete wasn't prepared, he thought she was going to ask a favour, "Er, I don't know. Stan is nearly fourteen, the twins nearly eleven."

"Not to worry," Liz withdrew slightly.

"No, no, please. They may be interested. I could ask them," proposed Pete. "Can you tell me anything about it? Have you any details, to help?"

Liz invited her neighbour into her home, it was a privilege for anyone to be allowed inside. She left Peter in the hall and returned shortly with a sheet of paper.

The lady explained. Her two sons, Luke and Mathew had been working an evening paper round for the last three years. As they would be going to university or starting work soon, they were looking for someone to buy it from them.

She continued, "The boys buy the newspapers from the paper man at Heathway station and deliver them to a list of people who make up their round. Each paper costs them 4d which they sell for 5d."

Pete was interested, "That is very good, can you tell me anymore?"

She was pleased to hear Stan's response, even more of a privilege he was invited into her lounge to speak with the boys.

They explained that each customer paid a weekly delivery charge of 6p, which meant the profit was 12p per customer a week. Also, on Saturdays, there were extra customers who bought the newspaper to check the Football Pools. With tips, they earned about £1 15s each a week.

Peter was impressed with the young business tycoons. He knew that early morning paper rounds operated by shops paid only 10s for a seven-day week. This was more than £1 extra for a six-day week. Better, it was after school.

The price to purchase their little business was £15. Pete played for time; he didn't want to lose such a money spinner. He thanked them and requested time to have a chat with the family.

That evening, after the boys were in bed, Irene and Pete talked through the paper round proposal. They agreed the simplest way to understand the value of money was to earn it. It is far harder to squander something that has cost you time and effort. Free money has no connection to endeavour.

The parents decided to talk with the boys. As Irene had been working from home for a year, she had secret savings for a rainy day. The boys mum had a workbench in Stanley's bedroom where she sat and painted plastic soldiers, hundreds and hundreds of soldiers for a national toy company. To boost earnings, she planned to paint additional figures while in front of the TV each evening.

The next evening after tea, the family sat around the table and chatted about the paper round purchase.

Eddie wasn't interested, he was earning more money working on a Saturday morning. His job was helping lorry drivers with the bread deliveries around Essex. At 5.00am, he waited in line at the large bakery factory near Gunter's Hall School to be picked by a driver. It was an early start, but he now had a regular driver who looked after him.

John and Stan were interested. Mum and Dad would loan the two boys £15. From their takings, they would pay back £1 a week. This meant the boys would have roughly £1 5s each to spend a week.

John's brain whizzed, a can of cola cost 10d, he could buy 30 cans a week. Stan was also happy: they would be rich.

Pete took the £15 fee to Mrs Williams. In no time, John and Stanley were earning a living, just like Mum and Dad.

The boys divided the round into two equal halves. From leaving home to returning, took each about ninety minutes.

Stan's favourite customer was a little old lady who lived on an estate for vulnerable people.

Each Friday, as he cycled into the estate, she would be standing waiting at the open door. A soon as she saw him the lady would turn and go inside. One minute later she would return to the same spot holding his due money, a 3d tip plus a piece of fruit.

Every time she would smile, her tiny bony hand gripped his with a squeeze. If he was a minute late, she worried about him.

One setback happened later that year. The three boisterous boys, as usual were flying around the house playing tag or fighting. Stan dived over the back of the settee and landed on his back with his right arm underneath. His fractured wrist was reset and wrapped in a plaster case.

As he was not allowed to attend school or cycle until the swelling had reduced the posting of newspapers became a problem.

Always supportive, Irene and Pete helped him deliver the newspapers. For the next five days after work, Pete drove the route with Stan in the front seat directing. It was Irene's task to leave the back seat at each client's home to post the newspaper through the letter box.

A year later, the two boys were informed by the newspaper man at Heathway station of another paper round for sale. Would they be interested in its purchase? The brothers bought it for £10, which increased each one's weekly income to £2 2s a week. On John's costing scale, equivalent to over 50 cans of cola a week.

John was the first to start a full-time job, so he no longer worked on his round. However, Stanley continued until he started work some years later. Surprisingly, he earned enough to buy clothes and have a social life with his friends.

06-08

CUPS

On Friday and Saturday evenings, Stan and John collected the paper round money from their customers. Most paid without argument, only a few 'accidently' forgot to answer the front door when they knocked. In the end, everyone paid their arrears, there were no debtors.

Trouser pockets bursting with coins signalled Stan had finished his round. A bit shaken he cycled home along Bullock Lane. About fifteen minutes earlier in Halibut Street he had had a squabble. Three boys had taken his bike while he was collecting a customer's money. When he walked along the front path from the house, his bike wasn't against the garden hedge where he had left it. Then he spotted it, about fifty yards away a boy about his age was riding it. Two others ran chasing the thief, trying to unseat him.

Stanley was angry, how was he going to get it back? With nerves of cotton wool, he tried to appear in control of the situation. There was no point in shouting, that was a sign of desperation. Anyway, his throat would probably dry and the shout finish in a squeal.

He had to act tough, without fear. Quivering inside he thought 'calm', then called to the thieves with authority.

The one on the bike rode back towards him. In a cocky manner, the thief started riding in circles around Stan. All three gave him 'verbal', but he didn't weaken. Stan understood, if he failed this test, he would never deliver papers in this area again.

He was about to chase the bike rider, then changed his mind. If he chased, it would become a game. Stand firm, make them come to him. After another five minutes without a response, the bored thief dismounted. The boy inclined the bike against a hedge and the three antagonists ran off.

Riding along on his beloved pale blue, drop handlebar bicycle he was still nervous. Stan worried about what would happen the next time he was in Halibut Street. Pleasingly, those boys never harassed him again.

He stopped at the newsagents shop on the corner of Waveland Lane and entered to buy the new edition of *Commando Comic Action*. The shop was a mass of Union Jacks.

They were on the ceiling, in the windows, everywhere.

On the counter, he spied a World Cup Willie mascot, a soft toy of a lion wearing a Union Jack waistcoat. It was £1, his comic was 1s, he didn't want to spend that much money. He looked around the shop at the souvenirs, there was a World Cup Finals Guide and Score booklet for 3s. It looked interesting. Information about the teams, fixtures and Group tables.

"When does it start?" he asked the lady behind the counter.

"Tomorrow, I think" she replied. "Silly, billy, look in the guide, you're holding it."

He bought the booklet, 17s less expensive than a stuffed Lion and treasured it for eternity.

The previous year, Stan had sat with his dad and brothers listening on the radio to West Ham winning the Euro Cup Winners Cup Final.

This year, most of the 1966 World Cup Final matches were being televised. Some, classed as 'not worthy', weren't shown. Only the second half of the England v France match was broadcast. They had to listen to the first half on the radio.

Stan checked every result fastidiously, entering the score from each match into the booklet. He loved football, now paired with the extra joy of following his Home Nation to the Final.

The weekend of 30 July 1966, Pete was at home decorating the hall. The World Cup Final would start soon, most of the anxious family sat huddled around the TV.

Stanley called from the living room to Pete who was hanging wall-paper. "It's starting Dad," They watched with fingers crossed for luck.

"Goal," twelve minutes of play, West Germany took the lead. "Oh no, but a long way to go," Pete noted, they were disappointed.

The game seesawed, each time West Germany scored Pete went back into the hall and continued decorating. Then, when the boys cheered, he would race back and stand behind the chairs to watch the TV.

England were winning 2-1, only one minute to play. Pete was back in the room, roll of wallpaper in hand.

"Goal," West Germany scored again, it was now 2-2, devastation. The game moved into extra time. Pete confined himself to the hall, 'West Germany only scored when he was watching'.

"Goal," one hundred and one minutes played, England took the lead again. There was cheering from the front room, "Dad, Dad, quick, quick, look," cried the boys.

"No, No," replied Pete. "Every time I come in, they score, I'll stay out here for now."

England scored again, it was over, the crowd waved their Union Jacks in celebration.

England had won.

The next year, the evening of 25 May Stan watched on TV as Celtic beat Inter Milan in the European Cup Final. In two years, he was lucky to have watched the first Home Nation win the World Cup and the first Home Nation Club win the European Cup.

06-09

RESPONSIBLE

Returning to school in September 1966 as fourth year students the boys were grouped to reflect their future employment plans.

Those leaving at the end of the school year were assigned different classes to ones scheduled for an extra year's study. GCE 'O' Level exams would be taken the following year when the boys were sixteen. These pupils formed the Lower Fifth class.

This meant that Stan and some of his friends were in different classes. Stan had been at school with Glyn, Roy and Jon for nearly ten years, they were good mates. Now, their friendship was paramount. They needed to help and support poor Jon whose father had passed away during the school holidays.

The grief and stress showed on Jon's appearance. He no longer looked, nor behaved like a boy of fourteen. Fate had changed his life, he now had responsibilities. His mum would argue but he was there to look after her.

Jon was a late child to his mum and dad, they already had teenager children when he was born. Unfortunately, when their father died, Jon's sister was travelling around South America and his brother touring the Far East. To ease the pressure on his elderly mum, Jon had taken the responsibility for most of the funeral arrangements. He had done really well, but the magnitude of the task had prevented him from grieving. The gang made sure that at least one of them was always available to be with him.

At school, even Stanley was surprised when he was made House Sports Captain. The appointment caused him to question his abilities of leadership. However, if Thomas thought he was capable, he couldn't fail the teachers trust.

Students at the school were assigned membership of a 'House'. These were, England, Scotland, Ireland and Wales. They provided internal school competitions between students.

Stan captained and managed the sports teams for the house of Wales. Wearing the red of that nation he also represented his house in football, rugby and athletics. His first duty, however, was at the Opening Ceremony of the School Summer Fayre and Family Day.

A very hot Saturday in September, the air was filled with the smell of cooking burgers, sausages and onions. The Beer Tent sign was changed from 'Closed' to 'Open'. The Summer Fayre was ready.

Among the attractions, were a Fire Engine and a helicopter to climb over. John Thomas and Alison volunteered as targets in the Wet Sponge Throw. Mr Butler had a stall called simply, 'Hammer a 6" Nail into a block of Wood in Three Hits'.

Mr Kerrigan the Headmaster, stood with Dickie Davis, other teachers and the Celebrity Guest in the main playground behind the 'wall'. Stan was in the Metalwork classroom waiting as Mr Roberts polished and buffed a wooden lamp stand on a lathe. The door opened: it was Dickie Davis. He was not amused, "Where is the gift? We are running late because of you."

He snatched the wooden object from the metalwork teacher and gave it to Stan. "Come on, quick!" They raced the fifty yards to the Presentation Area, Mr Kerrigan's voice boomed around the school and playing fields.

He was speaking on a mike, "bluurrr, bluuur." They could hear him introducing the guest. Did the Headmaster know Stan and the gift weren't there? "Who has just returned from the Commonwealth Games in Kingston, Jamaica, representing England, where he won Gold. And wish him well in Mexico in 1968."

Stan turned the corner, panting for breath behind him Dickie Davis was breathing out of his bum. Breathless, Dickie bent forward and pointed at the very tall man with blonde hair, wearing a suit.

Kerrigan continued, "I give you the amazing David Hemery, 120-yard hurdle gold medallist. Please accept this gift, made here by one of our pupils."

David Hemery turned at the same time as a small boy holding a wooden lamp stepped into the vacant space in front of him. Blushing like an orange, Stanley shook his hand then retreated to safety, next to Dickie Davis.

07

ADOLESCENCE

Chapter Marker

LOUNGE

Friday evenings were initially spent in the front room at Glyn's home, but his mum had complained that the smoking was staining the wallpaper yellow. Plus, the room stunk. To the rescue came Jon's mum. She was pleased to see them gather in the front room instead of wander around the streets or playing in the gravel pits. Besides, they were nearly young men. They spent hours at Jon's, smoking and playing cards.

Their favourite card games were Kalooki, plus Three and Nine card brag. They bet in pennies and preferred Nine card as it took longer to lose or win any money.

One evening when only four friends were in attendance, Jon and Glyn interrupted the gambling to announce some news. The previous week, they had been to the Lodge. Stan and Roy were flabbergasted.

"Did you get served?" asked Roy.

"Yeah," they both replied.

"What's it like?" wondered Stan.

Jon gave an account of their visit, then confessed, "Well, really it's our second time."

"Nooooo?" interrupted Roy.

Jon continued, "Yeah, you see we went in there the week before as well. Dave told us to go in a pub for the first time on a Tuesday when it's not busy. That way, we are not a problem. Plus, the landlord takes money he wouldn't otherwise be getting."

"And you got served? Did you buy a drink then?" Stan asked, in awe.

"Yeah, we had two pints," claimed Glyn, "do you fancy coming with us next week?"

"Yes please," Stan and Roy excitedly rejoiced.

The following Tuesday evening a sequence of assembly which would endure for years began. Roy would knock for Glyn, those two knocked for Stan, then they would knock for Jon. The smartly dressed boys waited for Jon to appear at his front door, then set off. Each one had taken the opportunity to apply gallons of Christmas present after shave to various parts of their anatomy.

The walk to the pub took less than fifteen minutes. Chatting about their understanding of getting drunk they walked swiftly along Dacca Road with open fields to the right where Brad had practiced golf.

The public house resembled a small detached mansion. Set back from the road, centred in a lawned garden with tables and chairs dotted about. Further along the road was the entrance to Beckvale Chase, after which were the fishing lakes. Behind it was Beck Quarry where they had ridden a conveyor belt. Closer was a pond where the boys went newting and frogging.

There were farm buildings, sheds and a tractor along from the pub. Farmer's fields in the distance where mums and sisters harvested the crop to earn seasonal pocket money currently displayed the green tops of vegetables.

There were two entrances to the Lodge, both above ground via separate concrete stairs. Nervously, Stan and Roy hung back. They followed Jon and Glyn to the entrance at the right-hand side.

At the top of the stairs, Glyn turned, "Ready?" he chuckled, "follow us, this is the Lounge, also called the Saloon Bar."

They walked into a large upholstered, carpeted room. There were comfy sofas and armchairs, net curtains across windows with drapes pulled back. A polished wooden horseshoe bar to their left also served the public bar. They walked towards a large sofa directly in front of them, opposite the door. To one side of the sofa was an ornate, black cast iron fireplace, filled with coal.

A voice came from the bar, "Good evening, gentlemen." The barman raised a hand in welcome. Jon and Glyn returned happy smiles, Roy and Stan troubled ones.

The quartet sat on the sofa in a line, facing the bar. As the barman was in earshot, the location now deemed the worse place possible for underage drinkers to decide on their choice of drinks.

Afraid the man could hear them, they whispered.

"What do you want?" Glyn asked Stan and Roy.

"Don't know," declared the boys.

"Do you want Bitter?" Jon asked.

"What's it like?" replied Stan.

"Don't know, suppose it's like sour, like the name," guessed Jon.

"Eh? I'll have a, umm, I'll have what you're having," answered Stan.

"Me too," chirped in Roy.

Glyn stood up, trying to appear confident he walked to the bar, "Four pints of Brown Ale please?"

Success, he was served. He thought he could feel the barman's eyes in his back. Being extra careful, he carried the four large bottles of beer to the table, then returned for the empty glasses.

"Ahem," a noise radiated from the bar. The four youngsters looked up in fear.

"Your change?" grinned a knowing barman to Glyn.

Seconds later, Glyn was back on the sofa. "How much was it?" whispered Roy.

"It's 1s 8d a pint, that's 6s 8d together," Glyn answered.

Stan thought it through, he had brought a 10s note, so he had enough money. He now earned £2 2s a week from his paper round which would buy twenty-four pints. He wondered if that was enough beer to get drunk.

The immature beer drinkers emptied their glasses a wee bit faster than a regular drinker. In less than fifteen minutes, each one had guzzled the lot. The problem was, none of them really wanted to walk across the open space to the bar. Glyn sat back without a care; it was now someone else's problem.

As Jon was 'experienced' in the ways of 'the pub' he went next, then Roy. Eventually, it was Stan's round, he would go last.

Stanley slowly crept towards the bar; three pints had made his cheeks flush. Alcohol had given him courage, but not enough to be poised. The barman served a customer in the public bar at the other side of the horseshoe, aware of Stan's movement he lifted a hand with a raised thumb. Stan waited.

The wait seemed protracted. Stan's confidence ebbed. His face was reddening, his mouth drying. 'Here I am', he thought, 'sixteen years old, not very tall, weighing seven stone when wet. Standing here trying illegally to buy alcohol. I bet I look more like a frightened baby than a man'. He started to count the shining beer mugs hanging on hooks along the top of the bar. The dimples reflecting light like a curved mirror.

A cheery voice broke him from his trance, "Four pints of Brown, is it?" enquired the jovial barman.

"Yes please," Stan heard himself talking. 'I'm going to get away with it', he thought.

"Do you want mugs this time, sir?" the barman asked.

"Uhm," Stanley looked puzzled, he reddened further.

"I saw you admiring the mugs," the barman lifted his eyes to the line of hanging mugs and jolted his head up.

"Eh?" Stan looked up, "Eh, no they'll do," the teenager answered pointing to the glasses.

Four pints of Brown Ale was enough to make any sixteen-year-old happy. Drinking them in just over an hour magnified the effect. The boys were even more excitable on the walk home than the one to the Lodge.

07-02

SONGS

As the boys had the day off school, Roy and Stan wanted to go ten pin bowling in the morning. However, because of Glyn they had been shopping in Romford instead.

For a period, when the boys were bored on a quiet Sunday afternoon, they would go Ten Pin Bowling at the twenty-four lane Princess Bowl. On one visit, Glyn was scouted by the bowling team captain. He sat with him at the lane offering advice, the young man thought Glyn's natural action could be coached to achieve a high standard player.

Glyn went with him to the first-floor area where the Professional Lanes were situated. Once a week, Club matches were partnered with training sessions twice a week. The captain promised that with coaching Glyn would become exceptional.

Glyn attended for only two weeks, the training and coaching taught him that he preferred to play for fun. He just never bothered to attend. Regrettably, he later felt that perhaps he should have resigned. So, because he was then concerned about letting the man down, he wouldn't visit the Bowl until years later.

Mr Kerrigan always choice the Varsity Rugby Match day as the discretionally school holiday for pupil's Christmas shopping. Roy and Stan sat galvanised watching the match on TV at Glyn's home.

The programme reminded Glyn of a conversation with his neighbour. The man had told him about the bawdy songs the players sang on the coach coming back from a match.

He had a collection of LP records of the ditties. Glyn was welcome to borrow them if he wished. The boys agreed, they organised a meet at Stan's home to play them.

A few days later Stan asked his mum if friends could come round and listen to music. He was too cute to declare the type of music. She agreed, but was surprised he didn't want to use the living room Radiogram and sit with the rest of the family. Pete and Irene enjoyed

311

the current styles of music plus the popular honky tonk, jazz type piano music. To the family's dismay Pete also played bagpipe music which brought back memoirs of matching behind a military pipe band when on National Service.

Stanley borrowed a Tansette record player from his neighbour Michael, at No. 155. He took it up to his parent's bedroom, placed it on the floor near a socket and laid out three notepads with pens. His parents were not happy the boys would be in their bedroom, but regrettably it was the only vacant bit of upstairs floor space with a rug. The clear floor space in the other two rooms was covered in lino, with just enough clearance to walk between the furniture. Stanley's room also housed Irene's painting workbench.

Glyn arrived with a pile of LPs, Roy joined them a few minutes later. They moved upstairs and sat on the floor by the record player. The plan was to play a song while the boys listened and wrote the lyrics on the notepads provided. Once the thread was lost, they checked each other's interpretation and agreed on the lyrics.

Numerous times the needle was played from the beginning, lifted from the record then restarted. As they had never heard some of the suggestive, raunchy words before they cheerfully argued about the spelling and meanings. Some suggestions caused howls of laughter. Roy took a list of rude words home for his brother Billy to check. The boys found the task tiring but rewarding. They had never before laughed with such amusement.

Irene couldn't understand why the trio met in her bedroom on another three different occasions. Pete guessed that they were up to no good, something the rogues were doing up there made them laugh. He was sure even the neighbours could hear the giggling and wise-cracks through the wall. As soon as they had created the master crude songbook of more than a dozen diverse songs, they each copied their favourite seven into the gang's own edition.

The Buccaneer's Song:

A Buccaneer told me before he died,
An I've no reason to believe he lied,
Ah-hum, titty-bum, titty-bum, titty-bum, Ah-hum, titty-bum,
titty-bum, titty-bum.

He knew a woman with a…
That she was never satisfied.

The Mayor of Dayswater:

And the hairs on her dicki di do
hang down to her knees,
One black one, one white one
and one with a bit of s*** on…

The Good Ship Anus:

Twas on the good ship Aenus,
By God, you should have seen us,
The figurehead was a whore in bed
****ing a dead man's *****.

The captain's wife was Mabel.
Whenever she was able,
She'd forn*** with the second mate
upon the kitchen table.

07-03

NELLIE

The three lads had spent a few hours sitting on the floor of Irene's bedroom unravelling the lyrics to some lewd rugby songs. They suffered 'brain freeze' so decided to finish for the day.

Roy slipped the ball pen hook over the hard cardboard cover of his notepad and made for the facilities. He was in need, positive the profusion of laughing had caused the cups of tea to reach his nozzle quicker than usual. Standing at the white porcelain, he prepared himself with a sigh, "Ahhh."

A sixth sense suggested not all was as it seemed. He was not alone? It was a small room with a bath, basin and W.C., there weren't many places for a predator to be concealed. Someone or something was watching him. Roy scanned the room; he looked below the basin.

He glanced to his right. Someone was in the bath. Cautiously, he leaned his body back and his head forward. A bit further, further, he jumped.

Two heads of an animal bobbed up and down independently of each other, one looked him straight in the eye. The second tried to peck at him. Roy's muted scream changed to laughter, there were two ducks looking at him. For F*** sake. He looked again. They weren't floating but had sunk. Their bodies were under water, but their necks and heads were waving around above the water. Only the Patersons could have two sinking ducks in their bath.

Still grinning, Roy left the room and met Eddie coming up the staircase towards him.

Stan's younger brother arrived carrying a towel. He explained that he had found the ducks when they were ducklings, a few months before. Their nest had been scragged, so he brought the birds home to look after them. They actually lived in the garden shed with Nellie.

Eddie was giving them swimming lessons as they were nearly ready to be released. His dad realised the ducks sank because of their diet of bread, milk an occasional insect.

There wasn't any provision of the oils to make their coats water-proof. Eddie and his mate Steve were now going to release them at Beck Lakes.

Glyn joined Roy to watch in wonderment. Before being placed in a bag, each juvenile Mallard was wrapped in a towel to prevent it flapping and damaging its wings. The youngsters then set off to the release area, about twenty minutes' walk away.

Irene called the boys into the living room for a cup of tea and some homemade Victoria cake.

"How was your music?" asked Pete. "We couldn't hear it down here?"

Stan replied, "It was good thanks."

Glyn let out a chuckle, stealthily grinning at Roy.

"We couldn't hear any heavy drums or anything," Irene intervened. "Perhaps, next time you can play it down here with us? You know we like to give new things a try."

"It's sort of, err, uhm, sort of comedy songs Mum," blurted Stanley, "I don't think you would see the jokes."

Roy decided to change the subject. "Mister P, we saw the ducks earlier. Will they be okay?"

It worked, Pete told them all about the birds and animals that people brought to him to nurse. There were hedgehogs, newts, frogs and lots of birds.

He told the story of Eddie bringing home five 'baby' bluetits from a wrecked nest. They weren't as unwell as supposed. The minute they were taken from the remains of the nest they soared into the air. Flying around the room they hung from the curtains, sat on the lightshade, collided with everything. Once he caught them Eddie returned them.

Pete explained how he treated baby and injured birds. To stop any damage, he would wrap them in a handkerchief to hold their wings down, then put them inside his shirt, in his armpit to keep them warm.

If a bird was egg bound, he would do the same and periodically massage warm olive oil onto its vent.

The black miniature poodle called Tracy was their current pet, plus a budge called Shush because he wouldn't be quiet. Mister P and the boys did once have pairs of tropical birds in the aviary, but mice got in and petrified them. Currently, he had canaries in there.

ADOLESCENCE

"Have you seen Nellie?" Pete enquired.

"No," replied Glyn, "but Stan has told us about him."

Pete called to his wife, "Eye, have you fed Nellie this afternoon?"

"Not yet," came the reply.

Pete continued, "Can you take the boys with you, when you do, please?" Irene agreed.

A little later, Irene guided Roy and Glyn through the kitchen to the back doorstep.

She used her leg to keep excited Tracy indoors as she shut the back door. Next, she asked the boys to wait and be quiet as she went to the shed. Irene stood back as she opened the door. A bird sang, as if saying "ello'.

The two boys watched as a black shape in the shed dropped from a height and landed at Irene's feet. Irene spoke to it, "Hi Nellie, are you hungry?"

With Nellie bobbing along behind her, Irene walked along the path. Glyn and Roy followed at a distance. Firstly the bird then the human passed the shed, next the lean-to, they stopped at the vegetable patch behind the aviary. While Nellie watched from the path, Irene used the garden fork to dig around in a muddy area. The male Blackbird stood in one position his head at ninety degrees to follow Irene's every movement with interest.

Once Irene had enough worms, while calling to Nellie she forced the fork vertically into the ground. Sailing up from his position to perch on the fork handle, he squawked and flapped his wings as a fledging should. Irene fed each fat, juicy worm by hand.

When he was satisfied, Nellie glided down to the path, hopping along behind his foster mother to the shed. He waited patiently for her to open the door, then took off to settle on his favourite perch.

"Is he a male?" asked Glyn, chuckling.

"Yes," answered Irene.

"Well, why has he got a girl's name?" grinned Glyn.

Irene responded, "Because he has two adolescent feathers on his forehead which look like horns, or tusks. So, Eddie named him Nellie the elephant."

Irene laughed, "I would never have picked up a worm, before. Now I feed him three times a day."

A week later Irene stopped shutting the shed door during the day to let him fledge.

Amazingly, over the next three years a pair of Blackbirds nested in the shed and had lots of babies. Surely, it was too much of a coincidence? The Patersons were convinced the male was Nellie.

07-04

MEET

Tony Clark was at home tidying the kitchen. He had just finished eating his Saturday tea of baked beans on toast with a mug of beef soup. He was a quietly spoken young man with two older sisters. Tone kidded them that they were the cause of his lack of conversation, as he could never get a word in edgeways. He was at home alone. His oldest sister had recently been married, his other sister with Mum and Dad were visiting her in Suffolk.

The quartet were on their way to Tony's home in Brushwood Road. When they got to Tony's turning, they also 'knocked for' Joe, Roy and Rick, before calling at Tony's. Glyn placed his thumb in his mouth and made loud sucking noises, joking they would be 'babysitting' Tony as he was on his own.

The gang settled in front of the TV to watch a popular spy-MI5 show. Jon helped Tone distribute cups of tea. During the adverts they caught up with everyone's gossip.

Since leaving school last July, Jon had become an apprentice working on a milling machine in an engineering company. Glyn was an apprentice electrician working on a building site. Roy worked in a posh London hotel and Tony was an apprentice tool maker in a factory opposite the Beck pub. Stan studied 'O' levels at Beck School. The remaining three were a year younger, they were still at school.

"Got anything to drink Tone?" asked Roy.

"Have a look in the cupboard by the front door," suggested Tony. "My mum and dad don't drink much, see what you can find."

Roy didn't have to be told twice. There was only dust where he had been sitting. "There's some here," Roy called.

"Don't touch them, or move them," commanded Tony, "we need to put them back in the same place or I'll get shot. I'll get a glass."

The boys sat on the floor around the open cupboard door. The strangely shaped and coloured bottles in the cupboard contained ginger beer, orangeade, sherry, whiskey and coffee cream liqueur. In turn, they tasted the drinks straight 'yuck', then mixed with another 'yuck'. All options draw twisted 'ugh faces', from the boys. Primarily, they couldn't understand why the 'beer' tasted so awful.

A glass of orangeade became the best option.

Back in the front room, Tony spoke about his girlfriend. He had been seeing Lisa Poppen for over a year. Sadly, her parents had objected. They wanted someone better than 'him' for their daughter. It had become so bad that she had been forbidden from meeting him, ever. Other than work, the poor girl was stuck indoors, the only time she was allowed out was to walk the family dog.

Around 8.30pm he would nip out to walk the two family corgis.

The only time the couple spent time together was of an evening when they walked their respective dogs. The good news was that her parents had begun to visit Lisa's older sister on a Saturday afternoon. Tone could now sneak round her house for a few hours without being discovered.

The boys all felt for Tone, they murmured their commiserations. It didn't seem the time to say anymore. Sometimes it's best to remain quiet, they couldn't really offer any meaningful comments.

Tone took the dogs for their walk and met Lisa. He returned full of smiles, but gradually his mood sank.

The rest of the night was sombre. The boys stayed until Tome's family returned home then left for home themselves.

07-05

CLUB

Stanley had finished his paper round as quickly as possible. He had wolfed down his tea had a bath and got ready. As previously agreed, his friends 'knocked for' him at 7.00pm. Dressed in their best bib and tucker the boys were going 'out, out'.

Mike Jones was with them tonight. Three years before his older brother Richard had had a terrible accident at school. They were pleased to hear that he was walking okay and no longer needed to attend six monthly check-ups at hospital.

The five sixteen-year-olds, with three fifteen-year-olds were walking along Regen Road towards Dacca Football club. Each had bathed in enough aftershave to sink a ship. All dressed very smartly, it was the first time Stanley had worn his new dark blue Reefer Jacket. It looked so sharp with two rows of black shaped seafarer's buttons and wide lapels. To help him buy clothes his mum had taken out a Provident Cheque to pay for the coat. He had promised to give her the monthly instalments from his paper round money so that she could repay the loan.

As they turned right into Queens Road, the main wooden gate to the ground became visible at the end of the street.

Jon spoke loudly to address the boys, "There's a little old bald man on the door who sits at a table and takes the two shillings and gives you a ticket. Only then does he look at your card. It's not a problem. When I was the only one with a card, Tone and Glyn used to get in with me.

With sleight of hand and bravado, eight of us can easily get in with three cards. This is what we are going to do."

The boys often watched the Athenian League matches at the venue; they knew the football ground layout well. From the car park, they entered through the red painted iron gate next to the turnstiles. They walked past the dilapidated Nissen hut used as a toilet then turned into the stand. Following the three-foot-high concrete wall around the pitch they arrived at the source of the loud Soul Music.

Jon called then to a halt outside the second old Nissen hut with a corrugated iron roof, now signposted as 'Social Club and Bar'. Everything was clear.

The enlightened boys walked into the lobby of the Nissen hut, forming a line back from the table. An old man sat at the far edge taking the money. The card holders positioned themselves first, second and fourth at the table, the others stood behind.

Jon was first, "Evening, how are you?"

"Okay thanks," answered the man. "Two shillings please?"

"Do you need to see my card?" Jon asked.

"Yes please, sonny," replied the man.

Jon showed the man his card, then palmed it. He continued, "I don't have any change, only a ten-shilling note."

That was Roy's prompt, third in the queue, "I've got loads of change, here," he fumbled about in his coat pocket then offered Jon a 2s coin, a florin.

Jon reached back to Roy switching the 2s coin with his membership card.

Mike took his coat of, "It's warm in here anyone want me to take their coat?"

Tone in second showed the man his card, then passed it backwards to Stan who had moved up close behind him.

Roy paid the man and showed him Jon's card. He then put the card into his coat pocket and gave Mike his coat.

With secret hand movements and deception, all eight of the crew gained access. Once, they established the man's name they talked to him about the war. After a few weeks, the elderly man recognised their faces, so he no longer asked to see their membership cards.

The crowd moved into the bar area of the Nissen hut which had enough space for about sixty people. The boys moved some tables together while three went to the bar to buy the drinks. As the cost of the drinks were at subsidised 'members' prices' they were much cheaper than the Lodge.

The DJ played Soul, Jazz, Stax and Tamla imports from the USA. The music was loud, the people calm but on the edge. There was an atmosphere of controlled energy and excitement, ready to explode into jubilation.

Joe, Mike and friends had little idea of dancing, they sat watching the shuffling around on the dance floor. Some steps and moves looked professional, the majority awkward. After a few drinks, Glyn, Joe and Mike took the plunge. They stayed near their table, upright, rigid with a slight bent stomach they waved like reeds in a storm. Tone suggested the trio were lucky it was dark. He joined them, "Try to move your feet," he shouted against the volume of the music.

Two rotating spotlights illuminated people for a split second, a white light flashed their movements in slow motion. A young girl ran into a corner and puked next to a concrete pillar heater. Her friend went to aid her but tripped over her legs. No one heard or saw the pair: it was too dark and noisy.

Time for a drink, the trio sat down and left Tone alone. He kept going, in the groove, alcohol consumption was working. Roy joined him. They giggled and wobbled, trying to copy the movement of what they thought were good moves from other people on the dancefloor.

The boys had been in the club for just over two hours, they had consumed nearly seven pints each. All self-restraint had been dismissed. They formed a circle looking inwards at each other and wiggled their way through the music. They were happy, they joked, with humour they mimicked each other's twirls and twists. Sometimes, bent over they laughed so much the ability to wiggle was lost. In pairs, during the slow tunes they danced close with each other. Sometimes two pair would become a four. Then it became an eight. A circle of friends, arms around the shoulders of the nearest two mates swaying drunkenly to music. Singing to a song when they didn't know the words.

The first bell rang, they ignored it.

Jon put his arm around Roy, "I'm going to pinch the Red Barrel ashtray when we leave," he giggled. "I've always wanted one of them." He staggered to the table and repositioned the big plastic ashtray from the top to the floor underneath.

The last bell sounded, the Disco stopped.

Boys got their coats then used the outside toilets for the last time.

Jon called them together, "Is it clear?" They looked at him in surprise.

"Is what clear?" Mike asked.

"Quick, let's go," muttered Jon. He undid his belt, bent down, seized the ashtray then stuffed it down the front of his trousers.

Jon turned and walked quickly towards the exit. A trail of dogends and cigarette ash followed him, flowing down his trouser legs. The others ran behind him in tears of laughter. Amazingly, without hindrance the Red Barrel ashtray later arrived at Jon's home. It became a trophy, with pride of place at the boys' card school nights.

07-06

LEAVE

Back at school studying in the Upper Fifth year Stan worked hard for his GCE 'O' Level exams. The previous year he had achieved top grades in all eight of the RSA subjects he sat. The school forecast the same in the GCE subjects.

He didn't really know what job or profession to follow. As he liked Maths and Technical Drawing, he presumed he would eventually work in Banking or Engineering. Stanley's parents would forever support his final decision which he was not yet able to establish.

Dillydallying without an occupation preference his future path led to unemployment or further education. The Borough's Career's Officer had few ideas and recommended Stanley take 'A' Levels, leading perhaps to university.

Stanley was elected as one of thirteen Prefects. Being slight of build he learned to use words rather than physique to control the pupils. He also worked in the school 'tuck shop' twice a day during morning and afternoon breaks.

One of his proudest moments was as Sports Captain of the Wales House. Although complete outsiders, under his leadership the team won the Rugby Sevens Tournament.

Being the only player in Wales House who represented the School Rugby Team he had to be astute. With his knowledge of the game, he selected a good kicker, two quick runners and three strong heavy behemoths for the team. The plan succeeded. Stanley controlled the play, the strong used their physique, the kicker his boot, and the runners their speed. John Thomas was very proud of all of them, he gave Stan a celebratory bear hug. Then, a final dead leg to confirm his joy.

The school year was coming to a close. Although the examinations had been completed, the Upper Fifth students were obliged to continue attending the school.

Mr Kerrigan gave them daily access to the main hall for recreation. Some, like Brad would continue at Beck to study 'A' levels.

The Headmaster was actually very content. The class had attained the highest average GCE passes per head in the whole country. For three weeks, the main hall was like a youth club. Mr Kerrigan provided a record player, dartboard and table tennis table.

Attendance times were relaxed.

At various times, members of staff on a break would join them. It was possible these teachers preferred playing darts and table tennis to sitting in a smoky Staff Room with a few coffin dodgers.

John Thomas, Reg Alison and Dave Wilson visited the most. Always arriving in pairs, the boys rumoured the three of them had started their own table tennis league. Mr Wilson even brought in some albums to play. The like of Dr Sohn, Dan Morrison and Jeff Peck, so the boys could hear some 'proper music'.

It blew the crowds minds when Dickie Davis dropped in to say goodbye. As every time before when the man entered a room, the building went silent as he walked into the hall. He was smiling and talkative, human. Dickie respected pupils who worked hard, those who understood he was doing a job of work. In a way, Stanley's grandad was similar. Stanley wouldn't want to work for Joseph either.

The Head Teacher wished them every happiness in their grown-up lives. He 'hoped' to see them again?

The school also arranged a joint Disco for the leavers from both the boys' and girls' schools. Stan and most of his friends didn't attend. The boys were too shy to speak to girls at the school gates. They wouldn't be speaking to any at a school dance. Anyway, the rumour was that most of the boys attending would be Flash Harrys.

Rather than drink cola and become embarrassed at a school dance, Stanley and his friends drank beer and boogied at the Football Club.

Saturday morning the boys heard rumours regarding the chaos at the school event.

On Monday, there was more gossip and details.

The supervisor had closed the Disco early because some pupils sneaked in alcohol and became rowdy. Also, a notion spread, that mixing headache tablets with cola gave that person a 'high'. In fact, it just produced a cola eruption which made the floor sticky. To combat the pill taking, a clever supervisor circulated a rumour that the Police had been called to arrest all drug takers. The result was a carpet of white dust where the tablets had been dropped to the floor and crushed underfoot.

Stan could see this was true, the whole floor of the main hall was covered in a sticky pink layer. Reg Alison was busy with a mop and bucket cleaning the floor before his arranged table tennis match against John Thomas.

That afternoon was Stanley's last at the Beck Secondary School, he had fond memories. The next four years the gang would return for the school Summer Fayre. They often bumped into Thomas, Alison and Wilson in the Beck and made a point of having a chat.

The last music Stanley heard as he left the hall, as the students said their goodbyes was 'Mony Mony'.

GIRLS

Jon lived with his mum in a house in Beck Avenue, opposite Mike Jones. He often saw Mike's teenage cousin Julie visiting. She was a lovely calm, friendly person of athletic build with straight long blonde hair to her waist. The pretty young woman usually wore figure hugging tops with short miniskirts to emphasis her shapely legs.

When she arrived on a visit across the road, the boys would hide behind the net curtains to admire her physique. For some time, when the boys met at Jon's house, he would declare his passion and promise that he would marry her.

One evening, the boys were playing cards, smoking and ribbing each other when there was a knock at the front door. Jon answered, the others could hear him talking to a girl. They looked at each other in amusement, a girl? Probably a neighbour borrowing half a cup of sugar. Perhaps Glyn's mum forgot where she lived, or someone was collecting the monthly Insurance instalment.

"Yeah, come in," Jon requested, "the boys are in here. Come and meet them." Tony moved to the window to have a look, Joe hid his cigarettes, Stanley and Glyn blushed.

Shyly, a head with blonde hair and pale blue eyes appeared around the door. "Go on," assured Jon from behind her. She stepped further into the room, relaxing as her cousin's smile greeted her.

"Wotcha," blushing Glyn broke the ice, he giggled. "You okay?"
She smiled.

"This is Julie," added Jon, "I'll introduce you to the gang."

Later, the boy's labelled Jon 'a sly old dog'. He must have been planning the chat up for ages, there was no doubt that she was a cracker. He then became 'a sly, lucky old dog'.

The boys were at the age when the one-eyed trouser snake would, without warning take control.

Irrespective of what the young man was doing, it would suddenly mutate and demand attention. Sometimes from a downward aspect it would rise and snag on clothing causing discomfort. Not only sitting on a sofa with an attractive young lady would arouse it. Common stimuli were TV adverts for coffee or chocolate, a newspaper cartoon or even the TV weather forecast. These could all easily trigger the same reaction. It had a mind of its own, able to render the owner motionless until it eventually got bored and went back to sleep.

Stan met and started dating Julie's best friend Rebecca. Stan and Becca were both still at school for a short while they enjoyed each other's company, but never went 'out, out'. He was naïve, still a boy, he never thought to take her to the cinema or out somewhere. He thought she was too young for her parents to let her visit a pub, but he was lacking confidence to ask.

Each evening together they would sit with her dad and watch TV. The draw for Stan was each evening at 9.30pm when her dad left to collect Becca's mum from work. The moment they heard his car pull away they smooched, then thirty minutes later when the car returned, they stopped, red faced readjusting themselves.

Stan couldn't wait for 9.30pm. He also loved the additional 'good night' kiss and cuddle at the front door as he left to catch the last bus at 11.45pm. There were no real feelings between them, just his lust. Stan didn't appreciate that she was bored. His teenager brain wasn't in control, something else would take over.

After a few months, she travelled to his home on Christmas Eve to secretly give him a lighter as a present. Politely, she then told him she didn't want to see him anymore. He wasn't upset, he shrugged his shoulders and understood her reasons. He was boring!

The following Spring, the boys had been playing football in Central Park. Stan's friends made their way home, he went to the Pavilion to buy a drink.

Three teenage girls walked past as he leant against a tree. He thought one was very attractive. They looked back, he smiled. The girls continued and moving closer to each other whispered together. They chuckled, playfully wrestling, the taller one was shoved towards Stan. Looking back at him again they laughed and smiled.

As shy as Stan was, he couldn't ignore this 'come on'. Especially as he did actually fancy the flirty taller, blonde girl. He walked slowly towards them. The three girls saw him coming and waited below an overhanging tree.

Close up, the nice one had acne on her face, but it didn't put the young man off, he could see laughter in her eyes. Stan sensed spending time with her would be fun, possibly insane. She was slim with nice eyes and long wavy golden hair. Her name was Christine. Stanley made sure most of his conversation was with her, gently neglecting the other two.

They decided to meet at the Odeon cinema in Heathway to watch a film.

Stanley was always hopeful that Christine would materialise at the cinema. On the day of the date, he spruced himself up, checked his money, applied aftershave then set off.

He was disappointed when he alighted the bus in Heathway. Christine was standing outside the cinema, but regrettably she had brought both her friends.

Although he had planned to pay for her ticket for the show, he couldn't afford to pay for all three girls. There was no alternative, he bought only his own.

The group of four made their way into the stalls to take their seats.

Being a gentleman, he led the way through the pitch black by the beam from an usherette's torch, stood at the end of a row of seats and waved them through. Because Christine had followed close behind him, she was now seated at the opposite end. The two other girls sat between them. He wasn't angry, he just didn't feel happy with himself. The three girls conversed, laughed and ignored him.

He felt like a 'spare one' at a wedding. When the lights came up as the film finished, he said his goodbye and left the cinema. He didn't have the desire to arrange another similar 'date'.

Later, when running the episode through his mind, he related it to his relationship with Rebecca. He had probably unknowingly treated her in a similar way as Christine had treated him. There was no malice just naivety, perhaps with a lack of self-confidence.

07-08

TRICIA

That Summer, Stan and Peter Roberts were returning from playing Pitch and Putt at the Central Park course. As they walked home through the park along a tarmac path, two young women called them. Stan and Peter looked up. The girls waved them over.

"Hi lads," the shorter one called to them. "Did you enjoy your game?" Her friend grinned, "she meant 'are you game'."

The four young people chatted for about thirty minutes. The taller one nodded to her friend, brushed the seat of her mini skirt with her hands as she stood and stated, "We have to go now, but do you know the Golden Hind in Romford?"

The boys nodded.

"Well, if you are near there on Saturday about 9.00pm you can buy us a drink."

The boys' eyes popped out of their heads. Together they answered, "See you there."

On Saturday, Stan and Pete were nervous but happy. They wore their best clothes with another dousing of aftershave.

Still believing they had been hoaxed, the boys arrived at the pub and entered the bar. Pete led them through the people sitting on stools or standing at the horseshoe bar. He ducked down nudging Stan, then pointed into a second room whispering, "They are here." The boys turned into the space to see the two girls sitting at a small circular wooden table.

The two girls had gone for it, they looked stunning dressed in the current fashion. Both were dressed similarly and looked immaculate. Shining black bobbed hair in a hairband, Mary Quant style flared mini dresses with white patterned lace tights and glossy patented shoes.

They smiled, waving Pete and Stan to them. After getting the drinks, the boys sat at the table.

The shorter girl blew cigarette smoke to the side and smiled, "I suppose it would be a good idea to find out your names?"

They laughed, Pete and Stan introduced themselves. The shorter girl was Tricia, the taller one Jacqui. The night flew, it got to 11.15pm before they looked at the clock. The date had gone so quick they couldn't believe it was time to go home. Pete escorted Jacqui home. Stanley left with Tricia.

As she lived a short distance from the pub, they agreed to walk the fifteen minutes to her home. Full of life, Tricia put her arm through his and held tight, she leaned closely against him bouncing with energy as they walked. They chatted, laughed, stopped for a kiss. There was no reason to rush, no reason to hurry the parting.

After thirty minutes, they arrived at Tricia's front door. Upbeat, she gave Stan a light kiss on his lips then asked if he would like to see her again. He confirmed he would, smiling she wrote her phone number on a piece of paper torn from her diary.

"Phone on Thursday after tea." She instructed him.

He turned and left.

"Don't forget to phone me," she called out.

"I won't," he called back, waving his arm above his head merrily skipping along the path.

Five days later Stanley was anxious. He had heard that Pete and Jacqui weren't bothering to organise a second date. He worried, hoping he would still see Tricia again.

Stan had managed to avoid using a Post Office telephone box for the whole of his life. Now, he was due to phone Tricia, and he had no idea what to do.

Why were there two buttons? "So what is the difference between Button 'A' and Button 'B'," he repeatedly questioned his dad.

Finally, he walked with his pile of 1d coins to the phone box on the corner near the Beck to phone Tricia. It went well, despite his lack of conversation they arranged to meet again.

To impress the young woman Stan had borrowed a Shen Berman shirt from his brother John for the date. He was delighted Tricia flatteringly thought the shirt was 'fab', she loved the button-down collar and back pleat. When they kissed good night, she was more amorous than the peck on the first date. She held him close, pushing her body against his, gently nibbling his top lip with her teeth to make it swell and tingle. Then she rubbed her teeth over his bottom lip, softly gripping and pulling a small portion from the rest to produce the same effect.

The third and fourth dates were at the local cinema to watch a film. Each time they met or spoke on the phone their relationship blossomed. At the end of the fourth date, she invited Stanley into her home for a coffee.

The next week they visited the Golden Hind, their fifth date. As Stan walked Tricia home, she cuddled up close to him. The young lady enfolded both of her arms around one of his as they chatted and laughed.

Tricia cleared her throat, "I know that you are not working, but are you looking to get a job?"

Stanley's feelings for the vivacious young lady would not allow him to tell her an untruth, he confessed that he was still at school.

"I had an idea you were," she admitted. Tricia appeared more sad than angry, she did not command but apologetically rasped from a dry throat, "So how old are you?"

The answer, "Seventeen," made her smile.

"Do you know how old I am?" she asked.

Stan replied, "I really hadn't thought about it. About eighteen or nineteen, I suppose?"

As they stopped at her front door, she turned to face him, looking deep into his dark brown eyes, she swallowed. Tricia lifted her left hand into the wavy blonde hair bordering his ear and playfully twisted it around her index finger. "You are cute, you sweet thing," she answered, "I'm twenty-five!"

"Oh, that's okay," Stan mused, "I don't mind, I li' like you."

"I'm sorry Stan," she took the keys from her handbag, "I'm really sorry, it's not fair on you, I'm too old for you. It's okay now, but I'm a lot older than you are, later on? I don't know? Well, what is best for you?"

Tricia took his head in her hands, "I'll be thirty when you are only twenty-two. If we stay together now, it will be harder to say goodbye later."

She wiped the corner of her eye with a finger, "I have been thinking of this for a while now. Look, I do think a lot of you, but it's probably better if I don't see you again. We can't get too involved."

She was genuinely upset, if only he was a couple of years older.

Stan was quiet, he enjoyed their dates, his time being with her.

He felt close to her, different to how he had felt towards anyone else. Perhaps he was in love with her, in love with the person, he had never thought about her age? Did he argue? No.

Tricia knew her own mind, after only five dates he already knew she was strong willed. There was no point in causing a scene, he truly didn't want to part under a cloud.

They had one last gentle kiss, a crushing loving embrace which neither wanted to withdraw from, then he turned and walked away. He looked back with a tear running down his cheek to see Tricia waving goodbye for the last time.

08

ADULT

Chapter Marker

08-01

STAG

Roy, Glyn and Stan had compiled a list of lyrics for seven rugby songs. They were in Jon's front room teaching a few friends the words. Jon and Mike were copying them.

A quiet 'rap, rap', on the window disturbed the activity. Jon pulled back the curtains to see Tony standing outside. He went to open the front door.

The crowd greeted him as he entered the front room, "Just in time Tone, we're learning these rugby songs," called Joe.

Tony looked flush, he nodded, not really absorbing Joe's welcome.

"You okay?" a few of the gang asked.

Something definitely was not right. "Here, have a fag," Glyn's extended arm passed a cigarette. Roy sparked his lighter and held it to the end of the white cylindrical object.

Tony nodded, "I've got some news. Well good news, but bad news." He pondered, "I'm going to be a dad." Silence. What could they say, he was only sixteen years old. A boy.

"With Lisa?" asked Roy.

"Yeah, yeah, of course," added Tony.

Jon joined the conversation, "But you was banned from seeing her, weren't you?"

"Yeah," added Tony.

"Sounds like the dog walking was fun," giggled Glyn. No one responded.

"Well, that's one of the problems," Tony added, "she hasn't told her parents yet. She swore that she wasn't seeing me. Now this!"

"Don't fancy having to tell Lisa's old girl, she's a battle axe," enlightened Rick.

"Are you going to get rid of it?" posed Roy.

"Have another fag mate, here are," Mike tossed Tony a cigarette, "what about your mum and dad. Have you told them?" He passed cigarettes to the others.

"Yeah, we told my mum yesterday, she's okay, Dad's a bit 'told you so'. We are thinking of keeping it," Tony mumbled. "We are going to tell her parents tomorrow."

"Come here, you wally. Too late now mate. No regrets, live with it. You love her don't ya?" Rick put his arm around Tony's shoulder, Tony nodded. The others stood and drew closer, together they formed a huddle.

About five months later on a cold, cloudy January evening seven smartly dressed boys collected each other as they walked from Jon's home to Tony's. On arrival at the groom's home, they entered the house to greet Tony's parents and sisters. The Clark family were gathering at the family home ready for the next day's wedding at the church in old Dagenham village.

Shortly, they left to travel to a pub Jon had recommended.

This was Tone's Stag night, they weren't going to the Lodge or the Football Club. Tonight it was going to be special. Only Jon had been there before, driven in his brother's car. But he roughly knew the route. After a thirty-minute journey by bus and then Underground, they arrived at Upminster station.

Jon the explorer led the way. "Turn right out of the station and walk about fifteen minutes." Boisterous and excited, they set off.

The group walked along a main road, eyes popping at the very big posh houses on each side. Most were detached with double drives and large gardens. They guessed that some of the vehicles parked on the drives cost more than a house in Dagenham.

After fifteen minutes, the houses gave way to a farm, then fields. They had been hiking for twenty-five minutes when they walked across a flyover, with a busy 'A' road running underneath. Jon was being verbally abused, 'walking for twenty-five minutes, pitch black, no buildings just trees and cars'. It was freezing cold, only the battering from the chilled wind stopped it from snowing.

"Be there soon!" He promised for the third time. "This way, not far."

They turned right into a narrow road. It was only wide enough for cars to pass each other. There was no pavement, just an uneven overgrown grass verge full of puddles and mud along one side. Without street lights, they walked in single file along the edge of the road, climbing towards the apex. If a car engine was heard or its lights seen, someone would shout 'CAR'. In unison, they would ignite their light-ers and jump onto the uneven muddy verge.

"It's like a F*** safari this," shouted Joe, "but all the F*** animals are indoors in the warm."

"They might be six feet away," continued Mike, "but we can't see F*** all."

A voice let out a 'whinny', another a 'neigh', they laughed and trudged on.

Another voice, "CAR," they flicked their lighters and stepped aside.

"S*** F***, puddle." Tony exclaimed, "I've got to wear these shoes tomorrow, S***."

The line of teenagers reached the brow of the knoll, then started descending. They could no longer see the car lights behind them now so had to listen more intently. Cheerfully, they could see streetlights ahead. At the bottom of the hill was a crossroads.

"Snake," shouted Stan, "where, where, S***," they all ran to the middle of the road.

Stan stood alone, laughing, "Got you," he cried.

"CAR," they ran back onto the verge.

Roy led them in the Buccaneer's Song.

The boys walked to the bottom of the hill then turned left. They didn't know which way, but there were more lights on the left. Eventually, set back from the road on the right, after an hour's walk from the station they found a pub. Any pub would have done, the teenagers tramped inside, a large open fire gushed heat into the room. It had taken them over ninety minutes from Tony's home.

Cold, wet and grim, they found the pub to be large and welcoming. An open fire, no live music just a jukebox. As normal the group made their own entertainment, wisecracking and bouncing off each other. There was a big cheer when Tone announced that Jon had agreed to be his Best Man.

There was a surprise at 10.00pm when the pub handed everyone a free plate of Shepherd's Pie. Jon asked the barmaid the reason and was informed that the following day, Saturday was 'Burn's Night'. They didn't know what 'Burn's Night' was, nor its connection to Shepherd's Pie, but the food was tasty if unexpectedly more spicy than usual.

'Chucking out time', the last bell had gone, slowly people drifted homewards from the pub.

The boys converged in the car park, now a lot happier than when they had arrived. Despite Jon's disagreement, they were determined not to go home the same route they had arrived. It was gone 11.30pm, there was no guarantee they would even catch the last train home from Upminster.

Nobody knew where they were, now cold, wet and drunk.

Tone kept mumbling about his muddy shoes. Brahms and Liszt, he continued to try and sit on the wet floor. Mike and Jon put him in the red phone box out of harm's way.

A decision was made, they would have to shell out and use the red telephone box in the pub car park to phone for a taxi.

Glyn moved around the group collecting change for the phone. Mike joined Tone and checked the inside of the phone box for taxi phone numbers. Joe stood by the phone box, removing shards of glass from the broken windows. Rick slide behind the phone box to have an 'eye lash'. Roy was already behind a tree, having one.

A faint motorcycle noise faded and died. The boys carried on with their activities.

Someone coughed, the boys looked up. A large policeman sat on a 'Noddy Bike', just in the kerb about ten feet away.

The policeman called, "We have had a report of a disturbance being made, by," he counted the boys, "Er four."

Roy appeared, "Five," he claimed.

Rick walked from behind the phone box, "Er six," he was concerned.

Mike stepped out of the phone box with Tone, "Er eight." He waited and looked around, "Yeah eight youths."

A second 'Noddy Bike' pulled up. The PC dismounted and joined the boys. "It's an offence to hang around in a group at this time of night," he informed them.

"We have just come out of the pub, trying to phone a taxi," Rick explained.

Mike pointed to Tony, "Tone's getting married tomorrow."

A 'Panda Car' arrived; it parked across the pavement to block any attempt of escape.

The first PC strolled to Joe, "Wanton damage to Her Majesty's telephone box. Sonny, you're under arrest. I can see you have smashed the windows."

Two Police Officers climbed from the first car to observe the scene. Another 'Panda Car' drove into the car park.

Joe argued, "No I ain't, I've been cleaning it up," he refuted the accusation angrily.

"You are under arrest," confirmed the PC.

Joe didn't like being called a liar. Furiously he pointed to the ground inside and outside the phone box, "If you look on the ground there is no broken glass. I was making it safe, someone cleaned it up ages ago."

The PC looked at the surroundings, the young man was right. The breakage must have been done some time before.

"Right," a voice boomed. The first PC commanded, "We are going to take your names and addresses. I want two youths in the back seat of each vehicle."

Stan and Roy were escorted into the back of a car. The PC took Roy's particulars. He turned to Stan, "Name? age? date of birth? home address? place of work?"

"I'm not at work," Stan replied.

"What do you do, unemployed?" asked the PC.

"I'm at school." Stan provided the information. He noticed when saying the words 'County High School' that the PC's attitude towards him changed.

Rick and Joe, who were too young to have even been inside a pub were told to stand, 'out of the way', adjacent the pub building.

After an hour or so of questioning, the Police warned the boys to 'move on' and left them to make their way home.

Tony, supported on Rick's arm waylaid the second 'Noddy Bike' rider to ask how they could get home. The PC was compassionate, he advised him to phone for taxis from the phone box but to wait a hundred yards away from the pub to prevent any further problems.

08-02
WEED

Mark Burns was a year younger than most of the boys, the same age as Joe, Mike and Rick. He lived in Glen Avenue, the turning next to Glyn.

One Sunday afternoon Mike spotted him on a motor scooter near Dog Shit Island. They stopped to have a chat. Scorch had two bags of cement on the scooter, one was on the back rack, the second inside the front wind breaker. They had been 'borrowed' from the building site where he worked as a brick layer. Mark had a private job organised for the following weekend so borrowing was a much cheaper method of funding the materials.

Mike laughed, he suggested the next time they met, Scorch would have a dozen bricks in the back rack. He didn't know how close to the truth he was, on Marks back was a rucksack containing six house bricks.

When saying their farewells, Mike invited the scoundrel to join the group for a drink in the Beck Lodge any time 'he was passing'.

Scorch dropped in to see them occasionally, eventually he became part of the group.

He was an immense man, over six feet tall and solid. Muscles, on muscles. However, he was a gentle, respectful person, who often caused to worry that he may have upset someone without knowing. He would worry that he hadn't apologised.

He tried to live as a Hippy, as if it were a religion, vowing never to get angry or hurt any living creature. His fine, dark wavy hair grew to his shoulders. Sometimes he would tie the end of his full wavy beard in a pink bow at his chin. Wearing long flowing clothes, he looked like a Yeti. Mark called everybody 'man', smoked 'weed' and used Hippy words. To save the planet, the Yeti shopped in second hand and army surplus stores.

One Friday evening at Jon's home, Scorch produced a letter from his girlfriend. She had dumped him, not face to face, but by letter. He was very upset; he had felt the world of her. The boys comforted him.

Mark took a small silver paper cube from his pocket. It was marijuana. He enquired if anyone would share a 'joint'. Stan was the only one willing to try, the others declined. At Jon's request, the two of them left the house, they decided to walk to the Beck Quarry. The pair settled down and had a 'smoke' on the banks of a lake, away from the cold wind. It wasn't very successful, in fact Stan would have rather had a pint.

Scorch apologised, he was upset because he had hurt his girlfriend, now he had wasted Stanley's time. He would rectify the matter for Stan. During the week he would travel to a Café in Kensington High Street to buy some 'high class' stuff.

Scorch fulfilled his promise, on the next Friday they met at Jon's then set off for the Quarry. There were people everywhere. When they did find a quiet place, it was windy, which made it difficult to 'cure' the lump.

Finally, after wandering around the fields and lakes they arrived at the old sewer pipe near Vickers Corner. Strangely, Stan noticed the top part of the old swing rope across the river was still in place on the tree. Opposite the swing where the pipe and river ran under the road was a small building which housed Public Conveniences.

"Ideal," rejoiced Scorch, "we can 'cure' it, then smoke it in there, away from the wind."

Stan was becoming excited.

Scorch clambered down the riverbank to the water's edge.

"Where you going?" questioned Stanley.

"Under the road to the other side," revealed Mark.

"I don't think you are, even I can't squeeze through there," laughed Stan. "Come on, we have to climb the fence and cross over the road."

Mark made one of his 'pitiful little boy' sad faces, then grinned, "That's the problem with being humongous."

Three minutes later, standing at the iron railings Mark smiled, "Climbing over this is another problem when you are humongous."

They found a gap in the fence, Stan tugged and helped pull the Yeti through to the pavement. The busy traffic slowed allowing the pair to cross the main road. Stan ran, behind him Mark strolled waving to the drivers. Finally, they were on the green which surrounded the toilet block. Stan stood back while Scorch crept inside.

He came out quietly, "There's someone having a dump, you can smell it, F***, we'll have to wait. We'll be better off out here, I promise."

They made camp on a slatted wooden bench on the edge of the green next to the path, about twenty feet from the building.

'Come on' they thought, 'the person in there must have diarrhoea'.

A middle-aged man walked along the pavement. The boys hoped he didn't need to use the toilet block.

They heard the cistern flush then a cubicle door slam, Scorch looked at Stan and smiled, "We'll, soon be in business." Stan returned the joy.

Where was the middle-aged man going? They checked he wasn't walking towards the Public Conveniences before they stood. He stayed on the pavement walking unhurriedly towards them. 'Great they thought, ten minutes before "smoooking time"'.

The middle-aged man stopped in front of them, "Where do I catch a 174 bus?" he asked. Next, he looked left and right.

The boys followed his glance, then looked at each other, "Over there by that big tree," Stan informed him, pointing to his right.

At the same time, the man reached inside his coat pocket to retrieve a card, "Don't move," he instructed.

"Police," he shouted as he flashed his Warrant Card.

More men joined them from each side. A big man, standing watching from the other side of the road was probably also a rozzer.

While two officers stood back, another two searched the adjacent area. The main officer questioned Scorch and Stan.

He took the boys names and addresses, then executed a frisk search. They both waited for the inevitable. At any time, he would find the 'Wacky Backy'.

From Scorch's inside pocket, the main officer pulled out the 'dumping letter' from Scorch's girlfriend. He opened it and put his hand inside.

"What's this?" he questioned.

'Curtains, put your arms forward', 'click, click', Stanley waited.

"Oh, it's some old letter I found over the Quarry," responded Scorch coolly. "Some poor dude got dumped, I thought it was so sad, so I kept it."

The officer opened the letter and started to read it.

Judgement Day, the boys were in deep S***.

The officer refolded the letter, placed it back into the envelope then put it back in Scorch's pocket. Stan could hear Mark's heart beating.

The officer signalled to his colleagues, as he whispered, "F*** off, go on, go." He waved his arm to gesture the direction.

The boys looked at each other, rose from the bench then scarpered across the road. A stationary bus waited at the traffic lights for the signal to change. The boys jumped onto the rear platform then raced up the stairs to the top deck.

"This is a 175, we don't want this," exclaimed Stan.

Scorch looked back out of the rear window, he declared that they needed any form of transport that took them away from the coppers.

He inspected his letter, the 'dope' was still in the envelope. Stan wanted to keep it, but Scorch threw the package from the bus window.

They couldn't believe the officer had not seen the 'stuff' in the envelope.

The name and address on the envelope was the same as the one Scorch gave as his abode. The 'Old Bill' are not 'stupid'. Scorch was certain the police would be tailing them.

Stan thought the police were probably after 'bigger fish'. The two boys had walked into an ambush, setup for someone else. They were caught in a planned police operation, four or five officers, just for a £1.00 lump of cannabis? No.

For weeks, Scorch worried that the police would pay his dad a visit at home. Later, to calm his nerves, he also destroyed the letter.

08-03

WORK

County High School was not a great move for Stanley. He had achieved remarkable 'O' Level results at Beck School, but this was different.

His thoughts went back to his first weeks at Beck School. The head, Mr Kerrigan had described the differences between a secondary modern and a grammar school.

'At Beck, the boys would be taught the mechanics of a subject, the process of acquiring an answer. They didn't need to know why, just how. But at grammar school 'A' Level students were taught the theory and relationships within a subject. It was for them to understand and determine the base facts'.

The lady who taught 'Pure Maths' was very old. Bent at the waist, arched back with silver grey hair. An archetypal grammar school mistress she wore a black gown, mortarboard and carried a cane. More a lecturer than a teacher, she acted as if she would prefer to be elsewhere, probably well past retirement age.

When studying subjects, she would write one 'proof' on the board explain the theory and leave the room. Five minutes before the lesson finished, she would return, enquire if there were any questions then leave again.

Stan found this method of learning very difficult to follow. There was no interaction between teacher and student, he had scores of unexplained functions and examples to calculate. The lady would probably have gone through the same procedure even when the classroom was empty.

He also found 'Applied Maths' difficult to study. Simply, he hadn't realised the close connection to Physics. At Beck, he had Science lessons for four weeks, then the teacher ran away.

He had decided to study Maths because he saw it as a path to employment. He didn't really know what trade to pursue. He really enjoyed woodwork at Beck, it was probably he's choice of employment.

346

However, two things concerned him, firstly could a person make a living at a craft. Secondly, most crafts were being dehumanised as machines took the place of people. Were there actually any craft jobs available?

As most of the students in his classes were friendly, he was accepted as one of the crowd. His friend Alan who moved from Beck to County High with him made lots of new social friends. Stan mixed with the new people, but he already had life friends at home. Some, like Glyn, Roy and Jon had been friends for twelve years. He couldn't desert these for a new set of friends.

One highlight was when he met Alan and his girlfriend with her friend Amy.

Stan thought Amy must be a model or film star, amazing long dark hair and beautiful eyes. She was so easy to talk to and friendly. Alan arranged for Stan to be Amy's date on a foursome to the pictures with him. She had treated him like her boyfriend for the whole date, given him her time as if she had known him for years, he would never forget her.

His dislike of the school situation came to a head, Stanley decided to leave County High. He was struggling with his studies; his social life was elsewhere. Although he stopped attending school, he still had no idea of his future.

He had two lives, most days he would be discontent, staying at home to hide from the world. Of an evening and weekend, he would skylark with his friends. Perhaps continuing his studies rather than starting work was just a way to hide from life?

Possibly, he was mentally shot after working so hard on his 'O' Levels?

As ever, Irene and Pete supported him. If he started a conversation, they would listen and try to help. They never questioned him about his life, just left him to decide on his next action. At least, he still had an income from the paper round.

After some months, Stan felt ready to move on. He had an interview at the Council Career's Office, but they had little to offer. He looked through the evening papers for job adverts.

Stan found an advert for computer training. It looked like the type of project he would enjoy, also computing was just starting. He completed the COED'S Agency form and shortly after received a 'Test Kit'. The Exam Booklet contained about one hundred timed questions

ADULT

grouped around series, shapes and codes. The candidate observed a line of shapes and selected the next or missing item from a suggested list.

He found it so refreshing. He loved puzzles and was able to see sequences in his head, without delay he sat and completed the test. He was excited. Even when playing football, he could see the movement of players as a pattern. The dejected young man hoped he had found a path away from his misery. He could see himself working with computers.

A week later, a letter arrived with his test results, he had scored 98%. The letter contained a telephone number for him to call to arrange a visit.

Stan's parents were overjoyed. They had read about computers in the daily newspaper. He was allowed to contact COED'S.

As scheduled, the very smartly dressed man with a large briefcase arrived at Stan's home. He explained the future would be all about computers and computing. 'Stanley's score was one of the highest his organisation, COED'S, had ever seen. The exam proved Stanley was made for the industry'. Stan's smile couldn't grow any wider, this was his destiny. He was so happy.

The man took leaflets and brochures from his briefcase. The proposal was that Stan would pay COED'S' to train him in computing. Money wasn't a problem as he could pay monthly or take out a loan. Later, after Stan had attained a high level of ability and passed the COED'S' exams, his CV would be passed to partners of COED'S'. The man promised that with Stanley's potential he would be offered a position with most of the partners.

Stanley was deflated, he thought the advert was for a job. This man was selling 'training'. He checked the company name again: it was 'COED Studie'.

What to do? The fees were expensive, astronomical. But if the payback was good, was it worth studying? He was unsure; anyway, his dad would have to sign all of the forms as a guarantor. The cloud hadn't been removed from Stanley he was more confused. He needed time to consider the proposal and asked the man to leave.

Irene, Pete and Stan chatted about the offer. They established there was no assurance the course was valid, nor that Stan would ever be offered a job. They agreed that computing may never 'take off'. It could be forgotten and replaced with something else before Stan was fully trained. Stan decided his dream was too good to be true, back to newspaper ads. At least, this exercise broke his malaise.

Finally, he applied for and was offered job interviews.

With his mum in tow, he travelled on the London Underground to various interviews. While he attended, she would sit in a nearby Café with her fingers crossed. Surprisingly quickly, within weeks he was offered a vacant post which he accepted.

He started going to work. Irene and Pete were relieved, Stanley alone had managed to tame whatever monster had been holding him back.

08-04

WALK

Jon's mum, Mrs Peters was loosely connected to the Christian Mission. At the end of her garden was a very large workshop with a door which opened directly onto the Mission's land. Before Jon's dad passed away, he helped by undertaking caretaker duties like cutting the grassed areas between the buildings and general handicraft repairs. These duties were now carried out by Jon and his mum. Sometimes, Glyn, Stan and Rick would help.

The Mission was open to anyone, the three large wooden halls built on the grassed area were used for Prayer, Sunday School, Scouts and Guides meetings.

Through people attending the Mission Jon's mum had heard about a 'Charity walk'. The lady used her position as Friday night card school tea lady to talk the boys into taking part. They agreed before they knew the full story, but the promise of a free concert by the country's top bands was a good enough incentive.

On 13 July 1969, they set off on the OXMAF charity walk. On the hottest day of the year, they took longer than eight hours to walk approximately thirty miles from Upminster to Wembley Stadium.

The walkers and guardians met at Upminster station at around 9.30am, they set off at 10.00am. The gang saw it as a giggle, a good way to chat to girls. No one was prepared for the endeavour or the physical task. Wearing soft plimsolls or sandals would make their feet sweat and blister. Heavy jeans and sweatshirts made them hot; few wore hats.

At first, the atmosphere was akin to the home support at a football match. Everyone smiled and nattered. The guides and marshals shared jokes with the walkers. Some joined hands to run in a wave along the street. Others held hands, dancing a waltz or Jitterbug. Any 'oggy, oggy, oggy' call would be met with an instant rapturous, 'oi, oi, oi' reply from everyone in earshot.

After about two hours walking, the boys started to notice casualties here and there. Not many, a few people sat on a wall or kerb, resting. Previously, a 'thumbs up' or a smile would receive the same back. But now, the responses were noticeably less cheery.

Roy requested the boys stop for a moment. He removed his left shoe and crumpled blood-soaked sock. The crease in the sock had caused a blister on two of his toes. After rearranging the sock, they carried on. By now, the walkers had passed three water stations the first two were not ready, the third had no water left.

The boys laughed as they walked past a group of four boys and girls spread across the pavement on their backs. In an attempt to soothe their tired, sore feet they had taken off their footwear and were laying with their bare feet against a Butcher shop's cold window.

There were now more people lying on the floor, some with their legs in the air to reduce cramp pain. Some stood on tip toe to push down and ease their taut calf muscles.

A blue painter and decorators van pulled up sharply next to them. A lady's voice begged through the open van window. "Pleease. Stop."

All about looked in the direction of the van. A middle-aged woman jumped from the van and ran to the back. She opened the doors, quickly the lady started to unload cardboard boxes onto the pavement.

"Pleease," she shouted, "water!"

Within seconds, a queue formed. Two people closes to the boxes ripped them open to gain access, passing the bottles to the line of desperately thirsty walkers.

The lady reappeared, standing by the boxes she helped hand out the water bottles. She confessed that the 'march' was travelling too quickly. She was supposed to operate at one of the first water stations, but when she got there the walkers had already passed through. 'How the people were moving so much faster than planned had baffled the Organisers. The heat would later take its toil'.

Rehydrated, the boys continued. The soles of their feet were now sore and blistered. Stan advised to walk on the outside of each foot. That produced a strange, hobbling gait but it limited the times the sore underside of each foot touched the floor. The pain from the soles of their feet was crippling. The others followed his idea.

Joe took a minute to hang back to watch them walk off. He blasted them. They looked like 'a band of dwarves who had messed their pants'. No one was going to scrag him, obviously they were not going to chase him either. He was safe.

On the opposite side of the road to them, they observed a garden hosepipe suspended above the path from a tall Poplar tree. A party of walkers were screaming and messing about under it to get each other wet. An uninterrupted string of others stood back from the melee awaiting their turn. The gang struggled onwards.

Later, they couldn't walk on neither the sole nor the outside of each foot, so they walked on the inside. There was no longer a continuous line of advancing bodies on the road, there were now small groups of grim-faced people spaced at intervals.

About six hours had passed when the boys came to a country village. While waiting at a crossroads for the traffic lights to change, Mike spotted a makeshift sign.

They were standing next to a tiny, old style 'Tudor' type cottage abutting the path. Inside a small dirty window was a torn piece of paper with the word 'WaTeR', scrawled on it.

"B*** H***! Water," cried Mike. The others looked around. The cottage looked old, resembling something from a Fairy Tale. Rick led the way.

The tiny front gate was jammed half open, laying askew as the top hinge was broken. It was difficult to pass. The trellis' at the front gate and front door were unkempt. A mucky empty milk bottle, plus broken and cracked flowerpots littered the garden and path, which were both overgrown. It looked frightening. The boys formed a line along the garden path, each waiting for another to use the knocker.

"Whoa," whispered Glyn. "This place is scary, like Hansom and Jetal."

"Like who?" questioned Mike, laughing, "you mean Hansel and Gretel."

"I don't care who the F***, I mean," answered Glyn, "I ain't F*** going in there. That sign could have been put there during the Great Plague. It's old enough. They could be kidnappers, in there?"

"Ooh, you sissy," berated Roy, "they could be pesky pirates. Caw, pieces of eight."

The front door to the cottage opened, they jumped back. It was only the inadequate free space at the broken front gate that stopped them trying to escape. A small elderly man with a balding head and grey ear moustaches appeared in the doorway. He was dressed in black. Glyn's heart jumped, "Dracula, S***!"

The old man spoke of the Charity Walk, he invited them into his home. The first two walkers gained entry into the front room not by choice, but by virtue of forces applied at their backs. It was only after they saw his 'dog collar' that they relaxed. The boys were in a vicarage, the man was the local vicar.

Once the boys were positive the man wasn't going to eat them, they accepted his kind offer to sit on soft seats to rest. They were given food and drinks, a warm flannel to wash their faces. The vicar offered them a foot bath, but they graciously declined.

Instead, they cleaned their feet, applied antiseptic to the raw areas and plasters to cover the blisters. Refreshed, now suffering only half of the foot pain they were renewed.

From then on, the walk was manageable. The boys continued with the other 50,000 walkers towards their goal. Soon, in the distance they could hear the sounds of rock music. As they walked along 'Wembley Way' towards the Stadium people cheered them, photographers snapped, marshals thanked them. People were walking in every direction, everyone was smiling. The 'oggy, oggy, oggy' call was working again.

The boys slowly, achingly climbed the stairs of the stadium to look out over the crowd and at the band playing. They bought food and drinks, rested then began the return journey. It would have been nice to sit in the sun listening to rock music, but it was work the next day. Slowly, limping on both feet they hobbled to the closest Underground Station to hitch a ride back to Dagenham.

Elated travelling on the Tube, the boys rested. But how every muscle in their bodies hurt the next day.

One 'Filmed News' item reported, 'It shows that young people, even with their long hair and strange dress, blistering heat and blistering feet, can do important things and do care'.

The boys hadn't learned their lesson. In the November, Jon's mum again persuaded them to walk with 17,500 others for REHAB. The course over the sixteen London Bridges that cross the River Thames was, when compared with OXMAF, just a baby totalling only twenty miles.

09

BOATING

Chapter Marker

09-01

BOZ

"Nice day for a swim," chuckled Glyn as he folded the front passenger seat forward.

Roy followed Stan, after squeezing between the open van door and folded car seat, the pair stepped onto the hot car park tarmac. The sun was shining. Above them a blue sky without a cloud. The journey from Dagenham to the boat yard had taken them three hours.

From the back of the van, they heard the thud, thud of sports hold-alls and grocery supplies dropping onto the tarmac as Jon removed them from the van.

They collected their belongings then wandered through the streets of a lovely old village. Although it was Saturday afternoon, the village was peaceful.

As they walked along the High Street Roy looked down the gaps between the houses on their left. He excitedly pointed as he saw a boat, "Look, look," he cried, trying to stay calm. The boys were now getting really eager. It was the first time Stanley had been on a paid holiday from a place of work. He definitely wouldn't miss the Tube journey to Gloucester Road station.

The boat yard appeared in sight, they turned into the enclosure coming to a halt at the edge of the dock. To both left and right were rows of freshly cleaned white and pale blue river cruisers. How could they not smile to each other? Roy had booked the holiday, but as Jon looked the eldest, he entered the office to sign in and collect the documents.

The boys stood looking at the scenery that encircled them, it was beautiful. The dark rippling water reflected white and silver shards of sunshine. The reflection of each boat added more colour. There were swans and ducks diving for food. A large swan swimming in front of them stretched tall to flex its wings. Trees and green fields fringed the river, families wandered aimlessly along a towpath. It was so quiet, but actually there was bird chatter, next an excited dog begged its master to launch a stick.

The smell of the countryside was different to that of Dagenham.

The office door opened. Jon reappeared accompanied by a tall slim man. The man was very tanned from working in the open he had the appearance and manner of a fairground operative. His shirt sleeves were rolled up above his elbows. He wore a dilapidated dark trilby on top of a ponytail hair style, on his feet were open sandals with no socks.

The man took an expired cigarette from the side of his mouth. "Wotcha lads," he greeted the boys, "I'm Boz, I'm gonna give you a quick instruction on the boat, follow me." Boz smelt of engine oil.

They proceeded along the jetty with a row of gently swaying boats to their left. Each boat was tied by its stern cleats to a pair of posts on the towpath. At the fourth cruiser, Boz stepped down onto the boat transom then leapt into the aft cockpit, he signalled the boys to follow.

Once everyone was aboard, he called an audience, "Right, this is Stalham Dyke, make a note of the name and how to get here because this boat has to be back here by next Saturday morning. Understood? She's called 'Staithe Blaze'. Has anyone cruised on a boat before?"

Stan, answered, "I have."

Boz ignored him and continued, "You have to give way to sail, be really careful when they are tacking. You must be moored from dusk to dawn. There is a speed limit, but you don't need to worry about that cos this has a limiter fitted.

Remember, these things don't have brakes. When you want to stop, you should decrease speed before cutting the engine then drift. As you get closer, if you are too fast, throw her astern. If you will be a bit short, give a tiny burst ahead."

He showed them the positions of the cap and fill points for diesel, fresh water and waste, naming the locations where they could be refilled. "Please don't mix these up," he implored, "it will cost you a lot of money to get them cleaned out."

"Are you ready? Let's go."

Boz turned the key, pressed the little blue button, the engine murmured. He moved to the back of the cockpit, reached out behind and lifted the mooring lines from the posts. Each rope was circled in his hands then laid by its cleat.

He took the wheel, "Ready lads?" Boz cheered, "here wee gooo, whoopee," his fist punched into the air.

They were cruising, smiles all round.

Boz called Jon to him, passing on tips and techniques he moved away to let Jon take the wheel. Roy was at the front sitting on the cabin roof enjoying every minute with the wind blowing lightly in his face.

After ten minutes, they were recalled to the cockpit, Boz wanted to demonstrate a special manoeuvre. He took the wheel, "I'm going to show you a quick way of turning round. Don't tell anyone I showed you, don't do it if there are boats or people about."

Boz turned the cruiser at an angle of about forty-five degrees towards the high riverbank.

He then applied full lock on the wheel and cut the engine. The bow remained nearly stationary as the stern continued moving, swinging forwards in an arc. When the craft had nearly stopped, he reversed the engines on max then turned the wheel to the opposite lock to pull the bow further from the bank.

Then at the boat's maximum distance from the first bank, he reversed the lock again then moved slowly forward.

The bow came gently into contact with the bank. Boz held her steady then applied full throttle. Staithe Blaze rammed into and climbed the bank, the engine roared as plumes of black smoke emanated from the exhaust at the rear. Gradually, with her pivoted on the stern the bow of the boat glided up and along the bank, finally slipping back into the river she swung to face the direction they had arrived. Boz cut the engine.

Triumphantly, he spoke to the boys, but they were too S*** scared to listen. They thought the front of the boat was going to break off, or the engine blow up.

"Grab the wheel Jon," he instructed, "it's all yours!" He stepped onto the gunwale then jumped to the riverbank.

"Have a brilliant holiday, lads." He waved.

Without power the boat was now drifting, it was floating in a slight sideways movement along the river. Roy got to the wheel first.

They heard Boz in the distance shout, "Sorry again, I forgot. Drive starboard, pass port to port," he ran off.

"F*** nutter," uttered Roy.

"Time for his medicine!" Chipped in Glyn.

09-01

09-02

SPEED

Staithe Blaze had drifted into the middle of the Cut. Roy started the engine to pull the boat out of its drift. He steered her to the right-hand side of the river then poodled along. "Be careful," he instructed, "it's slow to respond to the wheel, there's a delay. As you feel the boat start to react to one manoeuvre you need to begin the next one."

"Where to?" he demanded.

The others gathered round. "Shall we take a mo to relax and get sorted?" asked Stan.

The others agreed. They needed time to look at the map, unpack and have a cup of tea. Glyn was aching to get at the engine to remove the speed limiter.

"Let's find a mooring first then we can all start from scratch," Roy suggested.

Stan and Jon climbed on top of the cabin roof to look ahead for a place to moor. There were a few spaces on the left bank, but the inexperienced boys didn't want to navigate against oncoming traffic as their first exercise. Eventually, they saw a free mooring with bags of room around it on the starboard side of the river.

"What about that prat," moaned Jon, "was he alright in the head?"

Glyn joined in, "It was like showing us how to do a three-point turn in a car by using the front wing rammed up against a wall, barmy."

Jon replied, "I bet his last job was on the Waltzer."

Roy called, "You've done this before Stan, show us how it's done."

Stan took the wheel; he placed Jon at the bow and Glyn at the stern. "Can you each grab a sheet," he smiled, windup.

Looking around the cockpit floor, "There ain't no sheets," fussed Glyn, "there's only ropes?"

Next, he placed two hands on the gunwale and looked over the side, "Where do they keep the F*** sheets? Oi, wait a minute, what we gonna do with F*** sheets?"

"Only laughing Glyn, ropes on boats are called sheets," answered Stan.

"Mr B*** clever clogs," grinned Glyn, "just because you've been on the B*** Medway."

Stan laughed, "As we get closer, step onto the towpath with the rope and hold us steady. When we're fully stopped, take the weight and hold her in then tie the rope to the post."

"Okay, Cap'n," answered Glyn, sarcastically.

Stan had only recently returned from a river cruise holiday on the River Medway in Kent with his family. He was confident of mooring, slowly he brought the boat to dock at the bank.

The two crewmen jumped ashore holding their ropes. Stan joined them, he showed each how to fasten a rope to a post using a Clove Hitch knot.

Within minutes, Glyn had removed the engine compartment cover and was searching for the speed limiter.

Stan rummaged in his holdall for the groups navigational aid, 'The Map of Public Houses on the Norfolk Broads'. The strategy of their expedition would be based solely upon the time needed to travel between Public Houses. As pubs were only open at lunchtime from 11.00am to 3.00pm planning was crucial.

Roy came round with a small pull cord bag. He collected five pounds from each person for the 'kitty'. To guarantee everyone paid an equal share of all expenses, all purchases would be paid for by the money in the bag. Roy would take it with him every time they left the boat, more funds would be added when needed. For safe keeping, it was hung from a coat hook in the toilet / shower room.

The time was now 2.00pm, Jon went to make them a hot drink, Glyn joined him in the galley to procure suitable kitchen utensils to adjust the speed limiter.

Roy and Stan checked the map, they were on the River Ant. The pair agreed on their first target, a pub about two hours cruise to Ludham Bridge. Once Glyn had successfully isolated the speed limiter they cast off. Roy took the helm, Blaze moved on at a gentle, relaxing pace. It was peaceful, just the boys with nature. A blue sky, the wish washing of the river lapping against the bank.

Jon and Stan laid on the cabin roof to catch some rays.

Gradually, the expanse of Barton Broad opened in front of them. Now this was boating, a large lake appeared, it was beautiful. Glyn saw the potential to test the extra speed he had engineered. Glyn had only two speeds, fast and very fast, taking the wheel from Roy, he gave it full throttle. The bow didn't noticeably lift but a wake streamed from the bow, he was happy.

They were rapidly closing the distance to a line of boats in front, he reduced speed.

Roy told him to keep inline, round the two islands in front then follow the other boats to the outlet branch on their left. He started to enjoy the tranquillity, appreciating the beauty of the National Park around him.

Meanwhile, Arthur was sailing from the opposite direction. Being close to retirement he found his weekly sail along the River Ant relaxed him enough to get through the next demanding week at work. It also gave him a break from his noisy, uncontrollable grandchildren.

The expert sailor had just entered the Broad, hanging starboard his plotted journey took him towards his home in Sutton. At last, he was in open water, without the confines of the river. Now he could catch the breeze, travel at greater speed, manoeuvre more easily. Rather than tack through the straight between the islands and riverbank he decided to use the freedom of clear water to sail around the islands.

It was a pleasure. As he neared the first island the wind caught his sails, he skipped towards the second. Tacking back, he repeated the exercise. Then, on the third tack amongst the tranquil calm of the water he heard an engine. In dismay, Arthur looked up to see a cruiser bearing down on him. Instinctively he dropped the sail then observing the cruisers speed he prayed. The cruiser hadn't seen him, Arthur grabbed an oar to fend off the larger vessel.

Laying in the sun Stanley felt thirsty, he decided to make some drinks for the 'crew'.

The young man sat up to look around at the scenery he needed to lift an arm to shelter his eyes from the sun's glare. Ahead, in the glare he could just make out a shape, dead centre of the bow was a shape. It was a pole, or a mast? Whatever its purpose, it was swaying in the air and in front of the boat. He stood up, there was a muffled cry from the water.

"Glyyyn, reverse, maaax reverse," he commanded. The engine noise stopped, then roared, he could hear the water at the stern churning. Glyn turned the wheel to its lock then cut the engine. Blaze moved backwards away from the island.

09-02

As if peeping to see if the road was clear, the nose of a small orange sailing dingy floated slowly into view across Blaze's bow. The sailor standing in the craft held a long oar upright, he didn't appear to be very happy.

The boys waved, no one spoke. Roy standing next to Glyn pointed forward. He restarted the engine, very carefully he guided the cruiser around the stern of the dingy.

Later, they arrived at their target pub where they moored for the night. Over a very tasty pub meal with gallons of beer, the boys recounted the dramas of their first day.

POTTER

At the stern, Roy unlocked and folded back the sky-blue canopy that covered and protected the cockpit. Stan appeared, cleaning his teeth.

Through tooth brushing teeth, he spoke, "Just got kicked out the khazi, Glyn needed it bad."

He pointed to the canopy, "You moving that aft?"

Roy responded, "Aft, don't be daft, what on this craft?"

They laughed, Stan replied, "Er, that would be graft, I'll give you. Er, a blast, to help."

They laughed some more, "A blast? You wally," Roy grinned. He continued, "Then er, in the pub this noon aft, I'll buy you a beer a draught."

With toothbrush in mouth, Stan helped Roy. They swivelled the awning tubular frame onto the transom then smoothed out any creases in the canopy. Job done. They looked at the view, a few boats had moored up behind them.

The boat behind was casting off, a man onboard waved, "Morning," he greeted them.

"Morning," they replied. Then they saw the funny side, both standing in only their underpants. Stan with a toothbrush sticking out of his mouth waving to a stranger. They had a giggled.

"A fish," Roy excitedly declared, pointing into the river.

The boys had a closer look, they wrenched. It was Spaghetti Bolognaise, Glyn had just 'parked last night's dinner'.

They set off about 10.00am, first stop Potter Heigham. Stan had plotted the course, Ant, Bure, then Thurne to the infamous bridge. Jon was at the helm.

About twenty minutes before they got to their destination it started to rain. Stan was now steering; it could have become a calamity. As Jon, Roy and Glyn scrambled to erect the windscreens then connect the cockpit canopy they continually blocked his vision.

Half the time Stanley was 'flying blind'. At intervals, he sat, stood or leaned sideways constantly bobbed to and fro to scan, then avoid moored boats, oncoming traffic or the bank.

The rain became intense. Roy and Glyn were required as windscreen wipers each side of the boat. They stood inside the covered cockpit with an arm extended outside wiping the water from the screen with a newspaper. Suddenly, as a right-hand bend straightened the bridge came into view. Although directly ahead, in the downpour it was indistinct, just a large grey shape.

Stan slowed the engine; he aligned Blaze to the tallest opening which formed the central arch.

The boat moved forward, a large illuminated red sign on the near bank read 'SOUND YOUR HORN'. He hit the horn. Within seconds, Blaze's bow was under the arch. The windscreen wipers called to him, there was about four inches clear each side.

Through the gloom and rain, he realised his view was hampered by the cockpit canopy and windscreens. 'Oh, no', worse, as they were still erected the edges of these parts of the boat were higher and wider than the arch. He was steering a square windscreen through a curved arch. Blaze was eight feet away from crashing into the bridge, as he slammed the lever into reverse Stan shouted to the windscreen wipers.

Roy and Glyn stopped wiping the screens then sprang into action. They quickly passed through the gaps between canopy and bridge onto the cabin roof to unlock and lay the windscreens flat. At the same time, Jon unhooked the canopy from the top of the windscreens and rotated the frame back to the transom. As Blaze drifted slowly under the bridge Roy and Glyn lay prone on the cabin roof, their heads within six inches of the brickwork.

Stan set the boat moving forward again.

Blaze moved slowly, in a straight line under the bridge. Stan gently increased speed, even a 'short A***', like him needed to duck as the cabin moved below the curved structure.

The boys were euphoric, the boat popped out the other side to be saluted by silence.

Two boats sat off the bridge, the people on them looked frustrated. Stan didn't know if he had jumped the queue. Perhaps there was a priority protocol to adhere to. In the storm, he had a problem seeing something as big as a stone bridge? He didn't really care; they had narrowly dodged spending their holiday wedged in Potter Heigham.

It was still raining. They erected the windscreen and canopy before motoring further along the River Thurne. After ten minutes, they decided to turn back. Jon drove for the return journey. This time, they were prepared, so much so that Stan and Roy knelt on each gunwale to guide Blaze through.

The plan was to return along the River Thurne then have lunch at a pub in a small Cut. Around 12.00pm the boat turned left into Mill Cut. Glyn was steering, it was extremely tight. On both sides of the river, boats were moored nose to tail, some hadn't been tied up properly and were swinging into the channel. One with a broom, the other a mop Jon and Roy were designated 'lookouts'. Positioned on the cabin roof the pair studied obstacles to offer instructions to Glyn, if they could reach an obstructive vessel the pair used their tools to push it clear.

"Reduce speed now." Roy shouted, "I can see the end. It's like a round basin, like a frying pan."

Then he added, "Fishing, I can see fishing rods." Followed by, "Whoa, yahoo, there's a building over to the right, looks like a sign outside. It's okay, it's a pub, a few minutes' walk."

Glyn cut the engine Blaze coasted slowly into the circular basin, he noticed there were anglers positioned about every ten feet around its perimeter.

There was nowhere to moor, 'F***'.

Jon shouted from the cabin roof, "What we gonna do?"

"Get the F***, out of here." Glyn answered.

His driving of a car usually resembled Rally Cross; it was no different when he was piloting a boat. Initially, he thought of trying Boz's manoeuvre but decided on a three-point turn. As he restarted the engine the anglers were aghast. Blaze was about thirty feet long; the basin was maybe only twice that in diameter.

From his steering position at the helm, Glyn couldn't see the low perimeter bank. Each time he moved ahead the 'look outs' had to advise him when to stop. But boats don't just stop. Before every change of direction, the boat would hit the bank, most times tearing into the angler's equipment.

Not only was Glyn ruining the days angling by scaring all the fish away, he was also destroying their equipment. The furious fishing men hastily removed their equipment, keepnets, rods from the water.

A few anglers were now expressing their anger, shouting, swearing and waving their fists at Roy and Jon. One irate man swung the rod through the air at Glyn's head.

Glyn worked at the helm, the bow was nearly in line with the channel, he gave it max speed. Insult to injury the water churned, mud rose to the surface, another keepnet was destroyed. Blaze entered the channel at an angle, she struck another boat then straightened up.

Blaze was on fire, ploughing through the water. Glyn grinned, he wished he had a water skier on tow.

Stan helped Roy and Jon, now at the bow with the mop, the other two balancing on either gunwale hurriedly using their feet to stop the craft smashing into boats that lined sides of the Cut. The shouts of outrage faded as Glyn slowed the vessel.

The boys took stock.

"Phew, did you see that wrestler one with the long keepnet on a pole," enquired Jon, "he tried to hook me off the roof with it."

"When we nearly beached, one of them was running to jump onboard," added Roy.

"Not much of a pub," chuckled Glyn, "I won't be going there again."

The tour of the Broads returned to a leisurely pace. They sailed to Acle Bridge for lunch then continued to Stracey Arms Windpump for the night mooring. Glyn turned up for the evening meal like a bandit with a hanky over his face, "just in case Interpol was circulating his photo."

09-04

MUD

Monday came around so quickly. The boys planned a day in Great Yarmouth and were extra excited.

Departing on their next adventure they stayed on the Bure travelling east towards the coast.

The sun was shining again. After travelling for about sixty minutes, Roy became aware of a boat ahead. Blaze seemed to be catching it very quickly. Jon was driving, so it wasn't due to Glyn tearing up the river. They got a bit closer to see the agitated movements of people standing onboard.

About ten feet away Jon pulled into the bank and stopped the engine.

"Are you okay?" Roy shouted.

A voice called back, "No, we are on a mudbank, been here for F*** ages."

"Can we help?" asked Roy. He could see four young men about his age on the other vessel.

"Try giving us a tow? If you want," came the reply. "Your boat looks about the same size as ours?"

Jon looked up at his ship mates standing on the cabin roof. All three nodded in agreement. He pulled Blaze a bit further forward while Stan stood behind in the cockpit, waving oncoming boats through. Jon shunted the boat backwards and forwards, unable to align with the stricken vessel he pulled forward then did a full sweep.

Conscious of the mudbank he reversed then drifted to within twenty feet of the stricken vessel.

"Have you got one of those metal tee things?" he asked. The man replied, there was one at the centre of the foredeck.

Roy hooked a rope over an aft cleat on Blaze then threw the other end to the immobile craft. One of the men caught it and hooked it over the forward cleat. He stood and gave a thumbs up.

Stan looked behind along the river, the first boat was about the length of a football pitch away, he signalled 'all clear'. Jon started the engine, he pulled forward. The rope tightened.

A voice from the afflicted boat shouted, "Slowly, we're moving. Keep going."

Inch by inch Blaze moved forward, "Good, great, keep going," a delighted voice called to Jon.

The boat slowed. Jon watched their position in relation to a tree trunk on the bank to confirm they were still moving. He tweaked the accelerator. The distance from his position to the tree didn't change.

A shout from the other boat suggested the men would rock the stricken boat from side to side.

Jon eased the accelerator forward, the men behind stood two each side of the cabin and pushed forward and back to produce a rocking motion.

Jon was on full throttle, the water behind was whirling. He heard a creaking noise, then felt a slight movement forward. Blaze roared against the load, there was another louder cracking noise, the white and pale blue boat lurched forward.

"Hooray, done it," Jon yelled.

He was about to enjoy the jubilation of success when a soft voice behind him spoke, "Don't turn your head yet. Stay there."

"Wait." Roy instructed, he bent to release the rope from the aft cleat then dropped it over the side. "Now, go like the F*** clappers," he ordered.

Jon couldn't resist temptation, he looked back. The stricken vessel now had a four feet tall pyramid of ruptured wood on the foredeck. The other boat hadn't moved at all, Jon had just ripped the whole foredeck from its frame. He had transformed its polished, shining waterproof planking into a pile of firewood.

Once they were safe enough away Jon stopped to shout his apologises. The people on the mud tethered vessel didn't move, they were speechless.

It seemed that without trying the boys were still making enemies wherever they went.

They arrived at the Great Yarmouth moorings before lunch. Within fifteen minutes, the boys had moored and commenced the thirty-minute walk to the beach.

In true holiday style, they decided to have fresh fish and chips for lunch with toffee apples and ice cream for afters. After setting up camp on the beach, Roy disappeared for thirty minutes. He returned with a bucket and spade, plus candy floss for each of them. It actually made a nice change to relax, build sandcastles on the beach, to paddle and swim in the sea. When three of them were laying on the sand half asleep, Roy sneaked away with the bucket to organise a wakeup call. Minutes later the cold sea water from the bucket had the desired effect. The boys chased him for revenge, eventually all four ending up in the sea wave jumping and splashing each other.

Consistently acting as children, the funfair was next. They screeched in the Haunted House, bumped on the Dodgems, white knuckled on the Roller Coaster. They lost money on the Penny Arcades.

In a short time, three of them won a soft toy on the Crane Grab, then they unsuccessfully took another thirty minutes and a small fortune to try and win a prize for the Glyn.

Luckily, Glyn won a cuddly penguin on the Horse Race game. He named it Julie and presented it to Jon.

Rather than eat at the evening mooring location they decided to stay in Yarmouth a bit longer to have burgers for tea. Later, on the journey back to the moorings they shopped for groceries. Glyn chose doughnuts and chocolate biscuits for the next day's breakfast.

From the Marina, they sailed into the River Yare then under Breydon Bridge, left into Breydon Water. The boys had been amazed when they first encountered Barton Broad, this was different. Breydon Water was massive, over four miles long and a mile wide.

The wind was up, the tide moved against them. The boat actually rolled and pitched; it was similar to being at sea. Glyn checked where the life jacket was kept. Roy joined the long line of vessels travelling towards the Southern Broads, every vessel kept within the markers.

Around 6.00pm they reached their night mooring at Burgh Castle on the River Waveney.

09-05

NORWICH

The next morning before setting out on a walk, the crew feasted on doughnuts, chocolate biscuits and two cups of tea for breakfast. The quartet followed the towpath past the old ruins of Burgh Castle to Breydon Water. The views at Burgh Castle were amazing.

There were large black birds sitting on the river signs and markers. Some had their wings extended in a 'haunting' position to dry them. Wader birds explored the many channels in the marsh for food while Curlews called. The boys recognised Curlews by sight and call because they often flocked in the fields around the sandpits at Beck Quarry.

The junior sailors set off around 9.30am, destination Norwich. It was about a twenty-five-mile journey, possibly more than a five-hour cruise.

Travelling south from the evening mooring on the River Waveney they next negotiated an oblique sharp backward turn into Haddiscoe Cut. The first straight waterway they had seen. Glyn couldn't resist it, two and a half miles of 'toe down'. He applied his shades, removed Jon from the helm then took off. Leaving him to get on with it the other three retired to the cabin roof to sunbathe.

"Let's see how fast this thing really can go," Glyn applied full power. The wash rolled towards the boats coming from the opposite direction giving them a see-saw motion, it bounced off the starboard bank. The boat had been 'bombing along' for some time when Glyn heard a police siren? He wasn't sure, a police siren in the wilderness?

"F***," Glyn looked around, he couldn't see any cars or a road. He called the lads, "Can you see any cars?" No one could be bothered to sit up; they muttered an unintelligible noise in reply.

The siren sounded again. It was coming towards them on the river. A small white motorboat came into view, Glyn reduced speed. The craft had two policemen wearing life jackets in the cockpit. It raced along, crossed in front of them and moved left into the River Yare.

371

"Well, coppers on the Broads?" cringed Glyn, "who would have thought?"

The river became The Yare, Glyn was enjoying the 'drive'. A massive structure put them in shadow, the boys on the roof felt the drop in temperature on their bare skin. Above them was a low iron girder bridge which straddled the river. They looked back to see the Reedham Swing Bridge moving. Reedham was on their right.

Seesawing around the river bends, Glyn was lost to the world, imagining himself racing through the streets of Monaco.

Their attention was then drawn to a clanging sound in the near distance. The boys sat up to see an old weather-beaten ship crossing their path from left to right. The noise was coming from heavy chains at the front of the ship.

It was a gamble if Glyn could shoehorn between the bow of the ship and the towpath on their right before the ship reached the bank. Also, there was this chain to consider.

Perhaps it wasn't a good idea, he decided to cross behind the ship. Ever nearer, Glyn directed Blaze towards the centre of the river, then straightened her parallel to the bank. Blaze should clear the stern of the ship by about thirty feet or more.

Glyn smirked; he was genuinely impressed with his own navigational skills. Suddenly, taking him by surprise, when only twenty feet from the ship a large steel chain rose from the water, directly in his path. He quickly reversed the engine and swung the wheel hard a starboard.

More chain appeared at the rear of the ship. Fortunately the chain blocking his route returned to the riverbed. There was now plenty of room for Blaze to glide through the space. The others had been looking at the pub on the bank, fantasising the taste of a cool beer in this heat. Each had just shrugged their shoulders at the sudden, erratic movements of the boat, accepting it was only Glyn's haphazard driving.

It was too early for lunch, so they moved on from Reedham, towards Norwich.

They stopped at a pub in Cantley for lunch. Not one mate would believe Glyn's story of near disaster and daring do. He was definitely 'pulling their legs', craving 'hero status'.

The journey to Norwich resumed. This time Stan took the wheel. It was another three hours before they would arrive in Norwich, the abundance of free time gave them a chance to enjoy the relaxing silence and beauty of the scenery.

Roy was at the wheel as Norwich came into view. He moved slowly, negotiating the motorway style traffic of boats and yachts arriving and leaving the City. The principle to pass 'port to port' meant nothing. There were so many boats that they had to moor in pairs. There was no room to moor against the quay, so they tied up alongside another vessel.

Later, the boys wandered around the City until by chance they entered a street of pubs and restaurants. It was destined to be a long night, even longer when later they tried to find Blaze.

BERNEY

Blurry eyed, Jon scratched his head, a noise had woken him. Now another, people were talking and shouting, the boat rolled as if these people were on the deck. For goodness' sake, did he need to get out of bed to have a moan? From the crack in the curtain, it was still dark, these inconsiderate people outside should be in bed.

An engine drummed. The vibration made the window by his head oscillate. Right, he closed his eyes, 'I'll give them two minutes'. He heard the faint noise of water splashing into the river accompanied by the putt, putt of an engine.

Last night had been extreme. They had been in a few rowdy pubs where the locals had 'bogged them out', then they found an old-style pub. The funniest thing was trying to teach the 'Buccaneer's Song' to the old men in the pub. Jon estimated the crew had got back to the boat at around 2.00am. He wasn't sure of the time, but he now needed to sleep. Something was annoying him, there was a lump in the bed. He reached down to remove the irritating object and pulled out a cuddly toy penguin. For a minute, he was confused, then remembered that Roy had made him kiss 'Julie' goodnight before he would move to his own bed.

Next to him Glyn lay snorting. Jon closed his eyes; within seconds he was asleep.

Two hours later, the smell and sound of frying egg, bacon and sausages woke Jon again.

Glyn yawned loudly as he opened an eye, "Aww, can I smell toast?"

Roy and Stan were in the kitchen, which was actually the same room as the bedroom cooking an A to Z for breakfast.

"About ten minutes lads," Stan called, "tomatoes and beans, then we'll serve up."

"Come on lads," moaned Roy, "can you get off the table, we're nearly ready."

Jon and Glyn dismantled the bed. The pair folded the mattresses into two sofas, then pulled the tabletop from under the bed frame and placed it on top. Glyn retrieved the tablecloth from his wardrobe to cover the table.

"What day is it," questioned Glyn.

There was a short pause, he answered himself, "Wednesday."

Jon moaned about his sleep being disrupted, Glyn confirmed a third boat had tied up alongside them during the night. Confused and drunk he had stepped into their cockpit before realising it was coloured red and yellow.

Two hours later, they set off on their return journey to Breydon Water. A light lunch at a pub in Surlingham, the opposite bank to Brundall and a visit to a Nature Reserve.

When they reached the Reedham Chain Ferry, three of the boys ensured there was no repeat of the spectacle that took place on the way to Norwich. They still didn't believe Glyn's fairy tale, but all kept their eyes peeled. Through Reedham they followed the route the police vessel had taken the day before, turning port along the Yare towards Great Yarmouth.

At around 5.45pm, the Berney Arms Windmill came into sight, fifteen minutes later they moored up just passed the windmill and close to the Berney Arms Inn. Surprisingly, this famous beauty spot was reasonably quiet. The gang made themselves ready, smartly dressed as always. Ironed shirt and pressed trousers, combed hair, polished shoes.

Their mums would have been proud of them.

The boys stepped up onto the towpath. Jon secured the canopy to the cockpit and windscreens, zipped the canopy closed then joined them. The pub was bright and friendly, the records on the jukebox were the best collection the boys had seen.

Stan strolled to the bar.

"Good evening, sir," the barman greeted him.

Stanley requested the order, "'Ello, four light and bitters please."

"Mugs or glasses sir?" the barman enquired.

Stan asked for mugs. Everybody drank from dimpled mugs nowadays. The handles made it easier to carry a lot of mugs in one hand, especially through a crowded pub or Disco. Strangely, the opposite was fashionable while drinking. It wasn't held by the handle but backwards, by the body. The handle was held away from the person's face with the fingers between it and the glass body.

"That will be nine shillings, please me luvely," the barman requested.

Stanley passed him a ten-shilling note from the 'kitty' bag. The barman rang the sale at the till. As Stan offered his empty palm to receive the one shilling change the barman delicately stroked Stan's open hand with his forefinger. He smiled, winked then placed two sixpence coins into the bare palm.

The four boys sat in a large alcove set back into the wall opposite the bar. A jukebox was positioned on the adjacent wall, with a dartboard at the other side of the alcove.

Beer, darts, music, they were settled for the night.

One thing puzzled them. Was Stan going doolally tap? Had he been on the wacky baccy? Why would a man stroke a strange bloke's hand? Stanley was 'petite' with shoulder length wavy blonde hair, but to call him 'me luvely', didn't make sense. Was there something in the local water, first Glyn hallucinating now Stan.

The boys dismissed the episode to examine the large selection of food available on the menu. Roy took the boys orders then made a movement towards the bar. However on seeing him the barman waved, then motioned that he would join them at their table.

A second barman appeared behind the bar, the two spoke and the second one sauntered to the boys' table. He stood by them, right arm outstretched, wrist bent down, left hand holding the order book and pen, supported at his hip.

"Coeee, boys, how can you help me? Well, anytime, actually?"

He winked, "I'm Simone, your desire is my pleasure. Oops, sorry got confused," he smiled. "What do you want? Oh, can't stop meself, sorry luvs, must behave myself."

Roy stood, quietly whirling the order in his head, trying not to forget anything, 'come on mate, shut up', he was thinking. Simone's words and flirting were lost on the boys from Dagenham, both went completely over the boys' heads.

Simone wore very tight black trousers with a bright floral red shirt undone to his navel. A matching red handkerchief was tied loosely around his neck. Flirting, lightly touching their hands or placing his hand on the customers' knee or shoulder, while taking each person's order, he gushed with compliments.

After the meal, Glyn chaperoned Stanley to the bar because he refused to go on his own. Walking back to the table Glyn commented,

"Do you know what? I can't quite place it, but they are a bit different, ain't they?"

Later, Glyn argued that both barmen had black makeup on their eyes. No one agreed, but they did concede that the barmen's finger nails looked manicured, their tailored dark Verdi beards were probably dyed and looked immaculate.

The boys played darts while jigging about and singing to the records playing on the jukebox. They drank until the pub closed then made their way the short distance along the towpath back to Blaze. A cup of tea, chocolate biscuit then bed.

FUEL

Jon instantly fell asleep. He hadn't slept well the previous night because of the noisy people at the Norwich moorings. Happily, he'd remembered to hide 'Julie' to stop Roy mucking about.

A couple of hours after midnight, it was pitch black when something landed on his foot and woke him. An intruder or Roy clowning around?

'Pffffftt, rriirrp', Glyn released a raspberry in his sleep. Jon was laying up against his flatulent friend, he had to roll uphill to get out of bed. Was he dreaming, the bed was at a slant?

He stood up, the floor was on an incline. Too much alcohol? He looked out of the starboard window, pitch black.

In the darkness, Jon shuffled, arms stretched in front, he reached for the cabin door. As he opened it, it closed back onto him. He was dreaming, an Alice in Wonderland fantasy? He was too bemused to think of a swear word.

Rubbing his eyes, he made his way into the cockpit where he unzipped the canopy entrance. He was shocked, there was no sky, no pub. Jon stretched an arm in front of him, unprepared he touched a wet slimy material, 'Ewww', he jumped back.

"S***," he fell against the driving seat, landing on the cockpit floor. Sitting, dazed he assessed what he knew. The wet thing facing him had to be the river bank, perhaps the boat was sinking?

Jon crawled through the zip and climbed onto the port gunwale. By the light of the moon, he could now see a wall beside him but no towpath. He looked; the towpath was above his head. Then Jon realised, the mooring lines were taut but not horizontal, they were vertical. The boat was suspended above the river, in mid-air hanging from the mooring posts.

He managed to balance on the edge of the now angled cabin roof, at full stretch Jon pulled himself onto the towpath. By releasing and

378

resetting the mooring lines, Blaze slipped into the water. Jon lowered himself back onto the now perpendicular cabin roof, he entered the cabin and went back to bed.

Hours later, Jon and Glyn were woken by Stan and Roy. They were agitated, two drawers from the clothes cupboard in their room were on the floor. They thought Jon had been messing around.

Jon's explanation of what had happened during the night was ridiculed. "You're as bad as Glyn, looking for 'hero status'," claimed Roy, "like two twins."

Roy went back into the forward cabin to tidy the room, he pulled the curtains and saw the river bank wall to his left. More astonishingly, the boat in front was hanging from the towpath, the bottom of it was about three feet above the river.

Instantly, he returned to Jon and apologised.

Hearing Roy's news the boys rushed excitedly to the cockpit to observe the scene. They were not disappointed, there were dangling boats in both directions. They laughed with relief; how lucky they were? If Jon hadn't been a Super Hero, they would have been part of the same catastrophe.

The four young men were ready for the next part of their adventure. Although they were on a boat floating in the river, the deck was suspended six feet below the towpath.

Calling to any noise from the towpath the boys congregated in the cockpit. Perhaps, Jon being the tallest could use Roy and Glyn's stooped backs as a platform. But would he be able to get back down? If he removed the mooring lines the boat might float away from the bank. He didn't fancy jumping onto the boat from that height.

Eventually, a dog walker came to their rescue. She slid the lines from the mooring posts then threw them onto the boat.

Stanley took the wheel. The sight of so many airborne boats gave them the giggles. Three of them hid in the forward cabin to laugh loudly while observing the different configurations.

This journey was planned to steer them closer to the boatyard where they had collected Blaze. It was across Breydon Water, back to the Northern Broads. After about eight hundred yards, they turned into open water leading into Breydon Water. This was the most exciting waterway on the Broads. To gain the most from the experience, the missing boys left the cabin and took to its roof. They joined the long procession of cruisers moving towards Great Yarmouth and the sea.

09-07

Through Great Yarmouth then onto the Bure, they stopped at Stokesby for yet another pub lunch and oodles of beer.

Around an hour after leaving Stokesby, Roy noticed the fuel gauge was close to empty. He alerted the others. They agreed, luckily as the time was 3.10pm the petrol stations would be open.

Shortly after, they spied two petrol pumps to their right. These were located at the tip of a peninsular with the river on three sides. River access seemed to be at the tip, it was designed so that a boat could glide up and moor just in front of the pumps.

'Action Stations', moving to the bow Stan grabbed a rope. As Blaze drew close Glyn slowed then cut the engine. Stanley waited, waited then jumped onto the piece of land with the petrol pumps. He balanced then tugged on the rope to bring the boat into the mooring.

Roy at the stern noticed a 'closed' sign hanging from the pumps and informed Glyn.

Hearing Roy's shout Glyn restarted the engine, seconds later the boat was again travelling at Glyn speed.

Stan struggled. Blaze kept going. Like a tug of war match Stan was pulled running over the grassed garage forecourt.

Stan pulled and pulled but was gradually dragged from dry land into the water. Firstly, knee deep then underwater skiing. Eventually, he managed to release the rope. He swam to the shallows only to see Blaze powering away.

"Oy!" He angrily yelled, as he waded back onto dry land.

"Where's Stan?" asked oblivious Glyn, "I thought I heard him?"

Fifteen minutes later three hysterical teenagers on a river cruiser pulled up to a grass knoll to rescue 'Robinson Crusoe'. With tears running down their cheeks, they emphasised that swimming wasn't allowed because the river was one big toilet.

They laughed even more as the extent of his 'wetness' became apparent. Stanley 'stunk', he was only allowed onboard if he took a shower while wearing all his clothes.

Twenty minutes later the engine noise turned to a 'phut'. Glyn instantly turned the engine off to stop it sucking sludge.

The others appeared in the cockpit, "Aim her at the bank," shouted Roy, "get her close so we can moor up."

Blaze drifted, there wasn't a clear bank, it was all overgrown with trees and brambles.

The boat kept moving from the initial momentum. Close to eight feet from the bank Roy and Stan climbed onto the cabin roof and gripped bunches of overhanging tree branches to hold her steady.

The current took over, the boat drifting very slowly with the two boys changing the overhead tree anchors in relay. At least, they were keeping Blaze safely out of the main thoroughfare. Boats passed by, their occupants taking note and grinning at the spectacle. What goes around, comes around.

Stan and Roy had been grasping branches for over twenty minutes, they were hanging onto their third tree when salvation arrived.

As a rowing boat sat off Blaze Roy heard a call.

A slim fidgeting thirty-year-old man wearing a life jacket stayed seated in his dingy. The man seemed very nervous, which made it strange that he wanted to help.

He explained that he carried an emergency spare can of petrol for the small outboard motor fitted to his sailing boat. He would help them but was worried that they would take the fuel then power away and leave him.

His terms were, if the boys promised to replace the fuel, he would let them have his spare. They had to promise to pay for the fuel plus they must follow him to a petrol station where he could replace it. His trump card was that one of the boys would travel in the sailing boat.

The deal was done, Blaze was back to normal.

Stanley was voted expendable: he would be the 'hostage'. He lowered himself into the sailing boat they set off.

The boys just followed the sailing boat they had no idea where they were going.

Suddenly, a thought for poor Stanley. Could the man be nervous because he was planning to murder the hostage?

They hoped 'Robinson Crusoe' wasn't going to be kidnapped. Then laughed even more when Glyn suggested that the man in the sailing boat was actually Simone's barman friend looking for a date.

The two boats arrived at Ludham. The sailing boat man led them to the filling station. Blaze was refuelled, the man reimbursed, the hostage released.

BIKERS

Jon was dancing in bed, he was so itchy. Something had bitten him during the night. What with 'Norwich' then 'Flying Boats' he hadn't enjoyed a peaceful sleep for a few days.

He leaned to the side cabinet to admire his new beer glass, it would match his ashtray. The pub they were in the previous night used glasses with the Red Barrel logo, one had mysteriously found its way onto the boys' boat.

Glyn sat up. Twisting, he started hammering at the mattress, "F***, what's in the F*** bed," he complained. The young man sat up.

Jon removed the old newspaper he had used to conceal and magic the glass onto the boat. It was alive with ants, "F*** ants everywhere."

Glyn pushed pass him to vacate the bed. He tried to snatch the glass from Jon, but Jon held on.

"What do you want with it?" interrogated Jon.

"I'm gonna F*** chuck it overboard," promised Glyn.

They calmed down, deciding to work together. The glass was flushed under the shower by Jon. All the bedding, the boys' clothes from the night before plus the old newspaper were thrown onto the towpath and shaken.

Glyn wasn't amused. "When you nicked that F*** glass last night, did you hide it in the F*** flower bed at the pub?"

"Yeah," confirmed Jon.

"You wassuck, that's where the F*** biters came from," angered Glyn.

Finally, they sailed out of Ludham. It was their last day, the trip would take them along a section of the Broads they hadn't yet explored. Travelling west, along the Thurne then Bure towards Wroxham.

After the first stop in Horning for lunch, they continued west to chill, soak up the sun and indulge in the tranquillity of the Nature Reserves.

Earlier, while in the lunch time pub Roy had noticed a poster advertising a 'Friday Night Disco'.

Despite the ant feud, all agreed to put aside their grievances to return later, and spend their last night at a Disco. They returned to Horning with enough time for a kip and a shower before going out.

Again they had moored close to the pub. The distance from Blaze to the pub was only a few minutes' walk. Because it was their last night the boys arrived in the pub reasonably early.

The holiday was only seven days old, but they reminisced. Stanley brought up the adventure with the stranded cruiser. "I was lying in bed the other night and something dawned on me," he declared. "We should have towed the boat off backwards.

Forwards pulled it more into the mud, backwards would have pulled it off, the way it had gone in."

"Too late to worry about that Stan," replied Glyn, "you just hope Simone's here tonight to say goodbye."

"He's probably more dangerous to you than a mud bank," laughed Roy.

As the alcohol relaxed inhibitions, the boys wiggled to the music in their seats. A bit later they stood near the table and wiggled a bit more.

A lone figure boogied onto the dance floor. Stan wasn't impressed, the dancer was a show-off. Stan watched as the man strutted here and there, like a flamingo on heat. He wasn't even that good.

A new record started, Stanley would show him how it is done. Which proved he was pissed. He skipped confidentially onto the polished dance floor, with a rhythmic prowling motion he circled the first 'show-off'. The flamingo greeted him then created even more outlandish moves.

Stanley twisted, his standing leg shot up, with both legs in the air there was only one conclusion. Stan struck the floor with his back, his head followed shortly after. It hurt.

The cheering from his friends was louder than the music. Someone whistled.

The embarrassing had become the embarrassed. In pain, he rose as best he could. Crouched over he half danced, half hobbled back to his seat. His mates' eyes contained so many tears of laughter they hadn't seen him shuffle back.

A few more medicinal beers, Stan was as right as rain, ready to dance again.

Later, as Stanley waited at the bar to 'get a round in', a tattooed man with a west country accent, dressed in a short black leather jacket started a conversation.

"How's your back?" He grinned as he thanked Stan for the dancing demonstration. He stated his dislike of flash, posers. "Are you from London?" he quizzed.

"How do know?" queried Stan, drunkenly polite.

"From your accent," the biker divulged, "I'm from Bristol, on holiday with seven of my mates."

'I ain't got an accent', Stanley mused, he carried the beer order back to his friends.

Around 10.40pm the same man, called Fuzz visited the 'London Boys' table, as he called them. He had two friends with him, Chuf and Minge. For some strangle reason, they saw the boys as kindred spirits. Whereas the boys saw them as terrifying rockers. The three bikers pulled up chairs to chat about life in general even their holiday experiences. On the last bell, Fuzz invited the boys to his boat to continue the 'party'.

There was an embarrassing quiet, without warning breaking the silence Glyn agreed to accompany them. His pals were horrified. Glyn proposed to provide two cases of beer, but Fuzz waved the offer away. The Greasers had crates and crates of beer onboard which they were happy to share.

The pub shut, the boys followed the group along the marina's raised timber walkway to their vessel.

Jon slinked between his friends, "Don't tell them which one is our boat," he whispered, "in case they are going to do us in."

Apprehensive, worried they were going to be attacked and robbed, he quietly collected the boys' wallets and the kitty bag. Then, as they walked past Blaze, he surreptitiously slid them under the canopy, dropping them onto the cockpit floor. If they were beaten up, they would still have their money.

The only members of the 'Brotherhood' who knew the youngsters were Fuzz, Chuf and Minge. The other tattooed five, also clad in leathers emblazoned with chains and badges, with various styles of facial and head hair, bogged them out. They had no conception why 'these kids' were on their boat. They were not happy 'people from London', were drinking their hooch.

Fuzz introduced the other members, Gash, Clit, Bush, Kit and

Snatch. They were all about forty years old. Some ignored the introduction, some grunted, none acknowledged them. Glyn wished he had
kept his lip buttoned, his alcoholic daze was lifting. An adrenaline rush
prepared his legs for escape mode.

Each biker had a crate of beer, some sat on it, others had it next to
them. One used it as a footstool. Fuzz passed a crate to his guests. The
boys watched as Bush took a bottle of beer and used his front teeth to
prise off the crinkled metal bottle top. He spat the cap onto a pile of
caps at his feet then downed the liquid in one. Holding the bottle by
its neck a flicked movement of his wrist launched it into orbit. It was a
good fifteen seconds before a splash was heard.

This was the sign to leave. As one the Londoners rose, made
their apologies and skedaddled. There was no response, only Fuzz
murmured. Some bikers looked at them with blank expressions. Beer
brave Roy acted as rear guard in case they were followed or attacked.

It was also the end of an adventure.

The next morning they cast off to return Blaze to her home. Luckily
Glyn remembered to readjust the speed limiter before they arrived at
the boatyard. The boys said goodbye to Boz then jumped in the van
and left for Dagenham.

10
ABOUT

Chapter Marker

TONY

Back from the Norfolk Broads for a week the travellers visited Tony, Lisa and baby John. The new parents had set up home at Tone's mum and dad's house in Brushwood Road.

Three of the travellers presented baby John with the cuddly toy they had won on the Crane Grab at Great Yarmouth. Glyn didn't have a cuddly toy to give because he had forced his prize on Jon, as a substitute for Jon's girlfriend Julie.

To tell them an embarrassing story Tony pulled them to one side.

"Lucky you didn't come round last weekend," he revealed. "It was 'orrible. On Saturday afternoon, me and Lisa were doing what married couples do when we had a shock.

Lisa said to me, 'I'm bleeding look, the sheets are red with blood'. And they were, not a spot, I mean loads."

Four horrified faces paled as the details became more descriptive.

"F***, we stopped, quick, I can tell ya. We couldn't find any mark, she seemed okay. But it wasn't her, it was me. My k*** was pumping blood everywhere, like a fountain.

It wouldn't stop. We wrapped it in a sheet, I stuck it in pillow."

"I shouted to tell me dad, he said, 'it's 'cos you're excited, think of something other than sex'. Like what? I asked. 'Umm, err, I don't know. Food, a sausage sandwich, er! What about a banana?'"

Tony explained that his father offered to drive him to Oldminster hospital, but he didn't want blood all over the car. The answer was they wrapped a bath towel around his 'todger', then put it in a shopping bag. Because of the mass of wrapping, he couldn't wear trousers so he wore Lisa's pink floral dressing gown.

He continued with his story, "When we get to hospital, I have to wait with everyone else at triage. I got some really strange looks, I could see people looking at me and whispering. Dad told me the large bump under the dressing gown made me look pregnant. The triage nurse took all the wrapping off like she was unwrapping a Christmas present then threw it in a bin.

She says, 'Ahh, I see your little man's not well', then puts me on a trolley. She puts a paper towel over the injury and leaves me in the corridor.

It doesn't stop bleeding, another female nurse comes to have a look. She smiles and comes back with a friend. Everyone wants to have a look. She says the foreskin is split and I need a few sutures."

The boys are silent, but the suggestion of stitches makes them shiver.

"So, they don't put me behind a screen, she just gets this great big needle, 'Just a small prick', she says then sticks it in me k*** to freeze it."

"Ooooww," the boys sang.

"Then about fifteen minutes later, a female doctor turns up and starts playing with it."

"That's more like it," laughed Glyn.

"She put gloves on first in case I've got the pox." Tony took a deep breath, "She gets a needle and cotton and sews it back together."

"Ooow," the boys cringed.

"Okay Tone, can we talk about something else please," asked Roy.

10-02
HAPPENING

The group of friends always looked for new experiences, especially places to drink and have fun.

They all now had membership to Dagenham Football Social Club. It was a benefit because as well as attending evening Discos they could have a drink when watching the football on a Saturday afternoon.

Roy's older brother Billy told them about the staff Disco at a hospital in Ilford. Most of the staff were ladies from the West Indies, the music was Ska and Reggae, the drinks were cheap.

Many times they went to the monthly shindig. It took some nerve for eight 'dance retarded' white teenage boys to join the 'sisters' on the dance floor. But in the minds of the intoxicated, dancing ability improves when langered. The ladies whooped, giggled and made fun of the young 'honkies' when they asked to dance up close as a slow record was playing. Because of the amiable atmosphere, as part of the carnival the ladies generally agreed, but made sure there was a safe distance between them.

The boys' favourite venues in Ilford High Street were 'The Palais', sometimes 'Room at the Top'. Stan's first successful chat up to smooch with a young lady was at The Palais.

Tenderly, the pair held each other close, slowly moving their feet a couple of inches in time to the music. Magically, above them the dance floor ceiling of twinkling stars flickered like a genuine night sky complimenting the words of Woodstock sung by MSC. The couple spent time together in the bar, later he escorted the young lady home with a promise they would meet again, same time, same place.

The route for the boys to travel to Ilford needed two buses. However, without enough money for taxis, as the clubs closed at 2.00am they generally walked the four miles home.

Always in good spirits, mucking about chasing each other, pinching someone's scarf or bobble hat and posting it through a house's letter box the journey was never dull. One morning they walked past a Chinese takeaway that was still open. From that day, the traditional food to eat when walking home became Special Fried Rice, Curry Sauce with a plastic fork.

The first time, while waiting for the orders Roy spied a door in the wall beneath the shop window. On inspection, he opened it to find it was a store cupboard containing ancillary items bag, plastic spoons, till rolls, plus tins of lychee. Somehow, as if by wizardry one tin levitated itself into his coat pocket. On subsequent early mornings, other tins repeated the same manoeuvre. By chance, the next time he found a concealed tin opener in a separate jacket pocket which enabled him to eat the fruit on the walk home. From this development, Roy decreed that Lychee had two purposes, firstly he swore it prevented him suffering from a hangover, secondly it was great to throw at people.

On other occasions, they partied in music pubs along the High Street running through Chadwell Heath, Goodmayes and Seven Kings. There were so many within walking distance of each other, most with live bands, that the boys could choose the type of music they preferred.

Roy and Stan frequented the Birds Nest where each table was connected by telephone. The customer phoned the bar waitress service to order food and drinks or could phone another table to chat-up the occupants.

Initially visits to Romford were infrequent then suddenly the boys started to go on Friday and Saturday. When staggering home late at night, the walk from Romford was closer and easier on the feet. The Golden Hind became their 'local'. The King's Head was also popular, where they could watch top bands like Yea, Slack Babbath and Complimentary. Sometimes they might even catch the last bus home.

Generally, on Friday and Saturday evenings the group would 'knock for' each other and arrive at Jon's home last. They would jump on a bus for the fifteen-minute journey to Romford Town Centre.

Stanley always took £1 spending money. This would cover the bus fare, a pack of ten Embassy cigarettes, eight pints of beer and perhaps a bag of crisps. He would often return home with change.

On at least one evening over the weekend, they would leave the pub and stagger to the Blu Orchid Chinese Restaurant to eat. Full of like-minded intoxicated young people the popular restaurant was always rammed. Just before midnight queues of revellers would form outside waiting for a vacated table. Waiters, like infant school dinner ladies laboured to keep order. Two large Chinese men stood guard on the door to prevent anyone doing a runner. If it was a special occasion for the boys or someone was feeling flush the food might be washed down with two bottles of Liebfraumilch white wine.

The walk home always produced more entertainment, chatting, singing Rugby songs or skylarking about. Occasionally, they stopped in Oldminster Park where sitting and riding on the children's playground equipment they put the world to rights.

PLAYGROUND

The boys ran upstairs on the moving bus cigarette in mouth, smelling like the perfume counter at Debenhams. The prizes they aimed for were the two front seats. As there were seven of them each sat alone in a different two-seater. The few other passengers ignored them, with fixed gazes they kept their attention on the streets and fields outside.

"Where's Jon?" asked Mike, "at college?"

"Yeah," replied Glyn, "finishes late on a Friday."

It was a short walk from the bus stop to the Golden Hind. Just before 8.00pm they entered the saloon bar through the coloured mosaic glass doors marked 'Public Bar' and scattered around the horseshoe counter. This tactic gave them seven chances of getting served quickly, which was increased further because the staff knew their faces and recognised them as regulars. Stanley looked around to see if Tricia was in the pub.

Mike was the first to be acknowledged by a barman.

"Eight light and bitters please," Mike placed the order. The other six boys moved to him to collect their drinks.

They relocated in the larger room towards the rear of the pub gathering tables and chairs around them as a camp. After 9.00pm, Jon arrived, he had brought two young men from his class at college with him.

Firstly Jon introduced the group then his companions. The one with dark hair, "This is Ken," then the one with fair hair and freckles, "this is Bill."

With a soft voice 'Bill' corrected Jon's introduction, "Ben."

No one heard Ben speak. Forever to be known by the group as Bill, years later when he insisted his name was Ben most people thought he had just had his name changed by deed poll.

Nevertheless, the group was now ten. Ken was loud, confident and outgoing, always chatting up anything in a skirt. Bill was quiet and self-conscious, his shyness was far worse than Stanley's. Through making polite conversation with the pair Stan became aware that both Bill and Ken worked in the same industry as him. Both were trainee draughtsmen working at companies in London.

At chucking out time, they drank up, some waited on the pavement outside the pub while the others relieved themselves in the pub conveniences. Unoccupied outside, bored Glyn started clowning around. He sneaked behind Jon, "What you got in your pockets, sunny Jim," he laughed grabbing Jon's coat.

"F *** off," groaned Jon, "what are you? A policeman?"

They fought over the coat, Jon wary not to tear it, let Glyn easily gain hold.

"Have you any contraband?" he laughed, searching the pockets.

"What's this?" he hooted as he pulled out three Red Barrel beer mats. "You just nicked these from in there," he pointed at the pub.

Jon couldn't help loving the nutter, he placed his arm around the joker and joined in the merriment. Once he had Glyn's head under his arm, he rubbed his knuckles into the top of Glyn's head.

The denary moved on, walking in an unorderly line across the pavement width. Next they walked along the road, then in a line snaking through the hordes of people on their way home. Everyone travelled in a different direction. It was a typical Friday night.

There was a bundle about to erupt, five against about five. Two policemen hurried to break it up. The boys walked a bit faster.

A drunken young woman leaned against a lamp post, her equally inebriated friend tried to prise her hands from the upright to get her safely home. Another woman bumped into Rick, she looked up into his eyes then flirtatiously asked if he would take her home.

The sound of a man's anger, as he collided with half a dozen empty beer bottles left unattended on the pavement. Then the corresponding chink, clink and screeching as the bottles crashed into each other and careered along the pathing slabs, finally dropping off the kerb into the road.

Queues at the burger van, buying partially cooked salmonella fare. A young woman crying because she had had a row with her boyfriend. A young man punching the bus shelter because he had had an argument with his girlfriend.

The boys evaded a sick patch on the floor by the railway station. Leaving the mayhem behind them they turned right at the Army Recruitment office towards Oldminster hospital. Instead of walking across the zebra crossings at the large roundabout they climbed over the railings, racing between oncoming traffic to reach the other side of the road. Then a shortcut, walking through Oldminster Park saved a few minutes. The grass was damp underfoot, the air moist on the face. Without streetlights, their eyes gradually adapted to the darkness. The park was quiet, peaceful.

Bill, while commenting on the calm took a seat on a swing in the children's area. The sky was clear and black, clusters of stars shimmered through the gloom. He traced the shapes in the sky with is eyes looking for a pattern he could recognise. Then, pointing up, "Polaris."

Mike sat in the adjacent swing, "What's that, Bill?" he asked.

"Polaris, the North Star," Bill answered. "Just think, if you can see that you can navigate around the world."

"Em, is there a southern North Star, or a South Star near Australia?" enquired Mike.

Bill confessed that he didn't know, "I love the idea of space travel and things like that."

Stan joined the conversation, "Nearly every week we talk about the Universe, gods and things. You know, new books 'was god a spaceman' and things like that. Jon reckons that the universe we live in is inside a glass jar on the shelf of a grocers shop in another area of space.

In this other space, our size is equivalent to bacteria. Size, scale and time only relate to what your brain can comprehend? It's like, do germs and viruses know they are small?"

"Yeah, small to us and the planet but not to each other," added Mike, "perhaps a common flu virus is so small on our skin that when it travels from one person to another it's like space travel."

"Everything is designed to fight death and save its own life, or reproduce so that it's lineage continues," enlightened Bill. "The best way to make a plant multiple is to cut it back, it never dies naturally until after it has left a seed."

"Some people think plants are dumb because they can't speak," declared Mike.

"Again, that's relative because we can't hear it. Even plants and trees communicate with each other," reported Stan. "If one plant is attacked by disease, it warns the neighbouring plants."

"Well, believe it or not," continued Bill, "the smell when you cut grass is a cry of distress, the grass is actually calling beneficial insects to heal the cut."

"Probably the same when you're slaughtering a herb, it could be shouting 'don't eat meeee'," wondered Mike.

"You know those Venus Fly Traps that are all the rage in the shops at the moment?" questioned Bill.

"My mum's got one of them in a pot on the kitchen windowsill," interrupted Joe.

"Well, there're a plant that eats insects? How does that work?" questioned Bill.

Glyn listened, "Perhaps the first alien to land on Earth was a giant cabbage then?"

Bill ignored Glyn, he commented, "I love this, guys, this is cool, talking about the world and things."

The things he had thought about when alone with no real friends kept coming, "It's like everything is connected. If you remove cow dung from a meadow, you remove the nest for insects to incubate their eggs, the fertiliser for grass and flowers. No insects and flowers signals the extinction of bees, butterflies, bats, birds and small mammals."

In another area of the playground, Rick and Joe were running hard, spinning the roundabout. Rick jumped onto the rotating platform but Joe missed and crashed to earth.

He joined the group near the swings. "If you are talking about the meaning of life and things, what I'd like to know is, what is the inside of a sock?"

Roy joined them, "What do you mean?"

"Well," elaborated Joe, "does the seam at the toe go on the inside or the outside."

"The inside of course," answered Roy.

"No, the outside," chipped in Rick.

Everyone had their own opinion. Do you wear the seam outside so it doesn't rub on your toes? Or inside so it looks smarter?

Stan's mind wandered, he recalled the words of Oliver at work, 'always be yourself' and 'learn to be happy with who you are'.

Many times over the year and into the future, these boys with other friends would sit in this playground having drunken debates. Some were frivolous, others significant.

An onlooker would see only a gang of drunken hooligans, but these were sixteen- and seventeen-year-old boys trying to understand and discover the meaning of life. Why were they here? What is life about?

Conversations were based on experience mixed with information from TV and Radio News coverage which was reported as a statement without comment.

The boys questioned if democracy worked? The Trades Unions role. What would be the true effect if Government controlled the News and Press? Worse, what if the News and Press tried to control common people in order to manage Government?

It was easy to distinguish programmes which relayed only opinion as these did not have the word 'News' in the title. Simply by listening to the chosen words and tone of a question revealed the political persuasion of the interviewer and the answer they were pursuing.

Additional trends that disillusioned the boys were when someone's words were used out of context or misquoted. A simple example being when, 'for the love of money is the route of all evils', becomes "money is the root of all evils." Here the meaning of the phrase has been reversed because the original tells us that 'money is not the problem'.

The boys wanted to make the most of their lives. Also, they wanted to help others?

They were boracic lint, skint. There was little chance they would ever have enough money to permanently help the needy, nor enough political power to change the world. But they had compassion and realised life was about others, not just themselves.

Discussions and arguments continued to take place in Jon's mum's front room, in the Lodge saloon bar and the children's playground. Over time they agreed on the only manner in which they could strive to conduct their lives,

1. Help those less fortunate than yourself, not necessarily monetary.

2. Don't be judgemental, accept people for who or what they are.

3. Don't force your opinions on others, accept people have different priorities.

4. Debate not dispute, listen and observe.

5. Never knowingly hurt or harm another person.

6. Don't play the blame game. There is NOT always someone or something to blame for a problem or failure. Things that are out of our control do happen.

11
CAMPING

Chapter Marker

CYMRY

The summer after their adventures on the Norfolk Broads the boys were low on funds and decided to have a camping holiday.

Everything was borrowed, the only piece of camping equipment they had was the flask Glyn used to take his tea to work.

Luckily for them, Jon had agreed to loan them his brother's and sister's camping equipment. Because he was now completely in love, he couldn't join them. As an alternative, Julie had arranged a holiday for the pair of them on the same dates as the camping trip? The upside for Joe, he was first reserve.

They would travel in the same dark green Thames van that had carried them to Norfolk the year before. Glyn bought it because it had been adapted. Additional windows had been formed along the rear panels on both sides. The front seats hinged forward to allow access to a bench seat positioned just behind. A partition behind the bench seat created a secure area accessed from the rear doors.

They met at Glyn's home in Forest Avenue on the Saturday morning. The boys greeted his mum and waited in the backroom. Stan needed a waz, he climbed the stairs to the bathroom, pushed the door open and was greeted, "Well, 'ello son, how are you?" by Glyn's dad, Yorath.

The elderly man was sitting on the lavvy, wearing his favourite flat cap and a tweed jacket, with his trousers down past his knees, reading a sports betting newspaper. Yori placed a few betting slips with a pencil onto the wash hand basin, "I'll be with you in a minute son."

"We are leaving now Mum," Glyn called out as he opened the front door.

"Glyn, booy, I've been thinking?" his mum mentioned as she appeared in the kitchen doorway wiping her flour covered hands on her pinny. "Could you drop off your dad there, that would be nice, wouldn't it?"

"Muuum, drop off Dad where?" Glyn wasn't happy.

"Where you booys are going, Llan Talhaiarn, isn't it?"

"We are not going to Llan Talhaiarn," Glyn was getting annoyed.

"Noo, Glyn, but it's on the way to Llandudno, you can drop him off on the way, can't you?" The lady was persistent.

"Muuum," Glyn was angry, "we are not going to Llandudno, we are going to Porthcawl."

"Well. Well, I wouldn't go to Llan Talhaiarn then, if I was you, it's nowhere near Porthcawl. There's daft, why are you going to Llan Talhaiarn then?"

Glyn was livid, 'the problem being the youngest child of ageing, contrary parents'.

His mum was from South Wales, a Hwntw, his dad from North Wales, a Gog. Whether it was only his parents' relatives, but neither would speak nor integrate with the other.

When he took his parents to their family homes or collected them, neither would travel with the other. Also, they wouldn't travel into the other one's region. He always needed to make two journeys in both directions.

Glyn often wondered how his parents ever met, he also wondered how they had produced six children.

11-02
WILD

Glyn, Roy, Joe and Stan left Glyn's home to start the journey to Wales.

The holiday plan was to visit the seaside resort of Weston in Somerset, followed by a Safari Park in Wiltshire before crossing the border into Wales. The drive from east to west through London was horrendous. The traffic jam started east of the Capital at Upper Thames Street near London Bridge. That was even before they travelled the notoriously congested two miles along The Embankment to The Houses of Parliament. They would only break free from the gridlock once they reached the A303 at Chiswick, a further two-hour drive. Nine miles of road, nearly four hours of time.

At last, they could drive at the regulated speed. Glyn changed into Rally Cross mode. Roy sat in the navigator's seat watching the distance and directional signage streak pass. The delay caused then to change their plans. They would now drive direct to the Safari Park. Perhaps they would visit Weston on the way home.

The boys left the main road and cautiously picked their way through the meandering country lanes. The route travelled along roads bordered by high green hedgerows, trees and fields. The light varied from bright sunshine to dappled shade as they passed through tunnels canopied by overhanging trees. Roy pointed to a trace of rabbits hopping around in a field. Glyn slowed at designated passing points, but his aggressive driving persuaded most oncoming traffic to give way to the driver in the green Thames van.

They arrived at the Safari Park, paid the entrance fee then followed the line of vehicles into an enclosure. Everyone was thrilled. Seeing the 'animal danger' safety notices raised the excitement. They drove through the security gates where a squeaking sound as they slid shut accompanied by a reassuring 'clunk' of the lock eased the boys' nerves. "Do not leave your vehicle," read Roy aloud, "do not open the vehicle windows. That's it, lads, no going back." He smiled.

403

"Look, look," announced Joe, he could see the top of the large gate at the other end of the 'airlock' slid open. Slowly they moved forward, then stopped. The gate ahead slid shut, disappointment. The boys waited; the queue moved forward.

"Look, over there," pointed Joe through a side window. "Look, a grey bird." Acting similar to overjoyed five-year-olds the boys strained to see any animal. "What, where?" cried Roy.

"By that tree, there's two of them now, look."

Roy slapped him around the head, "They're F*** pigeons, you wazzock."

"Yeah, but these are wild ones," retorted Joe.

Finally, the vehicle moved out of the enclosed space into another.

"Monkeys, I can see them, look, racing to escape," Joe declared. The vehicles moved through the second 'airlock' gate into the Park. The monkeys sat in gangs, it seemed as if they had drawn a particular vehicle from a sweepstake and were waiting for their prize to appear.

It was possible to imagine the lead monkey in a troop sitting around holding a piece of paper containing the words 'Green Thames van'. As the vehicle came into view he would say, "Come on lads, this one's ours."

"That one looks like you," giggled Roy to Glyn. "Look at the size of its lugholes, but they're not as big as yours."

Glyn left a reasonable clear gap to the car in front, stopped the van and turned off the engine. That was the signal one troop wanted.

Instantly they were on the van, one was chewing the rubber blade from a windscreen wiper, Glyn laughed, "Do not feed the animals, no need to."

Another ape held the aerial and tested its strength, yes it could bend it double. A third had its belly on the roof while its face and hands were upside down looking directly at Roy. Glyn pressed the windscreen washer straight into the monkey's face. It screeched, had a paddy rolling over then fell from the roof. Sitting, looking forward, it noticed the wing mirror and slid across the bonnet on its bum. Then, seeing its reflection while trying to eat the mirror it let out a loud screeching laugh. The boys joined in.

Stan and Joe were having similar experiences at the sides. One monkey urinated over the window next to Joe. On Stan's side, one tried to unpick the rubber seal from around the window, another swung from the door handle.

Glyn started the car, 'jeet, phut', it took a few turns then sprang into life. He gradually drove towards the 'out' gate, ever careful of unexpected movements and actions from the monkeys. One remained on the bonnet enjoying the breeze as he digested a piece of rubber wiper blade.

Through the gate, they followed a 'Lions' sign with an arrow. After a few hundred yards, Glyn pulled to the side, the van stopped.

"What you stopped for?" asked Joe.

Glyn explained he needed to sort out the mirrors and the aerial. He continued, "I need to clean the windscreen, why?"

"You can't," Joe advised, "'Lions sign', look over there, 'Do not leave your vehicle', 'Do not open the vehicle windows'."

Glyn wasn't happy, he hated driving with a dirty windscreen. Monkey skid marks weren't pleasant. But, better safe than sorry. "I can't see any lions," he confirmed.

"They must be behind a bush or up a tree, waiting to eat you," suggested Stan.

"Roar," snarled Joe from behind as he clamped Glyn's head in an armlock.

Glyn fought him off, "Okay, we'll move on," he accepted. He started the engine, 'chut, chut, jeet, phut, jeet, phut'.

"S***, it won't start," expressed Glyn. He saw another sign, 'Need assistance, beep your horn, and wait for a warden'. He heeded the sign. They waited for twenty minutes, no assistance came.

Frustrated, angry, Glyn advised the others that he knew the trouble with the vehicle. An old worn part connected to the engine would stick. He just had to tap it, to free it.

After spending another ten minutes horn blowing, they agreed he needed to leave the safety of the van to clear the engine problem. 'Perhaps the lions were eating somewhere else or maybe they were having a nap in the long grass'.

The first issue to overcome was that his tool kit sat in the secure area at the rear of the van.

Glyn 'popped' the bonnet lever then took the keys, "Right if you see anything move shout like hell. Please don't let the driver's door shut. I'll walk around the blind side to stay out of sight."

With four sets of nerves jangling, Glyn walked to the front of the van, lifted the bonnet then supported it with the metal stay. He then continued to the passenger side and furtively moved to the back.

"Glyn, Glyn?" Joe shouted.

"What? What? A lion?" Glyn's trembling voice called as his body released adrenalin, quickly he turned towards the front of the van.

"No, no problem. Just don't slam the doors in case the noise attracts a lion," answered Joe.

"Thanks Joe, I'm now standing in trousers full of S***."

Glyn collected two spanners, the larger one for protection against a vicious animal attack, the second small one to rap the offending component. Task complete sitting in the driver's seat, on the second attempt the engine started. Relieved, he passed the large spanner to Roy, "Can you go round and drop the bonnet, please?" The gang moved forward and joined the line of vehicles.

Still on high alert, they kept an eye out for lions.

"That's funny, there's a man with two small children over there," observed Stan.

"Don't be silly," berated, Roy, "they'd get eaten."

"Look, above that tree, there's a giraffes head," indicated Stan. "Is that a zebra over there?"

"I don't know, perhaps the lions prefer to eat live zebras," suggested Glyn.

The procession of vehicles rounded a bend then proceeding to the right it entered the 'Animal Petting Area'. Cars were directed into parking areas by high vis wearing marshals. A father collected a pram from the boot of his car while a lady stood by holding an infant. Forty or so travellers disembarked from a coach to form a semi-circle around a guide.

There was no sound from within the green van, it didn't deviate from the road. Ignoring the parking area Glyn drove on. Joe and Stan sat on the bench seat, hands over mouths trying in vain to laugh silently.

A new type of sign appeared, 'You are now entering Lion Country'. Who in the van would dare to speak first?

Joe, "Look Glyn, Lion Country?" He pointed to the sign.

Roy convulsed as he held back a chuckle. He lifted his hand towards his mouth as a mixture of air and water droplets sprayed across the inside of the windscreen.

"Thanks, you twonk, now I have to clean the inside as well," angered Glyn.

Then the driver giggled, "What a F***, day?" He laughed some more. Tears ran from his eyes as they became blotched with redness.

The four 'creased up', together. It was never dull being with this lot.

Glyn sent Joe outside to clean the monkey mess from the windscreen. As Joe was beavering away, Glyn shouted, "Lion."

Thankfully, they travelled through 'Lion Country' without a further glitch. The size of the male's head that licked the driver's window was bigger than the window. By chance, the boys were there to watch the lions being fed.

After stopping for a quick meal, they made their way over the Severn Bridge and into Cymru. The holiday makers were making reasonable time as they drove through the Welsh countryside.

"E.T.A., Mr navigator if you please?" Glyn asked Roy.

"Eighteen hundred hours, skip," replied the navigator.

"Good show, old chap, two hours until Porthcawl," the pilot confirmed.

11-03
TENT

The green van pulled up at the yellow and black stripped barrier with a height restriction bar across the top. Glyn stepped from the vehicle, entered the reception at the campsite in Porthcawl and stepped inside to sign the arrival form. Roy added the money he had collected from the others into the small pull cord bag to organise the 'kitty'. Joe wiggled in his seat, he had lived with a tortoise head for an hour, he was now badly in need of a 'pony'.

Just behind the gatehouse stood a large building which contained a 'self-service' restaurant and dining room. Within the same block, across the foyer was a large function room with two bars. The main part of the large external grassed area ran at a wicked slope away from the function buildings. A more level plateau with groups of trees sat to the far side of these buildings.

It was after 6.00pm, so they decided to set out the tents first. Hunting around under the bench seat Joe pulled and swore as he fought to remove the two small, bagged up twin tents. By that time, the tents had already been well used by Jon's siblings, having seen service in different continents around the world. Each was a simple 'A' shape, with a wooden pole at each end and six rope guides stretched to metal pegs hammered into the ground.

Joe opened each canopy searching for scorpions, aardvarks and armadillos. He jumped back instinctively when he spotted two termites which to his chagrin were actually grains of rice.

In the blustering wind, the boys struggled to hold the poles, hammer the pegs into the rock-hard ground and secure the guidelines. Eventually, it required the four of them to erect each tent in turn.

Standing back to admire their handy work, the campers realised the tents were running down the slope. Then, when they entered the tents to lay down to test the comfort factor, their feet were higher than their heads.

Time to get ready for the evening, they prepared for a shower. For now, they would have to sleep with their heads near the tent opening. The only things of value, their wallets, aftershave and the 'kitty' bag were locked inside the secure rear compartment of the Thames van.

Bizarrely, although none of them had lived in a tent before, they hadn't considered the process of having a shower at a communal location. Wandering across the site, in the distance they could see two queues adjacent to a white concrete building. The occupants of one appeared to have just a towel around their waist. The others, generally wore a dressing gown with shower cap. Carrying large brightly coloured bags the people in this queue also held a towel or had one draped over an arm.

The boys, each smoking a cigarette, fully dressed and holding a towel joined the men's queue. A man turned to check on the rabble that was making so much noise. He greeted them with a nod of his head then asked Joe if he had brought his washing bag. Joe, shrugged his shoulders. The penny dropped, they had left their toiletries back in the van, quickly he took the key from Glyn then shot off to collect them.

The boys waited their turn in the queue and had another fag. Bored, Glyn flicked his towel like a whip against Roy's legs. Roy retaliated. The pair charged around whipping each other to the amusement of some in the queue. Others, tutted hoping the four boys from Dagenham would be gone by morning.

As soon as there were no more women queueing for the ladies' block, two men left their queue and moved across. One went inside the block to shower while his friend stood outside as a lookout. When the first was done, they reversed roles.

The shower block was dismal. Two shower cubicles each with half a door, the bottom positioned two feet above the ground. Two wash hand basins each side of a faded shared mirror were located on the adjacent wall, plus two sit down loos. There was a gap of about a foot from the top of the dividing walls to the corrugated asbestos roof.

Standing on the W.C. a tall person could see into the ladies' area. The laminate partition wall between the toilet cubicles contained two voyeur manufactured circular holes filled with compacted toilet paper by a nervous user.

It was 8.00pm by the time the boys entered the foyer. Joe sported a plaster on his chin due to Roy barging him as the pair fought over the use of the steamed up shared mirror. An official stopped them as they entered the restaurant, "Can I see your membership cards, please boys?"

They replied that they didn't have any cards. The official pointed out that to eat and drink on the premises they had to be members of the 'club', it was a way of meeting a legal requirement.

The boys followed the official to his desk, signed up and paid their annual fees. They turned back to see the restaurant was now shut. Ever resolute, they strode into the function room and ordered bar food and drinks. The Disco finished at 11.30pm, the function room closed.

As they walked through the legion of tents the air pressure seemed to be dropping. A foreboding sense of impending rain, the sky was heavy, wind gusting.

In near total darkness by recognising the black shape of Glyn's van, they identified the dilapidated structures adjacent to be their tents. The boys undressed to their underpants then slid into the sleeping bags. The sun-baked ground was so hard on their bodies, but they were knackered, sleep took them quickly.

It wasn't the lashing of the rain against the tent canvas, nor the wrenching of the tent flap by the wind that woke them, it was the wetness of their sleeping bags. Streams of water ran down the hill, some through people's tents. The air temperature had dropped the soaked campers also felt cold.

It was still chucking it down. With no reason to be in a tent, people stood outside talking, it was about 5.30am. Two young women from a tent near them were chuckling, they found it more comfortable to stand outside wet, rather than lay in the water.

The torrential rain prevailed until about 7.00am. Most of the campers were outside their tents by then, meeting and talking about the weather. Everyone was drenched.

Roy called his friends to him, he whispered, "I've been to the area with the trees. The ground isn't wet. It's relatively flat and sheltered by the trees, it's dry. Shall we move the tents?"

They nodded, "Do it quick, before someone else nicks the space."

The plan was to move each tent in one piece. The guidelines were released, the pegs, plus bits and pieces loaded into the van. Two boys stood inside each tent, at either end they lifted a pole with the tent attached at the top and set off blind. Within moments, their muted explosions of outrageous laughter brought them to the attention of other campers. The whole ensemble drifted as a ghost, snaking across the wet grass to a new higher location beneath the trees. However, as they couldn't see where they were going each tent stopped at regular intervals for the lead to check their location through the tent flap. As long as they walked up hill, they knew they were proceeding in a relatively correct direction. Once there, Glyn nipped back and collected the van.

The tents were set up in the new position, it was closer to the main building, but further from the shower block.

"I'm gagging for a cup of tea," broadcast Joe.

They organised breakfast. Stanley would find a 'water point' and fill the kettle, Joe would go to the onsite shop for milk and bread. Roy and Glyn were tasked with setting up the burner, and the 'kitchen'.

The weather was now good, the ground dry. Joe returned with the groceries, a Sports Betting Newspaper and a large rubber roll of material. He was so happy, when he had chatted to the lady in the shop complaining about the hard ground to sleep on, she was surprised he didn't have one of these.

The happy campers opened the roll to sit on it. It was soft and comfortable. They sent Joe back for another three.

CYMRU

Sunday was a day for chilling. Around lunch time they rambled along a small winding road through fields of cows and sheep to a nearby village.

Entering the village the road tracked into the square, past old weather-stained stone buildings with white painted window frames and doors, and grey slate roofs. There were two pubs in the square, but few cars. Glyn led the way. He tried the door to the first pub, it was locked. They strolled to the pub opposite and tried the door, it was also locked.

Puzzled, the boys checked their watches, it was 'opening time'. They could hear distant noise. The racket, with laughter was coming from the pub. Joe bent to look through the small low rippled block window, it was dark inside. Stan walked to the side, to where there was the smell of a barbeque.

Roy went back to the first pub, he followed the path into the car park at the rear. There were definitely people in the pub garden. He could hear them talking and enjoying the drink. The back gate was locked. From Glyn's previous visits to Wales, he could slightly remember that pubs were shut on Sundays. Each time he collected his dad for the journey home the old man had always been in the local. Something clicked, to get around the law publicans invited 'friends and family to a private Sunday party'.

It was a nice day, without an invitation the boys took a slow walk back to the campsite. Later, they drove the short distance to the Porthcawl Resort to spend the afternoon on the beach and explore the neighbouring area.

On Monday, they drove twenty minutes to Port Talbot, a much larger town. After spending most of the day on the beach, they ate an early meal at a Chinese Restaurant. After another wander through the streets, they journeyed back to the campsite. At first, the van 'misbehaved' again. Eventually, after Glyn again performed the trick with his trusty spanner the vehicle started.

Returning safe, they played a drinking game before the show in the function room started.

The game required the first person to choose a drink, the second person to choose a mixer. The third one paid for the round and the fourth went to the bar and bought it. Everyone received that same concoction. Anyone who wasn't able to clear their glass within twenty minutes added the total cost of the round into an empty prize jug on the table.

Playing the game on a holiday campsite had the additional benefit of the extra variety of drinks not usually available in a pub.

The first game Joe chose a pint of Dark Stout, Roy added a shot of Gin. Stan gave Glyn the money, Glyn went to the bar to buy it. All four boys managed to drink that 'cocktail'.

Next, Roy chose a pint of Cider, Stan added a vodka.

Stan chose a Port, Glyn added half a pint of milk.

Glyn chose Pernod, Joe added Tequila.

The next rounds had three different drinks in each 'cocktail'.

Tuesday, they struck camp and travelled further north to Aberystwyth where they found a holiday camp close to the beach.

For lunch, they entered a bar on the seafront where Stan was asked his age. "How old are you sonny?"

Stanley had been eighteen for three months, "Eighteen," he declared proudly.

"No, you're not, get out," came the reply.

He was shocked. He'd never been asked his age before, he had been drinking for two years. The irony now, he was legally allowed to drink but he'd been refused. He was going off the Welsh.

The boys chose another pub. To ensure they were served Stan was asked to sit outside while the drinks were purchased. Sitting in the sun Joe took time to scrutinise his Betting Newspaper. He soon wandered off in search of a bookies to place his bets.

After a few hours of food, drink and merriment they wandered to a sandy beach to sunbathe. Joe went off to check his winners?

The three remaining boys could hear a distant hum. Roy stood to see someone water skiing offshore. Excitedly, they chatted, "Who fancied water skiing?" Glyn couldn't swim, he proposed to go with them but he would only watch.

Walking towards the harbour they looked for the place that taught water skiing. In a loose cluster always one moving to or from another to chat, they strolled, never in a line nor a group, identifying things of interest, pubs, a chip shop.

Roaming along the promenade, typically Joe 'clocked' a very pretty young woman walking towards them. He stood and waited, then as she came closer bent forward with a smile to speak to her.

Roy saw an opportunity for some fun. He claimed the lighter from his breast pocket and concealed it in his palm. Slowing, he trod lightly behind Joe.

The young lady slowed, she looked at Joe and smiled then she saw Roy creeping behind him. Her expression changed, quizzically she frowned at Joe and kept going.

Roy ignited the lighter setting fire to the erect Betting Newspaper sticking from Joe's back pocket.

The three were hysterical, as flames rose from Joe's back Glyn grabbed the newspaper and threw it onto the floor. The girl, hearing the commotion turned to look back thinking Joe's screaming, terrified noises were him calling her.

Roy ran towards the campsite for salvation as Joe gave chase. Enough excitement, as they had returned to the tents they decided to remain on the campsite for the remainder of the day.

On Wednesday morning, they travelled the short drive to the amazing Lucifers Bridge Falls, in the Rheidol Jorge. Stan wasn't so sure, but Glyn assured him that it wasn't very high. Stanley wanted to stay in the gift shop at the entrance which led to a couple of nature walks but finally yielded to peer power.

The terrain rose and dropped, the holiday makers could smell the saturated fresh air, and blossoming plants. There was an abundance of brightly coloured dragonflies hovering in front of them then zipping away. Alas, when the trail burst through the trees into brilliant sunshine Stan was feet away from a vertical drop. There was little clear horizontal room to stand, people around him were not aware of the danger.

Stanley could only focus on a rickety, arched iron bridge which spanned the ravine. His fear of heights took control.

He became even more uncomfortable when his mates walked to the middle of the bridge and leaned to look down into the pools of water below.

He wanted, needed to go back. He could buy his mum a present from the gift shop while his mates were on the mountain. His friends explained that the bridge was stable and strong. Regrettably, the route was one way only, there was no route back. The paths they had walked to this location were too narrow and slippery for two-way traffic. They persuaded him that this was the most challenging bridge and ravine, if he could walk over this the others would be easy.

He agreed to continue. But only if they would hide his embarrassment and surreptitiously hold back the next pursuing people to allow him an unhindered crossing. Stan stood at the rear, waiting in the shadow of the trees a good distance from the drop. On Glyn's signal as the bridge became empty, Stanley strode in a controlled straight line, in a cold sweat eyes fixed ahead he crossed the bridge. Luckily for everyone he managed to complete the remainder of the hike without worry.

The afternoon and evening were spent enjoying the attractions, sights and beer of Aberystwyth.

The plan for Thursday was to visit Barry Island. It was a three-hour drive on the route back towards England.

UNCLE

The four campers had a good breakfast, packed away the camping equipment and set off for Barry Island. With luck, they would get there by lunchtime. The boys planned to complete their holiday with a visit to the renowned Pleasure Park during that afternoon and the whole of Friday before leaving for home on Saturday morning.

Luckily, the weather was glorious, it was very hot. The rips and tears in the tattered tents were now appreciated for their ventilation and cooling properties.

Travelling along a major route on a weekday they needed to negotiated the heavily congested roads carrying working vehicle traffic. A large double deck animal transporting lorry driving along narrow winding roads from a farm. A massive tanker delivering fuel to an isolated estate, shunting back and forth at a junction to execute a ninety-degree turn. Tractors rumbling along at ten mph without a passing place for miles. Around forty minutes from their destination the green van seemed to be losing power, it struggled to climb a hill. Glyn was about to notify the others of the problem. But the vehicles bunny hops made them aware that all was not normal.

Joe in the navigator's seat, cried out, "There's black smoke coming from under the bonnet! S***, Glyn?"

"Don't worry, I've seen it," answered Glyn in a false reassuring way.

His brain was doing somersaults, 'What had caused that?' 'Where's the first safe place to pull over?' 'Turn the ignition off and run'.

"There's thick black smoke coming under the dashboard," shouted Joe.

The vehicle shuddered as it reached a layby at the top of the hill, "Wait I'll stop, just a minute, I'll pull over," assured Glyn, turning the steering wheel hard.

The van stopped on the prow of the hill, Joe opened the passenger door. Before he could move a limb, his seat was thrust forward with his face pushed against the windscreen. Stan and Roy pushed past; they were standing on the roadside next to the van before Joe moved. Joe prised his face from the inside of the windscreen and joined them.

Glyn shut down the engine, he walked around the front of the van to the relieved trio breathing in the fresh Welsh air. On the way, he placed his hand on the bonnet. 'Ooww!' – it was red hot.

He placed three fingers in his mouth, "Give it fifteen minutes an I'll check the engine," he advised. "I'll have a walk to look for a telephone box, see you in a minute." He walked down the hill in front to have a slash in the bushes.

Upon his return, Glyn tried to start the engine, nothing, it was dead. He looked under the bonnet, everything was black, covered in soot. Possibly too much damage for him to repair. They needed help, at least at this time of day garages would be open. Glyn sat in the vehicle thinking, 'It was probably rings, S***, what to do? If it was rings it would cost a F*** fortune'.

He needed to contact somebody. Joe stood on the kerb with his thumb out, he was either ignored or verbally abused.

Stan was sent back down the hill, Roy directed forward, the pair's task to find the cars location. A signpost, a pub, a farm something with a name to indicate where they were. Roy came back first, "There's a place called Brinsadler on the signpost, it's a mile along a road to the left. There's a phone box a short way along from that turning."

Glyn had an idea, off he went. He came back over an hour later, smiling. The young man of Welsh blood had phoned his mum. Subsequently, the lady phoned round the family to ask for help. Glyn's uncle Dafydd had called a Breakdown Service to recover the van, his uncle was coming in the Land Rover to pick them up. Better, his mum was going to pay for both the recovery and the repairs. Being the youngest son did have some advantages.

A while later, Uncle Dafydd arrived with Tess a black and white sheepdog sitting in the passenger seat. Another thirty minutes later the Breakdown Vehicle drove up. Dewi knew the driver, Caerwyn was a friend from the village. The mechanic did most of the work on Dewi's farm vehicles. The enormous vehicle with a spinning orange lantern on top of the cab reversed, stopping a short distance from the van.

The boys climbed into the Land Rover with their belongings. About an hour's drive and Dewi stopped at a pair of white painted wooden farm gates. He left the vehicle, opened them, then drove into a court-yard. After a visit to the farmhouse, he loaded something into the rear of the car. Auntie Cerys appeared, waving she calling "haia, croeso y Cymru," then as they pulled away, she went to shut the gates.

Dewi steered along a dry furrowed track, passing farm buildings through a large grassed area to a copse of trees. They had reached the boundary of the farm, a wire fence ran behind the trees. Black and white patterned cows mooed in a field beyond the fence then lumbered over to see if any food was on offer. An old building of strange design flanked the internal edge of the copse.

Glyn's uncle unloaded a heavy shining metal milk churn, "This is full of fresh water," he announced.

He gave Glyn a toilet roll, "Here, you may need this, the toilet is over there," with a cheeky smile he pointed towards the trees.

Dewi clambered into the car, shouted, "Breakfast's at eight," then drove off.

WAGON

The boys woke up in the dark because the room they slept in had no windows. Roy used an elbow to lift his weight on the hard wooden floor. He struck his lighter with the other hand to check the time on his watch, it was 6.05am. 'Huh, only six o'clock?' He collapsed back, 'Yeow!', smashing his head on the hard floor.

The countryside had been alive with animal and bird noises for some time. Stanley was sure the cows were standing outside waiting for the boys to emerge. It seemed that they had been incessantly 'mooing' for ages. "What's time?" he called.

"Six o'clock," came the muffled reply.

Another hour passed. The bleak living conditions were not favourable for sleeping.

Joe was certain the noise was from a nest of vultures in the copse. Roy told him to be less stupid. But Joe reasoned, they could have escaped from the Safari Park and followed them, "Do you think those grey birds under that tree were vultures? A vulture could fly that far in a day. Couldn't it?"

"Clump," a shoe narrowly missed Joe's head and struck a wall.

Glyn stood to slide open one of the huge doors, he peered out through one eye, the sun was shining. He slid the door half way back, retreating into his sleeping bag he dozed.

The building by the copse was an old railway wagon, presumably used to transport animals. It still had wheels with straw on the floor. The grass in the field was overly long for camping so the boys had agreed to use the wagon in place of a tent.

Every one of them had held back their major body function for over a day. It was becoming more necessary by the minute. As they had received a gift of toilet paper from Uncle Dafydd, they guessed he wouldn't be offering them a place in the farmhouse to leave a deposit. It was now either 'copse or pants'.

419

Joe succumbed first, he gathered the bog paper and sped through the trees. With the long grass, stinging nettles and overgrown weeds he found it difficult to choose a comfortable location, but needs must. Comfort wasn't his primary requirement.

"Hurry up," a voice shouted, "we're all busting as well."

"Who's next for the 'woodland throne'?" Joe shouted back. "Oooh, who's next for a pony?"

Roy was off. At the first tree, their paths crossed, the one with the greatest need with the one who had been relieved.

"Watch the long grass," warned Joe, "it tickles your arris."

A minute or two later, "Where did you go?" shouted an alarmed Roy, "I have to find yours so I don't tread in it."

"Search for the paper," instructed Stan.

"Anyone got a hat, I can borrow," requested Glyn.

They howled, "*, I can't even swear for laughing," Joe cackled.

"What colour is the paper," shouted Roy.

"Roy, have you been yet?" Joe checked.

"Nearly, I'm hurrying. Nearly finished, why?" replied Roy.

"Cos I've still got the paper," hooted Joe.

"Use a dock leaf," suggested Glyn.

They howled again.

"What do they look like?" shouted a calm Roy.

"The same as a stinging nettle," laughed Glyn.

As Glyn was next in line, he supplied Roy with the necessary.

Finally, they used the ice-cold water from the churn to wash and shave. Once dressed it was time for breakfast. The quartet followed the dry track through the fields towards the farmhouse.

Joe stopped by a field of sheep to talk to one. As he tried to stroke it, he noticed that the sheep's pupil wasn't round, but a dark horizontal slit.

"Eww, that's disgusting," he yelled, "it's got vampire eyes, whew gives me the willies."

They endured farther across the fields until after twenty-five minutes they arrived at the farmhouse.

RINGS

The grey stone farmhouse was small, connected to a larger more modern brick building at the back. The boys stepped back as they approached the main door. Glyn instructed them to clean their shoes against the metal boot scraper alongside the low step, then remove them.

He rapped the heavy iron knocker against the white painted wooden door.

The door opened ajar, a small face appeared at the crack. Joe noted the long bluish-black shining hair and dark eyes.

"Let them in, Harad," a voice called from within the room.

The boys entered a low room with exposed dark timber beams on the uneven off-white ceiling and timber columns built into the walls. Through years of occupation areas of the slabs which formed the stone floor were slightly concave and inclined. The stone was cold on their stocking feet.

"Bore da," an older lady greeted them. The boys recognised her as the lady who had closed the white gates the evening before.

Glyn spoke in Welsh with the lady for a minute or two, then introduced her, "This is my auntie, my mum's younger sister, Cerys."

"Come on, Harad, get the 'men folk' a coffee, there," Cerys hurried about her work.

The room was poorly lit due to the small windows. The white-washed plastered walls were stained by the smoke from an open fire. Stan looked around, he saw a higgledy-piggledy mixture of pots and pans, some hanging from the ceiling. There was a shiny white butler sink beneath a window. An assortment of kitchen items, plus eggs, vegetables and bread sat in bowls on dark wooden cabinets.

There was a cured side of pork, with perhaps the remains of a second one hanging from a beam. Strings of sausages hung like Christmas decorations, looping along the beams.

Comfortable armchairs were stationed either side of a stone fireplace. The fire roared.

Cerys ushered the boys to chairs around a wooden table centred in the room. They had toast, cereal and fruit. Stan looked longingly at the bacon and sausages hanging from the ceiling.

Every time Harad topped up their coffee, Joe gave her a smile. The next time he tried Welsh, "Yaki Da," he proclaimed with a huge cheesy grin.

Glyn gave him a 'look', "Stay away from her Law," he whispered fiercely.

"Are you coming to the Village Dance tomorrow?" asked Cerys.

Joe's face was a picture, you bet he was. 'Open season'.

"Probably, if we are still here," responded Glyn, giving Joe the 'look' for a second time.

A while later Cerys answered the phone and passed it to Glyn. Dewi was at the garage.

The news wasn't good. As expected, the piston rings had failed, it would take more than a day to complete the work, perhaps more than two. Dewi had convinced his friend Caerwyn the mechanic to work late, he hoped the van would be ready by Saturday morning.

Stepping out of the farmhouse door the boys called back to thank Cerys for the hospitality.

Harad, shyly called them back, "Please wait, Mum wants you."

The lady appeared. "What would your mum say if I didn't feed you?" Cerys smiled, "I don't want you going home looking like a bag of bones."

"Which one is the cook?" she enquired.

"Me," claimed Joe.

"What?" The three boys laughed.

"I wouldn't eat anything you cooked," giggled Roy. "You even burnt a cup of coffee."

"I'll give this to you then," Cerys spoke to Roy, she gave them a hamper of fresh food and drinks for the next few days. Inside was a bonus of a new roll of toilet paper.

Having eaten and relaxed they strode back to the 'woodland throne'. There was nothing to do but sunbathe. Joe dreamed of Harad.

ANGHARAD

Early morning, Roy had set up the small gas cooker by the wagon. The boys were eating breakfast, to Stan's delight the lady had included fresh bacon and sausages in the hamper. Joe had his mind set on seeing Angharad, but he wasn't allowed near the farmhouse. Earlier, there had been some excitement when Roy came back from one of his countryside tours with a grass snake.

After yesterday's farmhouse breakfast, they spent the whole day sunbathing, there was nothing else to do. They would probably do the same today. The boys had been there so long, even the cows ignored them. Joe's vultures had flown back to the Safari Park.

The noise of a vehicle came from far off, a car appeared, it was the Land Rover. They waited in anticipation for news about the van.

Dewi stopped, he spoke to them through the open car window. Depressingly, the mechanic wouldn't guarantee when the works would be finished. But, Dewi had a scheme. He believed that if he drove Glyn to the garage and left him, it was unlikely Caerwyn would shut the workshop. It would be embarrassing if Glyn couldn't get back to the farm. The mechanic was a friend and Glyn was family there was a bond. Glyn approved, collected his ciggies, bits and pieces then climbed aboard, they departed.

Thirty minutes later, Joe made his apologies because he needed a dump. He disappeared but was seen walking along the track to the farmhouse. Missing for over an hour it was lucky he returned to some banter and leg pulling before Glyn returned.

Around mid-afternoon the lounging trio heard a car hooter, they knew who it was.

Although running in the new engine components, with Glyn in rally mode at the wheel the green Thames van raced across the fields. It bounced across the rutted track, broadsiding to a standstill by the wagon, engine revving.

"You took your time," barracked Roy.

"Yeah, I had a 'tom tit' in the garage toilet," hooted Glyn. "It was so comfortable."

They screamed. Roy whispered to Joe, "Is that where you went for your one?"

"I'm saving mine for the dance hall," declared Stan.

Glyn stepped from the van and opened the rear doors. The smell? Mouth-watering.

'What a diamond', the smell of hot fish and chips, they loved him.

"You are definitely my bestest mate ever," claimed Joe, "much better than these two."

"What else you got in here?" queried Stan.

"Cigarettes, special fried rice, curry sauce with plastic fork four times," yelled Glyn. "That's our supper sorted."

He was loved even more, "I love you even more than Law does," laughed Roy.

As Dafydd had advised they left early for the Village Square. The Village Dance always drew a big crowd. Generally, people from neighbouring villages also attended.

The boys arranged to get there for 6.30pm. They drove into the Square to see it was rammed, there were people and cars everywhere. Glyn nosed the van through the crowd, it seemed he would have to park a distance away. He dropped off Stan and Joe to get the drinks then left to find a parking space. They would meet near the War Memorial.

The two boys looked around there were four roads leading into the Square. A pub was situated near each junction. In turn, the pair frequented each, White Lion, Angel, Green Man and The Lamb. Two of them were so full the boys couldn't even open the bar doors.

Of the other two, the closest position they got to a bar had been behind a four deep rank of customers. The only choice was to return there, The Lamb.

Patiently, they waited. Stanley spoke to the man squashed up against him. The reason the pubs were so busy was because the Dance was in the Church Hall, which didn't have a License to sell alcohol. Everyone in the Village and the surrounding area was on a mission to get hammered before the Dance started at 8.00pm. The chaos had been like this since 5.00pm when queues waited outside each pub for it to open. In fact, the demand for booze was actually lapsing as more people became intoxicated.

Glyn and Roy walked through the Square searched for the other two. The pair saw picnics on the pavement, some people had brought their own tables and chairs. Buffets were laid out on grassed spaces, some with their own bar. There were fifteen-minute queues at a hotdog stall and outside the bakers. Everybody had at least one drink in their hand.

By chance, Roy eyed Joe through the pub window. They met up then returned to a corner of the bar in The Lamb which Stan had guarded.

The bar was thinning out, the boys were able to relax. Come 8.00pm they had a surplus of additional beers on the bar ready to take with them. The bombshell dropped when the barmaid explained that no drinks were actually allowed in the Church Hall. The man had told Stan that the Church didn't have a License. Not that alcohol was banned.

Outside, people were stashing booze behind telephone boxes, under cars, in shop doorways. Groups were leaving their booze with 'minders' and alternating dancing inside with drinking outside. Some had prepared stickers to identify the owner's name.

One reason people had arrived so early was so they could use the boot of their car as a bar.

The boys stayed in the near empty pub, they sat at a table and consumed their drinks at speed. Joe was getting restless, all three knew why.

Finally, they bought two bottles of beer each then made for to the Church Hall. The eight bottles were concealed under an Estate Agents 'For Sale' sandwich board.

There was a friendly atmosphere in the hall, what you would expect from a close community. Families worked and studied together, people of differing ages chatted. There were more standing around than dancing, but it was early.

Cerys walked over to say 'haia' to the boys. She had Harad and Lowri, her other daughter, with her.

"How's Dewi?" enquired Glyn, "Please thank him again for his help."

"That's fine, thank you," replied Cerys. "He is a man of few words. Not one for dancing either. Keeps himself busy, you know. He will pick us up later. I must go now to see a friend."

Joe had a massive smile, an absent Dewi, plus Lowri was even prettier than Harad. Did he keep chasing Harad? She was still beautiful, and he had spent an hour with her in the farm stables at lunchtime.

An hour later, Glyn couldn't find Joe. Stan informed him that Joe had gone outside to the concealed bottles for a drink. Glyn retraced the route, Joe was at the secret hoard having a swig from a bottle but Angharad was with him.

Glyn spoke sharply to her in Welsh, "Harad, your mother is looking for you," he lied.

Slightly shocked, Harad woefully left them and walked back into the hall.

"What did you say to her?" questioned Joe indignantly.

"Look," Glyn emphasized, "you can S*** her if you want, but I'll tell you one thing, if Dewi finds out it won't be me buried underneath the wagon."

"It's not like that," Joe fibbed. "I like her a lot. We can exchange phone numbers?" Joe suggested.

"Yeah, you could, but your mum and dad don't have a phone at home," argued Glyn.

"Good point." Joe slipped back into the hall.

The party was warming up, more than half the people were dancing.

'All Right Now' played. The boys from London loved the record, they did the 'greasers dance'.

Facing each other in twos, legs wide, hands on hips, body swaying left and right they dipped forward then backward from the waist. They could bend low on the front and back swings at speed heads just missing each other. The boys showed off to the audience. Others copied them, half the hall joined in.

Joe went missing again. He later came back looking behind him he spoke, "Watch your backs, could be trouble."

"Pardon?" they asked.

"In the loo, three blokes came up to me." Joe was agitated.

"And?" they asked.

They asked me if I was the 'F*** Sais' bothering Harad? "I tell ya, I nearly did for the big lumpy one. I would have got two of 'em. But another one was behind me."

"And?"

"I said me an her was mates. I told 'em, be careful cos we was from Chelsea."

"But we ain't from Chelsea," confirmed Stan, "why did you say that?"

"Cos people from Chelsea are hard ain't they, like gangsters an that," Joe explained, "anyway that scared them off. But, just be careful. So what's a Sais?"

12
OUTOUT

Chapter Marker

MARINE

The boys travelled to London on the Underground, twenty-two stops to Charing Cross followed by a short walk to Trafalgar Square. Their destination was the famous German Bier-Keller. Well, only Rick had heard of it and he had told them it was 'famous'. He wished to go somewhere special on his last but third night of being a civilian.

Strolling around the paved square bordered by the main road the boys were surprised by the size of the area, it was vast. Rick and Jon stopped a minute while a tourist took a photograph of her husband. Tone collected a camera from an outstretched lady's hand then waited patiently for her to re-join her family. Joe noticed three young blonde Scandinavian ladies walking towards him, he moved to one side to let them pass.

"Hi girls would you like me to take your photo?" he asked wearing his best chat up smile. The girls smiled and kept walking, "No camera" one shouted back with a grin.

The boys could see hundreds of tourists, Nelson and the Lions, but no Bier-Keller. Roy sat on the wall of the fountain's pond eating a hot dog. Mike had left home without eating dinner so he followed Roy's directions to the hot dog stall.

"I can't believe a German Bier Keller would be near Nelson and the historical stuff," questioned Jon.

"Well, on the tele on New Year's Eve they dance in the fountain," stated Mike fried onions protruding from his mouth, he swallowed, "perhaps they come straight out and jump in?"

The group walked around for a second time, Mike saw a sign. The entrance at ground level was a set of stairs obscured by scaffolding on a building site, the bar was underground. Following the cold, bare unlit staircase deep into the basement they had a slight feeling of fear, anxiety of not knowing what was next, leaving everything to trust.

Turning a corner at the bottom they were welcomed by an

illuminated sign above a heavy door. Leading the party Rick pushed the door open into a large bright space. The nightclub wasn't busy. Loud, throbbing Oompah music took them by surprise, an attractive young woman with blond hair in pigtails, wearing Bavarian costume came forward to greet them.

They smiled, what more could they want? Always hopeful Joe looked around for the Scandinavian girls.

The hostess requested they choose a bench then walked with them. Worried the lack of customers and atmosphere would prompt the new arrivals to change their minds and quickly depart, she explained that the boys were early. There would be a better atmosphere later.

"What would you like gentlemen," she smiled waiting for the order.

"Eight light and bitters please," requested Joe.

The waitress apologised, "I am sorry, we have no light and the bitters. We have bier only in steins, it is Bavarian strong bier. I will show you." Eight pair of lecherous eyes witnessed her wiggly walk to the bar.

The barmaid returned with an enormous glass, "This is a stein, two pint glass. Very big you see. We also have this, our one smaller?"

"We'll have that one," the boys cried in unison pointing at the large glass stein, "eight of those please."

"So, Royal Marine Rick Stevens, when does it all start?" questioned Tone.

Rick explained his position, "Well, I go into Lympstone on Monday morning, Mum and Dad are dropping me off. I do a first year as a boy soldier because I'm only seventeen.

Then when I'm eighteen I sign up for the real thing and another twelve years."

"Wow, that's a long time," added Tone.

"A toast," commanded Roy, "keep safe and well, remember we love you." The other six young men repeated his words.

The hall steadily filled with Friday night party people. Some who had finished work came straight from the office, others met friends in local pubs first for a warm up. It was a good time, they drank, stamped their feet and clapped to happy music played by the Bavarian band. The boys remembered old times, Rick and Joe's holiday the year before at a holiday camp, school teachers, they joined in the fun.

Glyn with a cheeky grin, fag in the corner of his mouth, arms gyrating above head level started a 'Conga'. The boys joined the line behind him. Other patrons hitched on the rear, weaving between the tables, then up and over the stage. As Glyn aimed towards the toilets a hostess took his arm and redirected him back into the hall. He steered the line of revellers along a path intended to dance behind the bar, but a 'knowing' waitress blocked his progress.

Rick was enjoying his send-off.

It was getting late, Stanley refused an eighth stein of bier. Seven had been enough, he made his way to the Gents for an eyelash. Too drunk to stand at a urinal, he chose to use a W.C. cubicle where he could sit down.

Asleep, he relaxed, only to be awoken by someone calling his name and thumping the cubicle door. Somehow, eyes closed Stan reached forward and flipped the door lock. Mike and Joe crammed into the tiny space and helped the unresponsive boozer. They stood him upright, dressed him then helped him ascend the stairs to the exit.

It was late and dark, they waited outside for the others. When everyone was accounted for the gang left for the station, Stan grasped an upright scaffold pole with both hands. He wouldn't let go of the metal pole. Holding on like a limpet he wanted to stay, he didn't want to go home.

"Come back and get me in the morning," he told his friends, "I'll have a sleep here first, see you tomorrow."

Tone removed Stan's hands, the drunk wrapped his legs around the pole. Tone grabbed his feet; Stan's hands gripped the pole.

Tone raised Stan's feet from the floor, now horizontal Stanley still wouldn't budge. Rick and Jon took a hand each and prised Stan's fingers from the pole. The three teenagers then carried their prone oppo to the station.

Finally, the eight drunks made their way to the Underground Station. Tone, Roy and Rick laughed as they plotted mischief.

The train was full of late-night revellers on the way home. Luckily, the boys didn't need to change tube trains on their journey. The group guided Stan into a vacant seat then left him. They stood in the open area beyond the seats at the rear, next to the single door on the back wall which provided an escape route into the next carriage.

After a few stops, Tone, Roy and Rick scragged Mike. Other able friends joined in, Stan snored.

Rick dropped the window in the escape door then reached through and opened the corresponding door window in the carriage behind.

On the wooden carriage floor initially laughing, Mike was now fighting for his life. He was losing, between them the six assailants pulled off his shoes and threw them through the two open windows into the next carriage.

Next his socks, then his shirt flew through the windows. The boys had Mike's trousers down to his ankles, the sight of his underpants gave them another option?

Mike shouted, enraged, "enough is enough!" He was angry, fighting mad angry.

Originally, he had fought back using playful resistance with his mates, now in one second they would no longer be his friends, he was about to use survival resistance.

Deep down the change in tone of Mike's voice sent a warning. Before somebody got hurt the boys stopped, he was released as they stepped back. Tone with Rick helped him to his feet.

Mike opened the two connecting doors and stepped into the next carriage. His arrival was greeted by applause from the laughing audience. He collected his clothes to return to the boys but the nutters held the door shut. Mike then turned to his spectators, bowed, he threw his clothes through the two open windows then followed them into the boy's carriage.

This stroke of dangerous entertainment was greeted by an even greater ovation from fellow passengers.

RUNNER

Everyone in the group enjoyed the taste of a good traditional beer, in 1970 they followed the trend away from keg beer to drinking 'Real Ale'. The boys would travel into deepest Essex to discover new beers, pubs in Ongar and High Easter were two favoured destinations.

Today it would be The Punch Bowl. The fourteen of them travelled in four vehicles, two Anglia vans driven by Glyn and Ken, a London Taxi driven by Bryan. Joe on his Vespa motor scooter.

Ten minutes into the journey the vehicles queued at the lights opposite the Hooper's Arms.

Stan stopped in the offside lane at a crossroads. A 'psycho' driver on a motorbike pulled level with him on the driver's side. The young man inched forward revving his engine. He turned his face back to Glyn, mouthed obscenities and made hand gestures. He eyeballed Glyn as he revved the motorbike's engine. With the traffic lights still showing red, Glyn looked forward then slipped the clutch. As the van jumped the mad man grinned, shouting 'loser' he raced forward.

His lane was still on a red light. On full throttle, he looked up to see a mass of intersecting traffic coming at him from left and right. Somehow, with luck he managed to scrap through the tiny gaps, zigzagging in and out to avoid oncoming vehicles.

After an hour's journey, they pulled up outside the old timber framed fifteenth century Tudor building. It was always quiet; they had never seen another car in the car park. The boys disembarked then walked around the front of the pub to the side entrance to access the small bar.

The old 'grumpy man' was serving behind the bar as usual. He stood hunched over wearing a grey knitted sleeveless cardigan over a formal shirt and tie. The grubby tea towel draped over one arm was his badge of authority. He watched the boys walk in and grunted. The boys thought his grunting was an involuntary body function to confirm that he was still alive.

The room was so small, the fourteen boys filled it. The bar was only long enough for six people to stand in two rows at any one time. There was just enough space in the opposite corner for a wooden table with four chairs. Without a table three loose chairs rested against a bare wall, while another was jammed under a door handle to keep the main door open.

To keep the rounds small, they set up individual whips for each vehicle. Joe was in a whip with himself.

Behind 'Mr Grumpy' was a waist high wooden bench where the barrels of beer lay on their side. There were usually four large wooden barrels with metal hoops, each with a hand operated wooden tap fixed into the front face.

Someone, probably 'Mr Grumpy', had scribbled the name of each beer and brewery on the back of a torn cigarette packet which was pinned to the corresponding barrel. At this time, Real Ale beers came from small independent brewers. Therefore, to project each beer and for it to remain in the drinker's memory they had strange, ridiculous names. Mr Grumpy's labels read, 'Droop Dangle', 'Pale Todger', 'Roger Inge', and 'Nook He'.

As the pub was in a small village with minimal police intervention the Licensing Hours rules were always relaxed. The 'last bell' sounded twenty minutes late, the boys grouped in the car park. It was decided to meet at a Chinese restaurant in Hornchurch for a meal.

The drive home became an adventure. While Bryan crawled along at the rear driving at speeds well below the regulation limits, Glyn and Ken played Grand Prix. When either of them stopped for a comfort break, Bryan would creep pass the line of young men lingering at the bushes, only to be overtaken shortly after. Joe preferred to be alone as the extra weight of a passenger slowed him down.

Joe was hammering along a minor road with Glyn in hot pursuit when a startled fox or similar darted into the road at the entry to a roundabout. He braked and turned the wheel which slid sideways across a large circular metal drain cover. Ching, kaboom, as Joe surfed on his stomach, spinning across a third intersection the scooter crashed into the roundabout kerb and jumped onto the grass.

Glyn hit the brakes. Everyone dashed to help the crash victim.

In the distance, Ken saw Glyn had stopped and recognised an

opportunity to take the lead, he accelerated towards the roundabout. Tone jumped into the road in front of Joe waving his arms.

Miraculously, Joe was up, back on his feet he muttered, "Ooww, whoa, that was close, nearly a gonna there."

Standing with scuff marks on his helmet and chest, the elbow ripped from his jacket, a knee from his jeans, he declined help. He stretched his legs, shook his arms then five minutes later with severe back pain sprinted away on his scooter to continue the journey to the Chinese restaurant.

After the countryside, they soon reached more congested roads and built-up areas.

They soon arrived at the Chinese restaurant. Bryan dropped off his passengers, said goodnight then left for home. The waiters at the restaurant were hesitant about letting such a large group of young men enter so late in the day. Nevertheless, they didn't wish to lose the takings for thirteen meals and drinks, so allowed the new customers access.

Although the boys sat at three tables, they requested a single bill so that the remaining whip money could be used to help pay the total. The food was excellent and compared to the heavier ales the Chinese iced beer refreshing. They finished eating, had a smoke and chilled. Tone, Bob and Bill collected the money from their tables and handed it to Scorch.

As the group collected their belonging Stanley used the facilities on the third level before leaving. On his return, he was conscious of the silence as he walked back and down to the ground floor. 'Had his mates ever been that quite?'

Still two steps from the ground floor Stan could see the restaurant was empty. His thoughts were they had forgotten him. Quickly, not wanting a ninety-minute walk home he made for the door, grabbing his coat as he ran past the stand. Agitated Chinese voices erupted behind him. Stan pulled on the door handle, the door was locked.

A group of waiters ran to him, shouting in broken English. A very angry, red faced one stuffed the bill in Stanley's face, "You pay!"

Stanley wanted out: his friends would have paid the bill? Surely. What was all the aggro about? He negotiated: would they open the door?

A hulking man holding a large cleaver unlocked the door and stepped outside.

Stan followed him. Now, he could now hear Glyn and Tone laughing, then the madman laugh of Ken. Ken would noisily wheeze sucking air in, then cackle as he exhaled. The number of hoots varied but always exceeded six, always very loud. His face and neck coloured crimson with tears running from his eyes. It was surely only time before he had a heart attack while laughing.

Scorch stepped forward, the whole gang were huddled together in a small alley between the restaurant and the neighbouring shop. He held up a hand containing a bundle of notes then passed them to the man holding the bill. The waiter with the cleaver coasted silently behind Scorch.

Everything ended amicably.

Stan requested that the next time they decide to 'do a runner' he is informed before they leave the restaurant. Glyn, grinned, "We were going to leave you in there until Bill warned that you might end up as tomorrow's spare ribs."

There were now twelve joyriders and three vehicles. Glyn could take four, one on the front passenger's seat and three squeezed onto the rear bench seat. Ken would take the remaining five, two on the front passenger seat and three rolling around in the rear cargo space. There were only two seats in his van. Joe was alone.

They set off, it was now very late with few people or cars around. The journey took them along Dacca Road towards the Lodge. For about half a mile as the road passed the Lakes and Chase, it incorporated three tight hairpin bends. The speedsters put their foot down.

Ken pulled into the Lodge car park and stopped with a handbrake turn. Glyn followed.

"What speed did you do around the bends?" Ken asked.

"Don't know," replied Glyn. "I was behind you, you slowed me done," he giggled.

Ken insisted that he had been quicker, the answer was to rerun the route, this time with a wager.

Each would race the course between the first and last bends. To be impartial a passenger would record the max speed from the vehicle's speedo.

The pair returned to the beginning of the bends. First was Glyn, he pulled away from the start increasing speed. Without warning a motorcycle raced passed him, Glyn swerved and hit the brake.

Glyn rerun his first attempt. The three on the bench seat fell to the floor at the second bend, arms and legs spraying in all directions. One sitting in the front nearly smashed the windscreen with his head.

Ken raced next, the three in the cargo space stretched across the width of the van to wedge themselves in. The moment Ken's foot hit the peddle they were fired into a heap up against the rear doors.

It was better than the Funfair. After each sprint, they met in the car park to check on the speed. However, bouncing around inside the vehicles, laughing and being thrown against the windscreens the observers hadn't been able to read the dial once. Each driver totalled three sprints, but neither would believe the opponent's time. Finally, they had to call it a draw and continue home.

12-03

FOOTBALL

Since the age of ten, when Stan played for the 'Five Jacks' football team he had loved football. He would play at any opportunity. Never able to walk along the road and pass a stone without side footing it 'into the goal'.

When the FA Cup Final was shown on TV, the whole nation would tune in. The TV broadcast started mid-morning until 6.00pm. All the family would sit together and watch 'Meet the Players', where the wives, mums or partners revealed the players bad habits. There would be live coverage of the local baker selling specially prepared food in the colours of his local team. A tournament or quiz show where residents of the home towns competed to win a plastic replica of the FA Cup.

Irene always went shopping on Finals day, she could get a seat on the bus and walk around the shops with ease.

Stan, Roy and Glyn even offered to help Jon babysit his sisters three young children because it was on Finals day and the family had a coloured TV.

All the boys had Social Membership at Dagenham FC. They watched the home games whenever they could. Then in 1970 the club reached the Amateur Cup Semi-Final against St Albans City which created a growing interest throughout the borough.

Tickets for the match scheduled to be played in south London at Willmall FC Ground sold quickly from the Daggers Clubhouse. Thousands of supporters bought tickets for the game and for the organised coaches to the stadium. The boys travelled in one of the many coaches. Everyone wore Daggers rosettes with red scarves, a few had red and white painted rattles. The coaches became mobile parties with everyone singing and loudly chanting.

Disappointingly, the game ended in a 1-1 draw. Rumours spread that the Willmall supporters had not been as welcoming to the St Albans City fans as they had to the Daggers ones.

A few weeks later the Daggers met St Albans City in the replay match. This time it was played north of London at the Tulon Town FC Ground. Even more club sponsored coaches carried the many red and white supporters to the stadium. Dagenham was closed, shops were shut. People of all ages, the elderly and young families embarked on the adventure.

The coaches dropped off the fans at the stadium then waited a mile away in designated coach parks for the return journey.

Excitedly, the boys took their place standing on the terrace behind a goal. There was a large crowd. The team's colours embellishing the stadium on all four sides of the pitch.

The supporters sang, 'dag an em, dag an em, dag an em', then, 'we're gonna win the cup, ee aye addio, we're gonna win the cup'.

The red of Dagenham, the yellow and blue of St Albans. The white and black of Tulon Town. The boys were engrossed in the game, end to end fast football. The atmosphere was crazy, the Daggers supporters were vociferous as always. Any chance of a score was received with loud applause and cheering. If an opposition player miskicked, made a foul play or was cautioned for misconduct he was greeted with scornful taunting and loud whistles.

'Goooaaalll', Dagenham scored 0-1. The crowd went berserk, the singing and chanting increased in volume.

A large assembly of people, conspicuous by its white and black attire gathered in the stands to the boys left. Slowly, this crowd began to move through the terracing away from the boys' position. In an erratic nature, the red group further from the boys was displaced and replaced by the bearers of white and black. The area behind the white and black became devoid of supporters. The boys watched as the clusters of differing colours moved around the stadium. The swarm of red moving away from the black and white as if being pushed. Suspiciously, the yellow and blue patches that intermingled with the other colours remained stationary. Some reds later filtered back into the empty areas.

After forty minutes, hordes of uprooted people wearing red appeared to the boys right. The white and black group were close behind them.

Warnings began coming from that side of the stadium. The white and black clad people were Tulon supporters, keen on causing injury to anyone wearing red. The rumour was these people were looking for revenge after aggression during the Willmall match.

Fifteen minutes later Ken felt a hand on his shoulder. He thought it was Glyn who was standing behind him and turned. Glyn, Mike, and Barry were no longer behind him.

Instead, sparkling in the sun was a large knife just six inches from his face. The owner of the hand holding the knife indicated to Ken's left. A giant of a man holding a large club hammer grinned with an evil expression. To Ken's right, a motorbike chain bumped against the holder's knee.

Ken's friends standing along from him were still engrossed in the football, oblivious of Ken's fear and the intent of the new neighbours standing behind them.

The knife flicked to one side signalling the direction of the Exit.

Ken coughed to gain his friends attention. When they looked to him, he nodded behind. Instantly, the message was self-explanatory, it wasn't open to negotiation.

The boys walked to the stairs then descended to the street, everywhere hordes of Dagenham Supporters were making their way to the Coach Park. The exodus was complete. Some supporters told how they had been sitting on the coaches for over an hour, listening to the match on the coach radio.

The final whistle sounded, Dagenham had won. The Coach Park exploded with noise, 'We're on our way to Wembley', they sang. People jumped from the coaches, dancing in the car park they sang and hugged one another. The Clubhouse would be bouncing in two hours' time.

"Put it in your diaries boys and girls, 4 May is Cup Final day," called out the driver. They all cheered.

Even more people travelled to Wembley Stadium in coaches on Cup Final day. Some vehicles were decorated with massive banners tied to the front, rear or sides. As the procession drove to the venue, each time one vehicle overtook another both coaches would explode in song as the occupants waved and cheered their peers.

Unfortunately, the match against Unfield in the Final was an anti-climax, Dagenham lost 5-1. But, never down hearted, the supporters cheered the players on. They cheered and loudly sang, 'Sing as if you're winning'.

12-04

FESTIVE

Christmas was always a happy time for the old boys of Beck School. When Christmas Eve 1970 arrived, they were aged eighteen and seventeen. At an age when parents and families find it hard to choose suitable presents, yet they were never short on love. A few had steady girlfriends. One was married with a young son, plus a second child on the way.

Another with a pregnant girlfriend joined them for a celebration drink with her blessing.

Each boys' arrival at the pub depended on the time they finished work and the amount of alcohol consumed at their 'works do'. In different states of inebriation, most of them managed to get to the pub even for an hour.

At the time, to boost his income Tony was now also working an additional evening job. Thursday was a normal working evening for him, but his boss had let him leave at 8.00pm to celebrate with his friends.

The Golden Hind was chocker, as was every building in Romford that sold alcohol. The benefit of being regulars was that the bar staff knew them. Although customers stood three deep at the horseshoe bar, the boys were always served before 'strangers'.

During the course of the night, siblings, friends and friends of friends put in an appearance. Many knew each other from school or older brothers.

Glyn was feeling distinctly green. He couldn't swallow another mouthful of beer, so he moved to Scotch. An hour later Roy and Stan saw him dive for the toilet where he was sick in the cubicle. Despite his protestations, the boys told him he had to go home.

Arguing as he went, he stumbled into the area at the back of the saloon, tripped and teetered. Roy caught his trailing arm and swinging Glyn in an arc steadied him into a chair.

Stan collected the P*** heads coat then the two boys heaved the sagging Glyn to his feet. They supported him through the side entrance of the pub which opened onto the enclosed courtyard of the original coach house. Roy left Stan to look after Glyn while he walked under the five-hundred-year-old arch formed by the overhanging building. Once on the pavement outside the arch he scoured the road for a cab.

Stanley told Glyn to act sober, then as he poured water into Glyn's mouth and on his head, it started to snow. He pinched Glyn's cheeks and leaned the dead weight against the whitewashed wall of the pub.

Within minutes, Roy had hailed a Black Cab, which was too soon. At the same moment. Glyn slid down the wall, the cabbie reversed with precision through the medieval arch.

The cabbie took one look at the sight of Stanley fumbling around trying to support a large ventriloquists dummy and started to pull away.

Stan called to him.

"I'm not F*** having him, in my cab," the driver declared, pointing at Glyn.

The two boys reasoned with the cabbie, he drove away.

"I'm gonna be sick," Glyn groaned, then roared, "raallth, blarggh." It didn't help.

Roy returned to the pavement. Ten minutes later he hailed another black cab.

This time as the driver shunted under the arch Roy stood with Glyn and Stanley against the pub wall. The new driver was going to pull away, 'What if the drunk was sick in the cab?'

The boys haggled, 'Glyn couldn't possibly be sick again'.

Roy promised, "That's the third time, he's got nothing left to bring up."

As trade was slack before 'kicking out time' the driver gave terms. Firstly, Roy would travel with Glyn. Then after dropping him off, Roy would return to the pub in the cab. If anyone was sick in the cab, Roy would be charged triple fare. All mess would be cleaned up by Roy, to the cabbies' standards.

Roy opened the cab windows, the boys dragged Glyn inside and slammed the door shut.

Pinching Glyn's nose Roy leaned into Glyn and in a menacing voice whispered, "If you are F*** sick, I'll be playing snooker with your B***."

As the cab pulled away under the arch Glyn stuck his head out of

12-04

a window. Roy saved him from being decapitated by yanking it back inside the cab by his hair. Luckily, Glyn only suffered a bit of hair loss and a slight abrasion to the top of his head.

Hours later, the last bell had gone, the pub was thinning out Roy was back. There were a dozen or so of the group surviving. Collecting their things, they stepped outside into the thick snow to chat.

A series of loud noises came from the market area at the distant end of the street. They could hear singing, swearing and shouting. Intermittently a thump, bang or smash as an object was punched, kicked or thrown.

In silence, they looked towards the noises. In the dim light and falling snow, they could see dark shadowy beings coming nearer. The groups' route home was to walk towards the shapes then turn right to the station. Should they stay at their current position or start walking home? Was there enough time to walk forward then turn right to avoid them?

The figures came closer, spreading across the width of the whole street and the market square. They were wearing short sleeved checked shirts, skinny braces supported tight three-quarter jeans with a small turn up, bovver boots on their feet. Skinheads!

Probably itching for a fight?

Nerves were jangling, most of the group resembled Skinhead prey. They had long hair and wore bright, big collared shirts with flared trousers. Run or fight? The Skinheads were closer than thirty feet away.

Breaking the silence of the standoff Joe started singing, 'We wish you a Merry Christmas', the mad man charged at the aggressors singing. He linked arms with the leading Skinhead swinging him around in a square dance style movement. The Skinheads looked bemused as their chief danced in a circle with the long-haired mad man while singing a Christmas song.

Scorch ambled forward, would a Hippy Yeti unleash the fighting desires of the Skinheads? "Hi man, peace," Mark Burns lifted an arm then crushed the surprised man in a bear hug.

The boys joined in the singing, so did some of the Skinheads. They danced together for a while then the boys slowly drifted into the street on the right. To their delight the mystified Skinheads, saturated with love, returned to their original route.

Stanley was attacked by an amorous girl who cornered him in a shop doorway for a festive kiss. Tone aided a drunk by hailing a cab for him. Bob placed his arm on a young woman's shoulder for a chat then she asked him to walk her home.

Joe spotted a pale blue Jaguar XJ6A one hundred yards along the road. The bonnet was up with a man leaning over the engine compartment.

Joe asked if he needed any help, Jon and Mike joined him. The man was very polite but stern. Jon walked round and started to open the car boot. The man intercepted him and reiterated, he did not need help.

Away to the fairies Jon shouted, "Ken you know about cars, come and help."

The innocent persistence to help from these boys made the man smile behind an angry face. He met Ken at the bonnet, the younger man looked down and recognised a police siren with a blue light to the side of the engine. He quickly apologised, assembled the group on the opposing pavement then moved away.

He was questioned, 'Why didn't you help that man'?

"Because, you dipsticks, it's a police 'Q' car, an unmarked police car," he informed them, "heavy duty Sweeney, the open bonnets probably just a cover for surveillance."

Twenty minutes later Bob caught up with the boys, he thought he was on a promise but the young woman had decided that she didn't fancy him anymore. He had been told to 'go forth and multiply'.

They walked on through the crowds of revellers, turned at Oldminster hospital, ran across the roundabout and through the park.

The snow was crisp under foot. They crossed past the front of the Hoopers Arms then turned left towards home.

The snow in front of a row of shops was deep and untouched. At this point, they had a massive snowball fight which turned into a riot. Everyone was slaughtered, struck by snowballs and rolled in the snow. Snow was rammed into pockets, down trousers and people's necks.

A twelve-inch diameter snowball that Scorch built was crashed onto Pete's head. Roy and Ken rugby tackled him to the floor, the other eight piled on top. Scorch was laughing so much he couldn't repel them.

Mike came away with Scorches' WW2 army surplus woollen greatcoat. He evaded spread arms with grabbing hands and a leg trip to enter a nearby launderette, Bob joined him. The pair stuffed the greatcoat into a washer machine, added the coins then switched it on.

Soon, a six feet tall snow encrusted Yeti shuffled into the launderette. He was looking for his coat. The machine's wash cycle took for ever, all the soaking wet boys sat in the warm watching the coat rotate in white suds and bubbles. When it stopped, Scorch rushed to collect the coat before any other scallywag could pinch it again. From previously fitting a six feet tall mammoth, it now fitted a ten-year-old skinny schoolboy.

It was so ridiculous the boys couldn't hold back their laughter. Always congenial Scorch played the stage, they openly cried from his theatrics, he was hysterical.

With the warm laundrette as the theatre, he acted in the guise and with the expressions of a silent film star. Forcefully pushing his body into the garment, he twice fell to the floor. The length which previously reached his ankles now reached above his knees. The sleeves stopped at his elbows, each button down the front was eight inches from its corresponding button hole.

Once Scorch was comfortable wearing the 'latest Paris fashion' they resumed the journey home though the ensuing blizzard. To Scorch's credit he wore his soaking wet mini greatcoat until he arrived home. He always told the boys that he still wore the coat for special occasions like his sister's wedding but in reality, he placed it in the dustbin in his front garden.

SABRE

Most days the boys would play football after work. Weekends, they could squeeze in a game between swimming and going on the lash. These were generally a 'kick about' with limited rules and the players clothing used as goal posts. The width of the pitch was determined by the distance someone could be chased before his pursuer gave up.

A bright spring afternoon, the gang and their friends were playing football in Central Park. The lines of the pitches used for Saturday and Sunday league matches were visible so they picked a true outline to play on.

A few bystanders watched, then more arrived. One of a group called to Joe and suggested a match. The boys from the Beck agreed, they were really content with the final result of Bystanders 8, Beck 10. Following the match Stan found that the bystanders were an established team which played regularly on a Sunday morning.

It gave him an idea, which grew. As the opponents were of Division Five ability could his friends play in a league of that level? He sounded out his friends, 'Would you commit to play proper football every Sunday morning if I organise it?' Not only did he have a good response but many knew other people who would also sign up.

Sabre FC was born.

Big mouth, he had again put himself in a pressure position. The doubts came to gnarl at his self-confidence. Stanley continuingly lived with a confusing personality problem. He was so shy he hated being in the limelight or leading, but he couldn't sit idle or do anything less than 110%.

Did he want to do this? If he started something he would never back away, just spend anxious days worrying about it. The answer was a positive. He had the ideas and mindset to organise, did he have the courage to fly solo. He decided to find out.

Stan searched through the phone book, he read through the local newspapers. He applied to join the Dacca and District Sunday Football League, rented a pitch for home games then applied to join the Essex Football Association.

He read the FA Handbook, then the League Handbook. Corner posts with flags of a specified height must be supplied, he made them. Nets for the goal posts were required, he bought them. Every player had to be registered with their signature on official League forms. He was interviewed by League Officers.

Stanley paid all the fees to get it started. Some money would be recovered later by a player subscription after each match. He already had a Store Credit Card for his clothes, which left him cash for other things. Now he took out a Bank Credit Card to pay for the football things.

Attendance at a monthly League Secretary's Meeting was mandatory. He attended these meetings at Dagenham FC. Although only the Officers spoke and more than a hundred people always turned up, he feared he would be asked to speak.

It wasn't 'a walk in the park'.

Stan found an advert for fifteen pairs of football socks. They were inexpensive so he visited the vendor and bought them. The colour, purple with two white bands at the top was the reason they were cheap. He later found out they were a famous Italian team's colours.

He wrote to all Division One football clubs, 'We are a group of xxxxx FC supporters who are joining an amateur league. We have always liked your xxxxx colour kit and ask if you have any throw away kits, we could have them please'.

Two clubs replied, one didn't have kit available the other from west London apologised that their old kit was always handed down to their Junior teams.

Next, he found an advertisement selling football shirts. Cheap again, yellow with white edging this time. The white matched the white on the socks!

He had run out of skinflint options, so requested catalogues from sportswear manufacturers. These were not branded names but again from newspaper adverts.

Unfortunately, he would have to pay full price. Analysing these he looked for a colour to match purple, yellow and white and unexpectedly found the answer. His dad suggested red or white, but to avoid the team looking less like a dog's dinner, he chose yellow shorts.

The upshot of the colour combination was he didn't need a second kit. The colours of Sabre FC's kit were unique, unsurprisingly it never clashed with another team's colours.

Once established, in order to help with finances Sabre FC held fund raising discos in the large hall at Hookery Swimming Pool. Vinnie who with Dean DJ'ed under the name Five Oceans Mobile Disco worked free of charge for each function.

Two other players Froth and Rory also operated a mobile disco. Among their clients were top London Hotels, they had a renewing contract with a hotel in London's West End for Christmas and New Year's Eve parties. These young men also helped fund raising by charging a nominal fee to provide the disco at Sabre events. Their speciality was a self-choreographed martial arts dance to 'Kung Fu Fighting' which always compelled the people on the floor to stop dancing and enjoy the exhibition on the stage.

To help them train during the damp dark winter evenings Glyn built four floodlights. He built frames from old pieces of pipe screwed together with a bracket fixed to the top. A car front headlight fitted into this bracket. Each was powered by an old 12-volt car battery.

The first evening training session arrived. The pitch would be on the grassed fields which adjoined the sandpits off Dacca road. Glyn parked the van on the pavement as the team members unloaded the lighting elements. The frames were heavy but double handed they could be lifted over the six feet high chain linked fence into the field. The car batteries were heavier, each one weighed forty pounds (18 kgs). The boys struggled, it took one pair each side of the fence to lift over, then lower each battery.

When setup, the lighting was weak and drew mist which made it harder to see. The experiment lasted for thirty minutes then the equipment was loaded back into the van and everyone went home.

12-06
MATCH

On an August Sunday morning at 9.30am, Stan stood in the car park of the Beck. His friends were arriving, football bags in hand, throbbing heads. Stace loaded the kitbags and water bottles into John's car boot. Glyn fought with the orange plastic goal nets to get them in his car boot. Jared and Rory had both borrowed match balls from their Saturday teams.

Stan did a count, one missing. It was Johnny the goalkeeper. Todd took Stan to collect Johnny while the others shared cars and made their way to Parsloes Park. The fixture was the first for Sabre FC. Besides providing the nets and match balls, the home team's chores included erecting the goalposts, corner flags, and unlocking the changing rooms.

Stan knocked at Johnny's house his mum answered, he was still in bed. Shouting up the stairs didn't wake him, so she went to his room. A ghostly half dressed, moaning creature slipped on the bottom step and fell down the stairs. It sat on the bottom step to finish getting ready then grumbled at its mum, "Where's my boots, and kit?"

"Come now, Willy, they are always in the same place." Mum collected them from the kitchen for him. Every week for the next fourteen years this scenario would be repeated during the football season.

Although a teenager, Johnny had very fair skin and white hair, "I didn't get home until 4.00am," he fussed. "Got anything to drink? Got a mouth like an Arab's jockstrap. Took some 'sort' home to Ilford, knackered."

The three footballers reached the park. As Todd parked the car Stan could see his brother John standing with Grandad Joseph and the other members of the team. He was touched, Grandad would be about seventy-three years old, but he had still made the journey to cheer them on.

Grandad presented him with a wooden First Aid box, it was painted white with a red cross on the lid. Under the hinged lid were bandages, smelling salts, a knee support, everything they may need.

But there was more, John showed him another bag which contained water bottles and pieces of sliced orange for half time.

Then Stanley noted the bucket of water and sponge at Grandad's feet. Not only had the elderly man supplied the full complement he had carried it all on two buses to deliver it.

Grandad had even checked the pitch number on the Park Legend. He pointed in the direct of the pitch, he would meet them at pitch number eighteen before kick-off. The brothers could see and feel the excitement and happiness in their grandad. He became a regular, making his own way by public transport to each match, supplying half time refreshments.

At half time, he would become involved with some of the players, not bossy but reassuringly speaking a few words. When Johnny had saved a shot, 'Do you know, that save was world class? When Joe missed an open goal, 'that was much harder than it looked, I'm sure you'll get another chance'.

Later Stan's mum told him that Grandad was very excited about the football. Each Saturday when she visited her parents he would ask where Sunday's match was being held them check the bus routes to map his route to the venue.

The result of the match was a 2-2 draw. Everyone was happy. The team and its first supporter travelled back to the Beck for alcoholic refreshment. They sat in the large Family Room which was used as a restaurant during weekdays. 'Pops' as Grandad became known was a celebrity, he relished the camaraderie and enjoyed a beer or two with the young men.

There were always scuffles between players during matches. Some players were skilful, others intimidating. On one occasion, Sabre was playing at Parsloes when a fight broke out on the neighbouring pitch. The team in red, from The Amber Light pub in Bullock Lane were playing. Because they also drank in the same pub some of the Sabre players knew most of the Amber Light team.

From the other pitch, Stan and his mates could hear sporadic swearing and cries as a heavy tackle took out a player. Sometimes a yell sounded so harrowing everyone, even the referee took a glance.

Then, they heard a Kung Fu scream. Looking across they saw a player wearing blue soar though the air and kick a red shirted player full in the face. As the injured player somersaulted and hit the ground with a shudder, deep red blood erupted as a volcano into the air above his mouth. All the players and the referee in the Sabre match stopped in their tracks. Everyone in the neighbouring match set about each other. It was mayhem, a bloodbath. They fought one on one, three on two. A player of the red team removed a goal net then used it like a gladiator's net to capture and pummel a blue. A player from each side thrashed corner posts at each other.

Vinnie, Doily, Scott, Paul and Stace stood restless on the touchline, they wanted to help their friends.

Just in control of themselves, yelling support and threats they were pumped up, ready to flatten someone, ready to put the boot in.

Vinnie was tough, he had been brought up in a violent suburb in the east of London. A gang had once beaten him, alone he slowly waited to take revenge on each individual. The last act of retribution was on the gang leader. Vinnie waited behind a corner of a block of flats holding an 80 x 80mm wooden stack in both hands. As the quarry turned the corner the pole swung with speed into the targets face. Evens!

The Ref advised the Sabre players if anyone left this pitch, they would be 'sent off'.

Three of the Amber Light team dismantled their goalposts. Each upright was too heavy to swing so they chose the top bar then a pair of them attacked the blues using it as a battering ram.

The fighting spread away from the pitch, the match on the opposite side was interrupted as the fighting spilled over. Around thirty minutes later a police siren could be heard as vehicles bounced across the playing areas towards the conflict.

The Ref blew his whistle, and Sabre FC and their opponents restarted the match.

12-07
DERRIE

Sabre FC was a success, winning promotion a number of times the team had risen through the divisions to now play in the Third Division.

Rory, one of Sabre's most skilful players was contacted by Derrie Sports FC to see if they could amalgamate. The truth was that Derrie Sports was finding it hard to field eleven players for their matches, they were looking to poach Rory and any good players from Sabre.

Stanley was invited to Rory's home to talk about the merger with Rory's father. Stan wasn't really interested.

Nevertheless, Derrie Sports booked a church hall for the two teams to have a meeting. All eyes were on Stan. He had worked hard to setup then run Sabre, funding a lot of the expenses. His mum washed the kit every week while he undertook all the administration duties.

The question was, if Derrie pinched the best players from Sabre what benefits went to Sabre in return? Derrie had everything to gain, Sabre everything to lose.

The answer from Derrie was that the merger would offer Sabre players the chance to play a better-quality football, in a higher graded league. It was nonsense, because everyone knew that most of the Sabre players didn't have the ability to play in a higher league. In reality, all those present knew that the merger was to move the best players from Sabre to Derrie and save that club from going under. Derrie cleverly pretended the decision was Stanley's. Even if he said no, he had no power or wish to stop his team members moving to play better quality football.

Stan wasn't the type to stand in the way of people's progression, thus he agreed to combine the teams under the Derrie Sports name. One club with two teams was a step forward.

After a very short time, most of the remaining original Derrie players deserted the club and the team ceased. This meant that inadvertently Sabre became a stronger team.

The merger meeting had introduced Derrie players to Stanley and his friends, now Derrie Sports was defunct those still wishing to play football joined Sabre FC.

Simon Flood who worked with Stan at Barham Council tipped him the wink that the Council were building a flood lit all weather surface training area. Complete with changing faculties it would be off Western Road in Dagenham. A mile from the Beck.

Stan's application assisted by a phone call from Si, was accepted and Scott accompanied Stanley to the interview. About fifteen clubs attended. After a tour of the new facilities, the club's representatives sat in a changing room as an audience to a charismatic grey-haired man.

With a childish grin, the witty, confident man introduced himself. A buzz went around the room, someone recognised him. A loud whisper revealed he was an ALLEN. A member of the famous London football-ing family. He asked each person to introduce themselves then talked football.

The new Derrie Sports were given a Thursday evening slot.

It was like 'real football'. Johnny received 'one to one' professional goalkeeper training. The others were taught tactics, followed by fitness exercises then a twenty-minute match. Mr Allen as a coach was just like John Thomas at school, he loved dead legging Stan during a match and spinning him when Stan was too fast to catch. He would play dirty with a smile, always there to help you up after kicking your legs away.

Stanley and some of the boys were super fit they now trained on a Thursday evening and played on both a Saturday afternoon and Sunday morning.

Derrie Sports won promotion to the Second Division, for the third time his brother John was top goal scorer.

Stanley was fatigued from the Club's Secretary duties. He also didn't like to choose one friend from another when picking the team. He took a gamble and placed an Ad for a Manager in the local paper. To his surprise there was an applicant. Jim, a quiet local man, made contact. The polite thirty-year-old watched them play, enthusiastically he took the role.

However, Stanley hadn't foreseen that as a stranger the task would be more difficult for Jim. As the core of the players and the supporters were friends and family some treated the new manager as an outsider. They contradicted his requests or just ignored him.

Jim persevered for ten matches but eventually had to abandon the assignment because not all the players showed him respect. Strangely, this failure actually highlighted how much respect the players showed their friend Stanley in the same role.

In 1978, a few years later Derrie Sports reached the final of their Divisional Cup. The opponent was Ben United at the Barham Stadium. The two league games had been close and spiteful, it promised to be a tight game. There was already bad blood between the two teams.

Stanley decided not to play. His excuse was to give someone else a chance to play in a Cup Final, but deep down he was nervous of not being 'good enough'. He would act as manager. A large crowd of girl-friends, wives, friends and family came to cheer both teams.

The match kicked off and so did the players.

There was niggle, 'off the ball' elbows and kicks at each other. Studs scraped down the back of a leg or stamped on a rival's toes. As the crowd could see more conflicts than the Referee it became agitated. The ladies were especially angry and vocal when their partner suffered physical abuse.

Ben's took the lead 1-0. They were the better team, controlling the game. The teams took formation for the restart, play continued. The next time the play was near the Ben's goal Paul the Derrie Right Back walked up behind the goal scorer and jumped two footed hard into the back of both the man's knees with his boots to scythe him down.

To make the point further he bent over the player, pointing a finger into his face. With spittle in his words and attitude that would scare a mobster, Paul warned, "don't you ever F***, do that again."

Into the second half Derrie were chasing the ball. Stan needed to do something, he decided to substitute Froth and replace him with Vinnie. The team needed some 'steel' in midfield.

Stan called him over, "See their number eight." Vinnie nodded. "He's running the show, play him out of the game." The substitute understood, he nodded again.

Within minutes, there was a 'throw-on' adjacent to where they were standing, Stan replaced Froth.

Vinnie watched a Ben's player throw the ball to his number eight. Slowly, in full view of the whole stadium he walked up and launched the number eight six feet into the air.

The silent assassin! Red card! He was sent off before he had kicked the ball.

The match finished 2-0 to Ben United.

The presentation table draped with green baize was carried by officials to the centre circle. A line of League Executives in navy blazers wearing Association ties added the League Cup and the Winners and Losers medals.

Expectant players from Ben United formed a line ten feet from the presentation table.

The Executives had a conflab then shortly after carried everything away. There was a rumble as a microphone was handed around. An official made an announcement.

"The League Committee has decided, that due to the unsporting behaviour shown by both sides during this match the Trophy and Medals shall be withheld."

Players chased after the Executives, the teams argued with the officials. The decision was not reversible. Deflated, everyone made their way to the changing rooms.

Twenty minutes had passed when they could hear a commotion outside. Scott and Todd wrapped a towel around their waists then left to investigate. The noise was from a scrap between the female supporters.

There was hair being pulled, fists and umbrellas thrust at people, handbags bouncing off people's heads. The men from both teams were summoned outside to calm and restrain their better halves. It took a while before it stopped.

The League Officials then withdrew to the safety of the Men's Changing Rooms but were then attacked by a joint force of ladies from both teams.

Back in the Beck the team licked their wounds, recounting events of the morning.

"What a day," proclaimed Drew, "they came for trouble, they got it."

"The ref was F*** biased," claimed Froth, "that was a fair tackle that Vinnie done, never a sending off."

The crowd were impressed with Scott's wife June, "I bet you do as you're told at home, Scott," Stace commented, "wouldn't want to be on the end of one of her right handers."

"She's mean with a brolly," added Todd, "bent the F*** thing in half hitting that big bird on the head. She'll be in the papers tomorrow."

"I was only looking after my baby," June declared with a smile.

'Pops' laughed with them. He felt tired, a bit woozy, being

seventy-seven was a chore. Joseph said his goodbyes as he collected his coat. He had offers of a lift but declined.

The drinks flowed, Bernie the landlord locked the front doors. He had a good crowd in spending money, may as well give them a chance to spend some more.

Around 3.00pm the crowd dispersed. John walked home with Stan, Doily and Stace went halfway with them then branched along different roads.

Scott and June drove Joe home. They had only travelled a few hundred yards from the Beck when the traffic slowed. Cars were navigating into the outer lane around a pile of rags and rubbish in the road by the kerb. Scott looked closer, it was only clothes he could scoot down the nearside to drive over it dodging the queue of vehicles.

Three metres from the rubbish June noticed a pair of legs protruding from the rags, she yelled for Scott to stop. Just in time Scott steered to the side as they came to a halt, the nearside front wheel just clipped the edge of the heap.

June was out of the car anxiously bending over the heap. The other two hurried to her side. The heap was a partly conscious man lying in the road.

"It's Pops," June whispered, "that's his hat." She pointed to a cap balancing on the edge of the kerb. Pops had left the Beck over an hour before, the old man must have been laying in the road for most of that time. Lucky he wasn't dead.

They brought him round, sat him on the kerb then dabbed the abrasions on his face and hands with spit and a hankie. Dazed and confused Pops wasn't aware of his accident.

From his recollection, it seemed he crossed the road and had stumbled as his foot caught the kerb. Against the younger people's judgement, the old man resisted being taken to hospital or phoning for an ambulance. So, once he was able to stand unaided and move a little without pain Scott drove him home. The three helpers supported the old man to his front door then hide so that Nanny would not become suspicious of his fall. She must never hear of this incident.

Sadly, Pops missed the next two matches, he was back for the third, but his attendance became more dependent on his health and the journey he would need to undertake to arrive at the venue.

12-08
WALTZ

The groups' drunken discussions when sitting on the playground equipment tended to ignite their imagination and curiosity. The alcohol did for them what Hippies looked for in drugs. Open unguarded conversation without rules, which led to a conclusion or agreement to disagree. There was no malice, if that was your opinion so be it.

Strange, extraordinary were all around them. There were stories in books which suggested that an alien was God, not just any god. Experts reported 'physical proof' that aliens had visited Earth. The Bermuda Triangle swallowed ships and aircraft.

Nostradamus had left prophecies that people only understood after the event had happened.

Even the TV showed classic black and white horror films every Saturday night.

Stanley wanted a set of Tarot cards because of the style of the graphics. Along with his friends, he was also intrigued with the paranormal, Ouija boards and seances. Scared to death when the boys were aged fifteen and sixteen, they peeped through the slit between fingers of hands held over their eyes as they watched the X-rated Rose's Baby.

Two years later, when *The Mephisto Waltz* was showing at the Romford Odeon, the boys queued for thirty minutes to get admission. Again, the film was scary, about people's souls and the occult. It had a similar effect on the boys' nerves as the previous film.

The boys shared the intriguing, eye closing parts of the film all the way home on the bus. They re-enacted the chilling scenes which made them jump the highest, referred to the most terrifying characters.

Bob invited them to his mum and dad's for a cup of tea, a sandwich plus a seance.

He lived above a newsagents shop in Regen Road. Bob asked them to be very quiet as his dad managed the shop and the man needed to get out of bed at 5.00am in order to receive the paper deliveries. His dad then assembled the paper boys' delivery bags with the correct newspapers and magazines.

After alighting the bus, Bob led the way. They walked through the muddy access road behind the row of shops lit only by a bright moon. A guard dog chained to a balcony at the rear of the Chip Shop did his job, waking the whole neighbourhood with his extra loud barking.

Bob held his hand up 'movie cavalry style', signalling the boys to stop. He continued to the shop while the others waited. Roy cupped his mouth with his hands, hooting with an owl impression. Joe flapped his arms out wide then asked what creepy noise a bat from the film would make.

Bob returned, because his dad had locked the back door and he would have to take them to the front door.

The gang retraced their steps through the mud to the main road then turned left to the shop door in Regen Road. Crouching low to remain undetected, they suspiciously huddled in the shop doorway waiting to follow Bob into the shop.

As there was a burglar alarm in the shop, it wasn't that simple. Before opening the door, Bob gave them detailed instructions. He couldn't turn the burglar alarm off because it was on a time switch, this was a precaution to prevent burglars deactivating it. Once Bob's dad shut the shop, it was alarmed until five in the morning.

Less helpful, some floor tiles were connected to the burglar alarm.

The trainee burglars looked at each other. Why weren't they home in bed? Why were they trying to break into Fort Knox?

As the boys turned to leave Bob shared the good news. So he could pinch cigarettes from the shop he had learned which floor tiles were wired. Helpfully, one tile by the counter wasn't alarmed. Once the door was opened, he had fifteen seconds to turn off the door alarm.

The newsagents trusted son divulged the method of secret access. Step onto the second tile from the door, pull yourself onto the counter. Keep your weight on the counter then slide over and step on the staff side. He had to be last over the counter because the front door needed locking.

One by one the raiders executed their assignment. Bob took them into the ground floor lounge, "Mum and Dad's bedroom is two floors above here so don't worry about making a noise."

He strolled away to make the refreshments. Passing the sofa, he called, "Have a look at this," he pointed to a small stain on the sofa cushion. "That's where my sister 'had it off' with her boyfriend," Bob claimed. "I smelt it the other day, some of her fuzz was on it."

The others were dumbstruck, 'the man was deranged'.

After the snacks, he called them to a large circular table. Jon spied an ornamental brass bell on the fireplace and slipped it in his pocket. Mike took control, they sat around the table with hands open, arms outstretched. With his finger pressed against the clanger, Jon took the bell and placed it between his knees.

Nervously, the young men glanced around the table at each other, was this the right thing to do?

"Spread your little fingers out to touch them against your neighbour's ones on each side," Mike directed.

Glyn stood bolt upright, walking into the kitchen, he panicked, "You lot must be crazy, I'm not doing this. You don't know what mumbo jumbo thingy will happen."

Mike was calm. "Okay, you can turn the light off when we ask."

Glyn agreed, he had no problem moving further away from the table.

"Okay Glyn, light please," requested Mike. The room fell into darkness.

Bob jumped up and walked towards the window, "Forgot to close the curtains."

The room was now in total darkness. To yelps and yells of 'get off', Bob's outstretched arms touched unsuspecting parts of his friends' bodies as he returned to the table.

Mike called out, "Is anybody there, talk to us?"

The boys giggled, the room felt colder.

Again, "We are assembled here to talk to you."

Joe and Roy started to argue, "Stop stroking my hand," demanded Roy.

"I'm not, it's not me," declared Joe with a quiet chuckle.

"Look, stop F*** about or I'll go home," threatened Mike. The others promised to behave.

"We are here to talk with you," continued Mike.

No one giggled this time.

"If you are there, give us a sign?"

"We are waiting."

"Please, give us a sign."

A bell rang.

12-08

Like a bullet from a gun, the chairs toppled backwards. Glyn didn't turn the light on; he just ran into the corridor.

Joe opened the window to escape but hit the security railings. Roy joined Glyn in the corridor, their path blocked by the locked door to the shop.

Bob and Stan hid in the kitchen.

Mike calmly walked to the switch and turned the lights on to reveal a sniggering Jon still sitting at the table.

CPSIA information can be obtained
at www.ICGtesting.com
Printed in the USA
LVHW050633220423
744985LV00003B/30